INTRODUCTION TO FRACTALS AND CHAOS

Mathematics and Meaning

Crayton W. Bedford

Venture Publishing
9 Bartlet Street, Suite 55
Andover, MA 01810

PREFACE

This book was originally written with a very particular audience in mind: a group of high school students who had completed a precalculus course, who were bright, curious and motivated, who did not want to take on the pressure of the usual calculus course, but who were interested in keeping mathematical skills alive. Intrigued by fractal images and the vocabulary of chaos theory, students elected this course to gain some understanding of the concepts. Soon they were joined by others who *had* taken calculus, and the skills they brought made the non-calculus students want some instruction to level the playing field.

And so an unusual course evolved for which this book is the text: predominately relying on precalculus skills but introducing some elementary calculus techniques, playing with the dazzling images but requiring some careful mathematics, pointing toward the need for higher powered mathematics while exploring the metaphorical implications for the poets in the class.

The audience also dictated the technology. Normally, a course in chaos and fractals would rely on sophisticated computing equipment, which these students did not have. On the other hand, every one of them owned a graphing calculator, a TI-81 in the beginning, then a TI-82, and more recently a TI-83. So this text relies on a graphing calculator, the TI-83, as a kind of compromise between technological sophistication and ease of access. The text should be read with a TI-83 in hand so that both the explanations and the exercises can be followed.

Of course, the TI-83 has its limits, and when they are obvious (a bit in Chapter 2, more clearly in Chapter 6), suggestions are made for using the software WINFEED (freely available on the Internet) with a PC. Even without a PC, one can get much of the benefit of a computer exploration of Julia and Mandelbrot Sets by watching Robert Devaney's videos (listed in the Bibliography).

In this book, the following conventions are followed in the description of the use of the TI-83:

- Bold print indicates a key. **PRGM** means the key labeled PRGM.

- Square brackets are used for 2nd functions. **2nd[INS]** indicates a two-stroke command: First press the gold key labeled **2nd**, then press the key that has **INS** as its second function (indicated in gold print over the key labeled **DEL**).

- Numbers followed by a colon indicate a selection from a pull-down menu. **VARS 4:Picture** means press the **VARS** key, and then press **4** to select the option concerning pictures.

- **>** indicates a cursor arrow to move to a submenu. **VARS>Y-VARS** means press the **VARS** key and then press the right cursor arrow to select the **Y-VARS** menu.

- When describing information that appears on the home screen, a typeface approximating the calculator font is used. For example, "When you press **ENTER**, you will see `Ans` on the home screen."

Chapters 1-6 of this book are designed to be within the grasp of anyone with normal high school precalculus math; Chapter 7 is for the more mathematically inclined; and Chapter 8 explores some of the non-mathematical ideas that emerge from the notions of chaos and fractals. The first six chapters can serve as a text for a self-contained, one semester course in chaos and fractals, and the last two chapters can serve as the basis for a more exploratory second semester involving student projects in math and science or in non-scientific areas. Whether you are a teacher, student or general reader, I hope this book helps support your learning about, and browsing among, the ideas of chaos theory and fractal geometry.

February 1998
Oakland, California

Crayton W. Bedford

TABLE OF CONTENTS

Chapter 1

INTRODUCTION

§1. Dynamical Systems

A *dynamical system* is a system that evolves over time. Anything that grows is a dynamical system – a plant, a person, a population. A river is a dynamical system; so is the weather, the stock market and your heart. Dynamical systems change their state from moment to moment, hour to hour, or more generally, from one time unit to the next. Chaos theory can be thought of as the study of dynamical systems whose long-term behavior is unpredictable. The complex geometric patterns traced out by a chaotic dynamical system are best understood using the concepts of fractal geometry. This course will introduce you to the insights of chaos theory and fractal geometry.

To model the evolution of a system, we will use sequences of numbers. First we make two simplifying assumptions:

1. There is one number that characterizes the system at any given moment. For instance, in studying a population's evolution, we might be interested solely in the size of the population at each generation.

2. The evolution can be broken down into discrete time periods. In the evolution of a population, this might mean measuring each generation as if it burst into being at one moment and then expired just as the next generation was born. The population simply jumps from one measurement to the next.

For instance, suppose we were interested in a population of 100 bacteria that doubled in size every hour. Then we would model the system with the sequence:

$$100, 200, 400, 800, 1600, ...$$

Sequences

A sequence can be thought of as a set of numbers, called *terms*, whose order is specified by counting; that is, there is a 1st term, a 2nd term, a 3rd, a 4th, and so on. In other words, there is a one-to-one correspondence between the set of positive integers and the terms of the sequence. The correspondence for our doubling population example would be the function $f(n) = 100 \times 2^{n-1}$ for each positive integer n. Other examples are given in the following table:

Sequence	Correspondence
$1, 3, 5, 7, 9...$	$f(k) = 2k - 1$
$-1, 2, -3, 4, -5, 6, ...$	$f(n) = n(-1)^n$
$a_0, a_1, a_2, a_3, ...$	$f(m) = a_{m-1}$

A *sequence* is usually defined formally as the function that makes the correspondence; that is, a function whose domain is the set of positive integers. The formula for the function tells us how to compute the nth term of the population sequence from the number n. This kind of formula is called a *closed formula*.

Informally, we often speak of the sequence as simply the range of the defining function; that is, the set of numbers that results from applying the function to every counting number one after the other. The terms of a sequence are often denoted by subscripted variables such as $a_1, a_2, a_3, a_4, \cdots$. The closed formula might be expressed in either function notation or variable notation. So for the population sequence we might see either $f(n) = 100 \times 2^{n-1}$ or $a_n = 100 \cdot 2^{n-1}$, for $n = 1, 2, 3, ...$

Sequences can also be defined *recursively* using a formula that tells you how to get from each point to the following point. A recursive formula uses the value of the $(n-1)^{st}$ term of the sequence to compute the next value, the nth. For instance, saying a population doubles every hour makes use of a recursive definition. You are told to multiply the population at time $n-1$ by 2 to get the population at time n. A more formal way of giving the recursive definition would have been:

$$a_1 = 100$$
$$a_n = 2a_{n-1} \text{ for } n = 2, 3, 4, ...$$

In chaos theory, it is common to denote the initial term of a sequence using the subscript 0 instead of 1. Once you are used to working with sequences such as $u_1, u_2, u_3, u_4, \cdots$, you will have no trouble using the same ideas with sequences such as $u_0, u_1, u_2, u_3, \cdots$.

Iteration

While you may be more familiar with closed formulas from your previous study in math and science, recursive formulas will be more common in the sequences we will generate in this course. The key concept underlying the use of a recursive formula is *iteration*. A function is iterated when its output is used as input for a subsequent application of the function. The process is repeated with each new output becoming the next input. (Figure 1.1.)

Figure 1.1. Iteration.

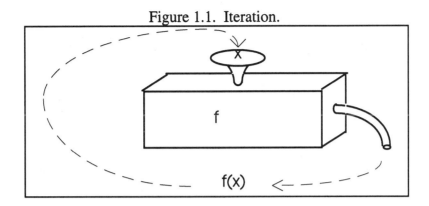

Example 1. What is the sequence generated by iterating the function $f(x) = x(x-1)$ starting with $x = 3$?

Solution: Taking 3 as the initial term and iterating the function four times gives:

$$3 \xrightarrow[x(x-1)]{} 6 \xrightarrow[x(x-1)]{} 30 \xrightarrow[x(x-1)]{} 870 \xrightarrow[x(x-1)]{} 756030 \xrightarrow[x(x-1)]{} \cdots$$

Clearly the sequence is going to continue to increase without bound.

Iteration with the TI-83

      A calculator is a good iterator. The answers in Example 1, for instance can be generated as follows: Press **3** and **ENTER**. The calculator now stores 3 in memory as Ans. To compute $3(3-1)$, press **2nd[ANS] (2nd[ANS] – 1)** and then **ENTER**. The answer is 6. When you press enter repeatedly, the calculator computes Ans(Ans-1) using the last computed value for Ans. You should see the results in Figure 1.2.

Figure 1.2

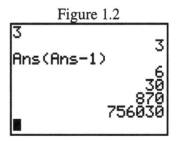

Example 2. Iterate the function of Example 1 using an initial point of $x = 1$.

Solution: You can do this one in your head. When $x = 1$, the second factor, $(x-1)$, is 0, so the first output is 0. Now when $x = 0$, the first factor of the product is 0, so again the output is 0. Continued iteration produces a string of 0's. The sequence is 1, 0, 0, 0, ...

There is a nice feature of the calculator that makes it easy to do other problems like Example 2. First press **1** (or whatever initial value you want) and **ENTER** to put the initial value in Ans. Then press **2nd[ENTRY]** twice to recall the formula Ans(Ans-1) to your home screen. The calculator stores a stack of previously entered instructions or expressions which you can access in order, from most recent to most ancient. After they appear on your screen, you can edit if you wish, and then execute again by pressing **ENTER**. The result for Example 2 would look like the screen shown in Figure 1.3.

Figure 1.3

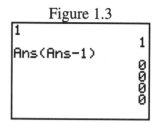

§1. Exercises

In Exercises 1-6, write the first six terms of the recursively defined sequence.

1. $a_0 = 4, a_n = 0.5 a_{n-1}$.

2. $a_0 = -3, a_n = 2 + a_{n-1}$.

3. $a_0 = 0.4, a_n = 2|a_{n-1}| - 1$.

4. $a_0 = 1, a_n = \cos\left(\dfrac{\pi a_{n-1}}{2}\right)$.

5. $a_0 = 256, a_n = \sqrt{a_{n-1}}$

6. $a_0 = 3, a_n = \sqrt{a_{n-1}}$

7. Write a closed formula for each of the following:
a) The sequence in Exercise 1.
b) The sequence in Exercise 2.
c) The sequence in Exercise 4.

In Exercises 8-13, use your calculator to iterate the following functions using the given values of x as initial points. (For trigonometric function, radian measure is assumed.)

8. $f(x) = \sin x$, $x = 0.8, 4, -\pi, 100$

9. $f(x) = \cos x$, $x = 0.8, 4, -\pi, 100$

10. $f(x) = 3\sin x$, $x = 0.8, 4, -\pi, 100$

11. $f(x) = 2x(1-x)$, $x = 0.2, 0.8, 1, 2$

12. $f(x) = 2|x| - 1$, $x = \dfrac{1}{3}, \dfrac{3}{4}, 0.9, 1.2$

13. $f(x) = e^{-x}$, for $x = 0.2, 1, 4, -10$

In Exercises 14-17 find the next term of the sequence and determine a recursive formula.

14. 1, 2, 4, 8, 16, 32, ...

15. 2, 5, 10, 17, 26, 37, ...

16. 1, 1, 2, 3, 5, 8, 13, 21, 34, ...

17. $\dfrac{1}{5}, \dfrac{2}{5}, \dfrac{4}{5}, \dfrac{3}{5}, \dfrac{1}{5}, \dfrac{2}{5}, \dfrac{4}{5}, \dfrac{3}{5}, \ldots$

In Exercises 18-21 find the next term of the sequence and determine a closed formula.

18. 1, -1, 1, -1, 1, -1, 1, -1, ...

19. 2, 5, 8, 11, 14, 17, ...

20. $1, \dfrac{1}{2}, \dfrac{1}{4}, \dfrac{1}{8}, \dfrac{1}{16}, \ldots$

21. 1, 3, 7, 15, 31, 63, ...

§2. Sequences

In this section, you will become familiar with the properties of two particular kinds of sequences that are frequently encountered in mathematics. Then you will learn how to use the TI-83 to simplify your exploration of any sequences that come up in the iteration of functions.

Arithmetic and Geometric Sequences

An *arithmetic* sequence is a sequence whose successive terms differ by a constant. For example:

$$0, 5, 10, 15, 20, 25, \ldots$$

In this sequence, the initial term is 0 and the common difference is 5.

$$a_1 = 0$$
$$a_n = a_{n-1} + 5 \text{ for } n = 2, 3, 4, \ldots$$

In general, if the initial term is a_1 and the common difference is d, then the defining recursive formula for an arithmetic sequence is:

$$a_n = a_{n-1} + d \text{ for } n = 2, 3, 4, \ldots$$

It follows that:

$$a_2 = a_1 + d$$
$$a_3 = a_2 + d = (a_1 + d) + d = a_1 + 2d$$
$$a_4 = a_3 + d = a_1 + 3d$$

and in general, for all positive integers n, we have the closed formula

$$a_n = a_1 + (n-1)d$$

Example 1. Find the 54th term of an arithmetic sequence if the initial term is 21 and the common difference is 0.5.

Solution: If the first term is a_1, then the 54th term is $a_{54} = a_1 + 53d$, the result of 53 successive additions of 0.5 to the initial term, 21. Thus

$$a_{54} = 21 + (53) \cdot (0.5) = 21 + 26.5 = 47.5.$$

Hence the 54th term of this arithmetic sequence is 47.5.

In contrast to an arithmetic sequence, a *geometric sequence* is one in which successive terms are *multiplied* by a constant. Here are some examples:

$$1, 3, 9, 27, 81, \ldots$$
$$1, \frac{1}{2}, \frac{1}{4}, \frac{1}{8}, \frac{1}{16}, \ldots$$
$$1, -1, 1, -1, 1, -1, \ldots$$

In these examples, the initial term of each is 1, and the multipliers are respectively 3, 1/2, and –1. The multiplier of successive terms in a geometric sequence is called *the common ratio*. The last example would be denoted:

$$a_1 = 1$$
$$a_n = (-1)a_{n-1} \text{ for } n = 2, 3, 4, \ldots$$

In general, if the initial term of a geometric sequence is a_1 and the common ratio is r, then the defining recursive formula for the sequence is:

$$a_n = ra_{n-1} \text{ for } n = 2, 3, 4, \ldots$$

Thus

$$a_2 = ra_1$$
$$a_3 = ra_2 = r(ra_1) = r^2 a_1$$
$$a_4 = r(a_3) = r^3 a_1$$

and in general, for all positive integers n, we have the closed formula

$$a_n = r^{n-1} a_1$$

Example 2. Find the 8th term of the geometric sequence whose initial term is 4 and whose common ratio is $\frac{1}{2}$.

Solution: You can write out the first 8 terms without difficulty, or you can use the short-cut formula. Here's the short-cut. If a_1 is the initial term, then the 8th term is $a_8 = r^7 a_1$. Hence the 8th term is:

$$a_8 = (\tfrac{1}{2})^7 \cdot 4 = \frac{1}{2^7} \cdot 2^2 = 2^{-5} = \frac{1}{32}.$$

Sequences with the TI-83

To access the sequence functions of the TI-83, first press **MODE**, and then use the cursor arrows to select Seq; press **ENTER** (Figure 1.4). Then you can define as many as three different sequences called u, v, and w using the subscript n. If you open the **Y=** menu (Figure 1.5), the first thing you'll notice is the default initial value for the subscript, nMin, is 1. Then you'll see two lines concerning the sequence u. In the first line, u(n) = , you can enter a closed or recursive formula. Suppose we use the arithmetic sequence of Example 1 which was defined recursively with a common difference of 0.5. For u(n) = you would type in **2nd[u] (n - 1) + . 5**. (You enter each one of these symbols: **2nd[u]** is over the 7; n comes from the **X,T,θ,n** key.) Press **ENTER**. For u(nMin) = you enter the initial term of Example 1 which was 21. (Figure 1.6.) (When you press **ENTER**, the calculator automatically inserts curly brackets around the 21 for reasons that don't have to do with this kind of sequence.) Now if you return to the home screen by pressing **2nd[QUIT]**, you can type in **2nd[u] (5 4)** and press **ENTER** to get the answer 47.5 in Example 1 (see Figure 1.7).

If you want to see a table of several terms of the sequence, press **2nd[TABLE]**, and the screen in Figure 1.8 will appear.

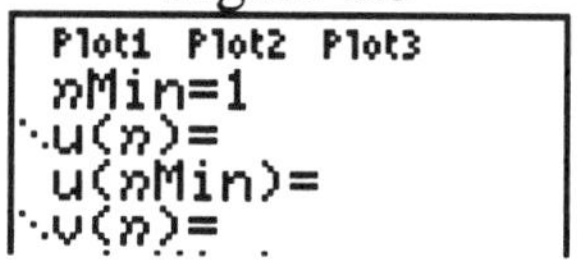

You can scroll down using the cursor arrows until you reach $n = 54$, but that is a lengthy procedure. Instead you can change the range of sequence terms displayed by pressing **2nd[TBLSET]**. To start at 50, change Tbl Start to 5 0. ΔTbl is the size of the steps between successive values of n, and it should be left at 1. Then press **2nd[TABLE]** again, you'll see a screen as in Figure 1.9.

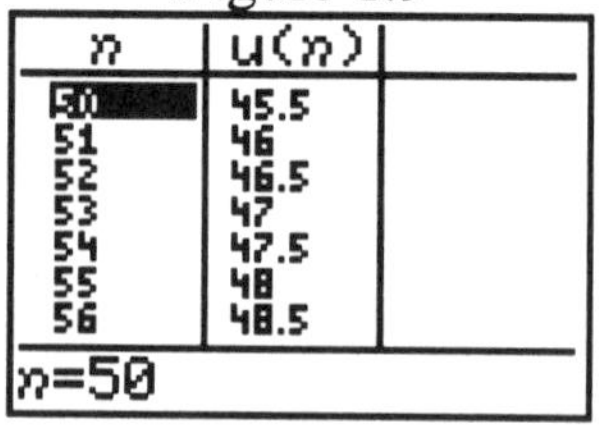

You can also define sequences using a closed formula, but in this case you do not include a value for u(nMin). Instead, you include the initial value as a number in the closed formula. For example to do the geometric sequence of Example 2 using a closed formula in the **Y=** menu, you would enter u(n) = 4 * . 5 ^ (n - 1) as in Figure 1.10. If you then press **2nd[TBLESET]** and enter an

Figure 1.4.

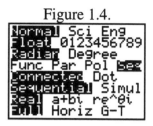

Figure 1.5

Figure 1.6

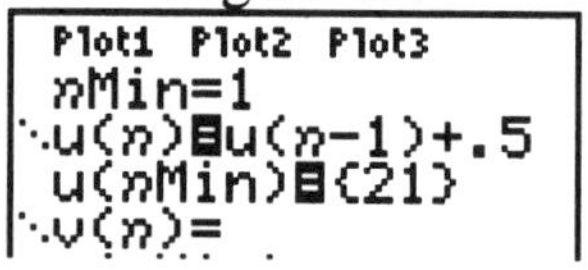

Figure 1.7

Figure 1.8

Figure 1.9

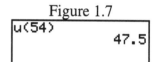

Figure 1.10

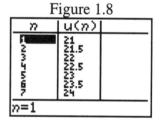

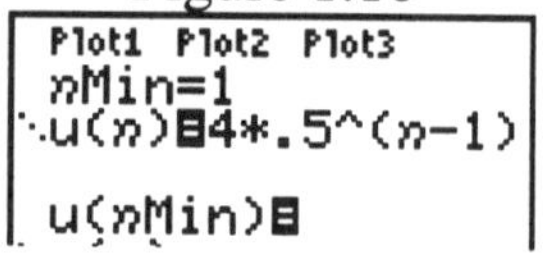

appropriate value for TblStart, you'll be able to display a table of sequence terms. For example, if you start the table at 5, you would see the screen in Figure 1.11 when you press **2nd[TABLE]**.

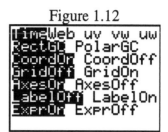

Figure 1.11

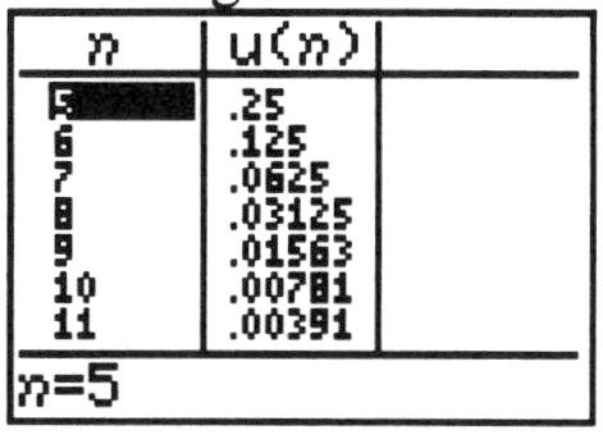

The calculator will also give a graphical representation of a sequence. The values of n are plotted on the horizontal axis and the terms of the sequence $u(n)$ are plotted vertically. To set up a graph of the sequence in Figure 1.10, first press **2nd[FORMAT]** and make sure that Time is selected in the first line, as in Figure 1.12. If you simply press **GRAPH** now, you may get a picture, depending on what window parameters have been defined. Better yet, you could press **ZOOM** and select Ø:ZoomFit to have the calculator choose parameters that fit the points to be plotted. Or if you want to be completely in control, press **WINDOW** and fill in the values you want. If you choose the parameters as in Figure 1.13, you would see the graph in Figure 1.14.

Figure 1.12

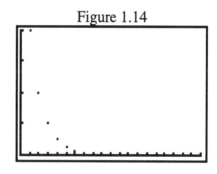

Figure 1.13 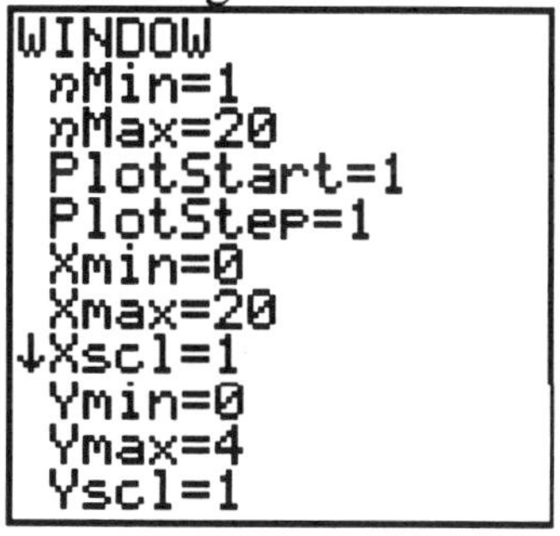   Figure 1.14

If you find the dots hard to see in Figure 1.14, you can change to a line or a thick line back in the **Y=** menu. Next to $u(n)$, $v(n)$ and $w(n)$ are little icons denoting the nature of the plotting style; the default is dots. To change to a line, use the left arrow to place the cursor over the icon and press **ENTER** once. If you do that (as in Figure 1.15), you will see the graph in Figure 1.16. (Pressing **ENTER** repeatedly cycles through all the style choices.)

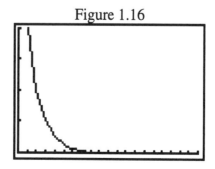

Figure 1.15   Figure 1.16

Finally, you can see a graph and a table of values displayed simultaneously by returning to the **MODE** menu and choosing G-T (Graph - Table), as in Figure 1.17. Then when you press **GRAPH**, you'll see the screen shown in Figure 1.18.

Figure 1.17   Figure 1.18

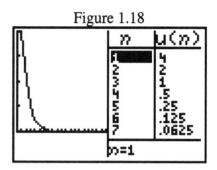

§2. Exercises

In Exercises 1-4, write the first six terms of the arithmetic sequence whose initial term and common difference are specified.

1. $a_1 = 5, \quad d = 3$

2. $a_1 = -2, \quad d = 4$

3. $a_1 = 6, \quad d = -1$

4. $a_1 = 0, \quad d = 3000$

In Exercises 5-8, write the first six terms of the geometric sequence whose initial term and common ratio are specified.

5. $a_1 = 1, \quad r = 3$

6. $a_1 = -1, \quad r = .5$

7. $a_1 = 5, \quad r = 10$

8. $a_1 = \pi, \quad r = -1$

In Exercises 9-16, determine whether the sequence is arithmetic, geometric, or neither. For arithmetic sequences, specify the common difference; for geometric sequences, specify the common ratio.

9. 1, 2, 4, 7, 11, 16, ...

10. 1, 3, 5, 7, 9, 11, ...

11. 2, 10, 50, 250, 1250, 6250, ...

12. 0, 1, 0, 1, 0, 1, 0, ...

13. 32, 16, 8, 4, 2, 1, .5, ...

14. .1, .01, .001, .0001, .00001, ...

15. 10, 0, –10, –20, –30, ...

16. 5, –5, 5, –5, 5, –5, 5, –5, ...

17. Find the 30th term of the arithmetic sequence whose initial term is 3 and whose common difference is 21.

18. Find the 19th term of the arithmetic sequence whose initial term is 13 and whose common difference is –7.

19. Find the 9th term of the geometric sequence whose initial term is 243 and whose common ratio is $\frac{1}{3}$.

20. Find the 10th term of the geometric sequence whose initial term is 2.783 and whose common ratio is 10.

Use your calculator to (a) write out the first 7 terms, (b) find the 25th term, and (c) sketch a graph of the first 30 terms of the sequence defined by the closed formula given in Exercises 21-24.

21. $u_n = -2 + 3(n-1), n = 1, 2, 3, ...$

22. $w_n = 1 + 10 \times (0.3)^{n-1}, n = 1, 2, 3, ...$

23. $a_n = 2^{n/n+1}, n = 1, 2, 3, ...$

24. $t_n = \dfrac{n+1}{n^2}, n = 1, 2, 3, ...$

Use your calculator to (a) write out the first 7 terms, (b) find the 25th term, and (c) sketch a graph of the first 30 terms of the sequence defined by the recursive formula and initial term given in Exercises 25-28.

25. $b_0 = 1, b_n = \dfrac{11b_{n-1}}{10}$

26. $t_0 = 40, t_n = t_{n-1} - 3$

27. $u_0 = 48, u_n = \dfrac{1}{\sqrt{u_{n-1}}}$

28. $a_0 = 1, a_n = a_{n-1} + (2n+1) \times (-1)^n$

In Exercises 29-32, (a) write a closed formula for the general term, and use the calculator to (b) find a decimal approximation for the 25th term, and (c) draw a graph of the first 30 terms of the sequence indicated.

29. $1, 3, 5, 7, 9, \cdots$

30. $\dfrac{3}{2}, \dfrac{5}{4}, \dfrac{9}{8}, \dfrac{17}{16}, \dfrac{33}{32}, \cdots$

31. $3, \sqrt{3}, \sqrt[3]{3}, \sqrt[4]{3}, \sqrt[5]{3}, \cdots$

32. $100, \sqrt{100}, \sqrt{\sqrt{100}}, \sqrt{\sqrt{\sqrt{100}}}, \cdots$

§3. Series

A series is the expressed sum of the terms of a sequence. If the sequence is, say,

$$1, 3, 5, 7, 9,$$

then the series is

$$1 + 3 + 5 + 7 + 9.$$

Because the sequence and series are finite in this case a sum is easily computed; it's 25.

If the sequence is infinite, such as, for example, the positive integers, then the series would also be infinite:

$$1 + 2 + 3 + 4 + 5 + \cdots.$$

For the series of positive integers, we cannot add up all the terms and get a finite sum, so we say the series is *unbounded*. Surprisingly, some infinite series *do* have a finite sum, but more about that later. First, we present formulas that give the sum of finite series, starting with the arithmetic series.

Finite Arithmetic Series

Example 1. Compute the sum of eight terms of the arithmetic series whose initial term is 2 and whose common difference is 3.

Solution: The series is

$$2 + 5 + 8 + 11 + 14 + 17 + 20 + 23.$$

Though you could easily add this up either in your head or on the calculator, I want to show you a useful trick. Notice that the sum of the first and last terms is 25. Then work your way toward the center, looking at the next pair of terms, 20 and 5; once again the sum is 25. Then you have 8 and 17, and then 11 and 14, all the pairs adding up to 25. You have four 25's, so the sum is 100.

The technique of adding the series in Example 1 can be generalized to give a formula for the sum of *any* arithmetic series.

The sum of a finite arithmetic series with initial term a_1 and final term a_n is:

$$a_1 + a_2 + \cdots + a_n = \frac{n(a_1 + a_n)}{2}.$$

Proof: If the sum is called S_n and the common difference is d, then

$$S_n = a_1 + a_2 + a_3 + \cdots + a_{n-1} + a_n = a_1 + (a_1 + d) + (a_1 + 2d) + \cdots + (a_n - d) + a_n.$$

If you write out the sum twice, once backwards and once forwards, you'll see a familiar pattern when you add:

$$
\begin{array}{rl}
S_n = a_1 & + (a_1 + d) + (a_1 + 2d) + \cdots + (a_n - d) + a_n \\
S_n = a_n & + (a_n - d) + (a_n - 2d) + \cdots + (a_1 + d) + a_0 \\
\hline
2S_n = (a_1 + a_n) & + (a_1 + a_n) + (a_1 + a_n) + \cdots + (a_1 + a_n) + (a_1 + a_n)
\end{array}
$$

The n terms on the right are all equal to $(a_1 + a_n)$, so we have

$$2S_n = n(a_1 + a_n)$$

or

$$S_n = \frac{n(a_1 + a_n)}{2}.$$

It may be easier to remember this formula in words instead of symbols:

$$\text{Sum of finite arithmetic series} = \frac{\text{number of terms} \times (\text{first term} + \text{last term})}{2}.$$

Example 2. Find the sum of the first 10 positive integers.

Solution: The sum of the first 10 positive integers is a finite arithmetic series with common difference $d = 1$. The first term is 1, the last term is 10, and there are 10 terms in the series. Therefore:

$$S = \frac{10(1 + 10)}{2} = 55.$$

Finite Geometric Series

A finite geometric series also has a formula that gives the sum in general, and its proof uses an idea similar to the arithmetic proof. You may have seen the idea in use before when you found a fractional expression for a repeating decimal. Recall, for instance, that to express as a fraction the number

$$n = 0.717171...,$$

you would first multiply by 100 and then subtract:

$$100n = 71.717171...$$
$$n = 0.717171...$$
$$99n = 71$$

When you divide both sides by 99, you obtain the fraction $\dfrac{71}{99}$. The technique –

multiplying and subtracting – works because n is actually an infinite geometric series:

$$n = \frac{71}{10^2} + \frac{71}{10^4} + \frac{71}{10^6} + \cdots.$$

The same technique will prove the following formula for a finite geometric series.

The sum of a finite geometric series with initial term a_1 and common ratio r is:

$$a_1 + a_2 + \cdots + a_n = \frac{a_1(1 - r^n)}{1 - r}.$$

provided $r \neq 1$.

Proof: If the sum is called S_n and the common ratio is r, then

$$S_n = a_1 + a_2 + a_3 + \cdots + a_{n-1} + a_n = a_1 + a_1 r + a_1 r^2 + \cdots + a_1 r^{n-2} + a_1 r^{n-1}.$$

Once again we write down the sum twice, but this time multiply the second sum by r, and then subtract:

$$S_n = a_1 + a_1 r + a_1 r^2 + a_1 r^3 + \cdots + a_1 r^{n-2} + a_1 r^{n-1}$$
$$(-)\ \ rS_n = \phantom{a_1 + {}} a_1 r + a_1 r^2 + a_1 r^3 + \cdots + a_1 r^{n-2} + a_1 r^{n-1} + a_1 r^n$$
$$S_n - rS_n = a_1 \phantom{+ a_1 r + a_1 r^2 + a_1 r^3 + \cdots + a_1 r^{n-2} + a_1 r^{n-1}} - a_1 r^n$$

Simplifying we have

$$(1 - r)S_n = a_1(1 - r^n)$$

and finally

$$S_n = \frac{a_1(1 - r^n)}{1 - r}.$$

Of course the division by $1 - r$ can only be done if $r \neq 1$. But if $r = 1$, then all the terms of the series are the same and you don't need a formula anyway.

This formula can simplify the task of adding up a geometric series as shown in Example 3.

Example 3. Find the sum of the sequence $1, \dfrac{2}{3}, \dfrac{4}{9}, \dfrac{8}{27}, \dfrac{16}{81}$.

Solution: This is a finite geometric sequence with common ratio $r = \dfrac{2}{3}$. If we call the initial term a_1, then $a_1 = 1$, and $n = 5$. Using the formula for the sum of a finite geometric series, we have

$$1 + \frac{2}{3} + \frac{4}{9} + \frac{8}{27} + \frac{16}{81} = \frac{1\left(1 - (2/3)^5\right)}{1 - 2/3} = \frac{1 - 32/243}{1/3} = \frac{211/243}{1/3} = \frac{211}{81}.$$

§3. Exercises

Find the sum of the finite arithmetic series in Exercises 1-8.
1. $2 + 4 + 6 + \cdots + 30$
2. $16 + 17 + 18 + \cdots + 35$
3. $-5 - 2 + 1 + 4 + \cdots + 40$
4. $8 + 5 + 2 - 1 - \cdots - 19$
5. $5 + 15 + 25 + \cdots + 105$
6. $-3 - 6 - 9 - \cdots - 30$

7. Ten terms of the arithmetic series with $a_0 = 7, d = 5$.

8. Eight terms of the arithmetic series with $a_0 = 4, d = -3$.

9. Find the sum of the positive integers from 1 through:
    a) 20   b) 100   c) 512   d) 1492

10. a) Find the sum of the even integers from 2 through 100
    b) Find the sum of the odd integers from 1 through 101

Find the sum of the finite geometric series in Exercises 11-16.
11. $4 + 2 + 1 + \frac{1}{2} + \cdots + \frac{1}{64}$
12. $1 + 2 + 4 + 8 + \cdots + 512$
13. $16 - 4 + 1 - \frac{1}{4} + \frac{1}{16} - \frac{1}{64} + \frac{1}{256}$
14. $1 + 1.1 + 1.21 + 1.331 + 1.4641$

15. Seven terms of the geometric series with $a_0 = 10, r = 0.2$.

16. Six terms of the geometric series with $a_0 = 1, d = -3$.

17. Find a fractional expression for the following decimals:
    a) 0.24242424...   b) 2.12121212...   c) 0.999999...

§4. Programming the TI-83

The formulas presented in the last section are handy calculation devices for evaluating the sum of finite arithmetic and geometric series. With the TI-83, you can make the process even easier by programming the calculator to do the arithmetic.

Evaluating Series with a Program

A *program* is a set of step-by-step instructions telling the calculator how to solve a problem. In this section, you'll see how to write a program to evaluate a finite arithmetic series using the formula (and you can follow the pattern to write your own program for the geometric series). Then you'll see how to write a program to evaluate *any* finite series whether it has a formula or not. (For a more complete treatment of to programming for the TI-83, refer to Chapter 16 of the TI-83 Manual.)

To write a program, you break a problem down into bite size steps that the calculator can perform one after the other. For the finite arithmetic series, there are four steps:

1. Start by getting the numbers the formula requires – the first term, the last term, and the number of terms.
2. Store each number in memory as it is entered.
3. Retrieve the stored values and combine them using the arithmetic operations of the formula.
4. Display the result of that operation on the screen.

Actually you have to repeat the first two steps three times to get three numbers and store each. Then you proceed to the last two steps. All you have to do now is learn the language the calculator uses to perform those instructions.

You start a program on the TI-83 by pressing **PRGM** to open the three programming menus: EXEC (execute), EDIT, and NEW. Since you are creating a new program, select NEW with the cursor arrows and press **ENTER**. Your only choice is 1:Create New, which is, of course, exactly what you want to do; so press **ENTER** again. Now you get to name the program you're about to write, using no more than 8 letters. Notice that the cursor is a flashing A, indicating it is in alphabetic mode. So you type out (at most) 8 letters (which are indicated in green above the keys). For instance, you might call this program FINARITH to remind you that it evaluates finite arithmetic series. When you type in **F I N A R I T H** and press **ENTER**, you have finished the preliminaries, and the calculator puts you on the editing screen (Figure 1.19) where you are ready to write your program.

Figure 1.19

```
PROGRAM:FINARITH
:
```

The calculator gets a number and stores it with the single command Input followed by a variable name. You find Input by pressing **PRGM** again to bring up three menus of programming commands: CTL (control), I/O (input/output), and EXEC (execute). Select the I/O menu, and from it select 1:Input. Complete this command by including an alphabetic name for the variable that will store the input value. Suppose the first value requested is the initial term and you decide to call it A. Press **ALPHA[A]** and **ENTER**, so your screen looks like Figure 1.20. (The Input command interrupts the program as it is running, puts a question mark on the screen, and waits for the operator to enter a number. When a number is typed and the **ENTER** key is pressed, the value is stored as the variable A.)

Figure 1.20

```
PROGRAM:FINARITH
:Input A
:■
```

Repeat the Input instruction twice more, using B for the last term and N for the number of terms, as in Figure 1.21.

Figure 1.21

```
PROGRAM:FINARITH
:Input A
:Input B
:Input N
:■
```

Now you are ready to substitute values into the formula and compute the sum. You instruct the calculator to compute by typing in the formula and storing the result in another memory cell, say S (for sum). You type **ALPHA[N] (ALPHA[A] + ALPHA[B]) ÷ 2 STO> ALPHA[S]** and press **ENTER**. (See Figure 1.22.)

Figure 1.22

```
PROGRAM:FINARITH
:Input A
:Input B
:Input N
:N(A+B)/2→S
:
```

Finally, you need to instruct the calculator to display the results. The command, Disp, is found in the same place as Input: press **PRGM> I/O 3:Disp** and then **ALPHA[S]** to complete the program as in Figure 1.23.

Figure 1.23

```
PROGRAM:FINARITH
:Input A
:Input B
:Input N
:N(A+B)/2→S
:Disp S
```

To run this program, you leave the program editor and return to the home screen by pressing **2nd[QUIT]**. From the home screen, you press **PRGM**. The EXEC menu is automatically displayed, and you select FINARITH. You'll see the screen in Figure 1.24, indicating the calculator is ready to execute the program. It starts when you press **ENTER**. Then you'll see the screen in Figure 1.25, the question mark waiting for you to enter the first term of your series. Suppose you want to add up the first ten positive even integers:

Figure 1.24

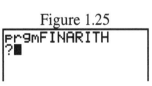

Figure 1.25

```
prgmFINARITH
?■
```

$$2 + 4 + 6 + 8 + 10 + 12 + 14 + 16 + 18 + 20.$$

(You should confirm that this is indeed an arithmetic series.) Then you type **2** and press **ENTER** to place the value of the first term in the variable A. Continue with the last term

2 0 for the second question mark, and **1 0**, the number of terms, for the third. Now when you press **ENTER**, you see the sum 110 displayed along with the word `Done` indicating the program has finished its work. (See Figure 1.26.)

Figure 1.26

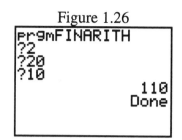

This program is a bare bones model, and you might want to make it more user-friendly. For instance, it would be easy to forget the right order to enter the numbers required, and an unadorned question mark is no help. If you replace `Input` by `Prompt`, the calculator will print the variable name before the question mark to jog your memory. You can edit the program by pressing **PRGM > EDIT**. You see the `EDIT` menu where you find the program `FINARITH`. Select it and press **ENTER**; now you're in edit mode. With the cursor on `Input`, press **PRGM > I/O 2:Prompt**. If you make this change in the first three commands (Figure 1.27), the program run looks like Figure 1.28.

Figure 1.27

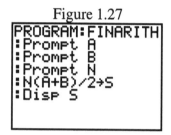

Figure 1.28

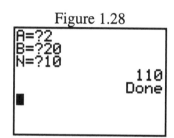

You would not have gotten as clean a screen as the one in Figure 1.28 unless you took the precaution of pressing **CLEAR** before you ran the program. Of course you can instruct the calculator to do this for you by adding `ClrHome` as the first command of the program. To do that you would return to the program editor by pressing **PRGM>EDIT**, and once again selecting `FINARITH`. This time you want to insert a command, not replace one. So you press **2nd[INS]**, then press **PRGM > I/O 8:ClrHome**. When you press **ENTER**, you'll see `ClrHome` inserted into the first line as in Figure 1.29. Now press **ENTER** once again and you insert a carriage return, putting `ClrHome` on its own line and `Input A` on the second line as in Figure 1.30. Now if you run the program you'll get the clean screen of Figure 1.28.

Figure 1.29

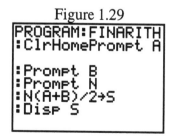

Figure 1.30

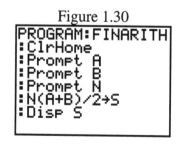

Suppose you are still not confident that the prompt is sufficient to remind you which value to input. Once last modification might be to insert written instructions that appear when the program is run. This is done by using the `Input` command, followed by a message enclosed in quotation marks (located as an **ALPHA** command over the + key), followed by a comma and the variable. The space between words is the alphabetic symbol over 0 (zero). Finally you can collapse the last two lines into one, because the `Disp` command also performs computation as shown in Figures 1.31 and 1.32.

Figure 1.31

```
ClrHome
Input "FIRST TERM",A
Input "LAST TERM",B
Input "HOW MANY",N
Disp N(A+B)/2
```

Figure 1.32

```
FIRST TERM
?2
LAST TERM
?20
HOW MANY
?10
                 110
                Done
```

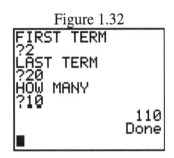

Now that you have seen how to program the calculator to compute the sum of a finite arithmetic series, you can probably see what modifications would make it work for a finite geometric series. You will have that pleasure for yourself by doing Exercise 2.

Loops

As a final example, this section ends with a program that relies on no special formulas but will add up any finite series, using the technique of a *loop*. A loop is a series of commands that are repeated in order several times. If a program requires the same sequence of steps to be performed many times, you write the instructions necessary to accomplish the task once, and then add a few lines to instruct the calculator to repeat the instructions as many times as you want. What makes the technique useful, is that you can use a changing variable in the commands so that they are slightly modified each time through the loop.

Every loop has a command to tell you where it begins, another to tell you where it ends, and in between the commands to be executed repeatedly. On the TI-83, there are several ways to build a loop, but for the programs we will need, the simplest way to start is with the command `For(`, and to end with `End`. You will understand the use of the command most easily by looking at the program `LOOP1` in Figure 1.33 and comparing it with the output shown in Figure 1.34 after the program was run.

Figure 1.33

```
PROGRAM:LOOP1
:For(J,3,7,1)
:Disp J
:End
```

Figure 1.34

```
prgmLOOP1
                   3
                   4
                   5
                   6
                   7
                Done
```

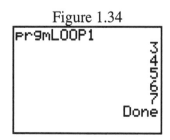

The command For(J,3,7,1) would be read, "For J going from 3 to 7 in steps of 1." The next command tells what to do with J – display its value. And the final command ends the loop. You find both For(and End in the CTL menu. When you are creating or editing the program LOOP1, press **PRGM**, and the CTL menu is automatically displayed. Select 4:For(and type in **ALPHA[J],3,7,1)**. You follow the same procedure for End except you select 7:End from the CTL menu.

J is called the looping variable; 3 is the starting point for J, 7 is the stopping point, and 1 is the amount J is increased each time through the loop. Because the step size is 1 in LOOP1, J runs through each integer from 3 to 7. If the step size is changed to 2, J would take on the values 3, 5 and 7 as in Figures 1.35 and 1.36.

Figure 1.35

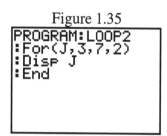

Figure 1.36

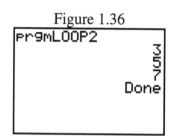

Now you know how to make a loop; next you have to learn how to add. You can understand the logic if you think about how you would add up a string of numbers being read aloud to you. Before you hear the first number, the total in your head is 0. Then each time you hear a new number, you add it to the subtotal you already have. After the last number, you've got the sum of all the numbers. For example, to add up the first six positive integers, you would make a loop with J running from 1 to 6 in steps of 1, and each time through the loop you'd add the new integer to the total so far. If you call the running subtotal S, you start S at 0. Inside the loop, you add each new J to S, and the result becomes the new subtotal S. The finished program is given in Figure 1.37 and the result of running the program in Figure 1.38.

Figure 1.37

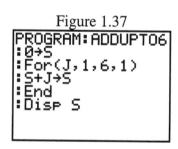

Figure 1.38

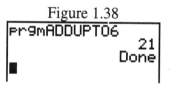

We can use this adding technique in combination with a defined sequence to find the terms of the corresponding series. For example, to add up the squares of the first six positive integers, we have the sequence defined by the closed formula $a_n = n^2$ for $n = 1, 2, 3, 4, 5, 6$, and we want the sum of the series $1^2 + 2^2 + 3^2 + 4^2 + 5^2 + 6^2$. With **MODE** set to Seq, define u(n) in the **Y=** menu as in Figure 1.39. The program SERIES in Figure 1.40 would generate the first six terms of the series and keep

Figure 1.39

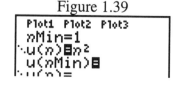

a running subtotal S. A run of the program gives the sum 91 as in Figure 1.41.

Figure 1.40

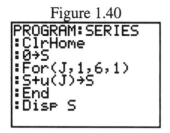

```
PROGRAM:SERIES
:ClrHome
:0→S
:For(J,1,6,1)
:S+u(J)→S
:End
:Disp S
```

Figure 1.41

```
                91
              Done
```

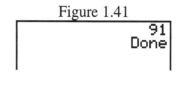

To make this program more general, you could have the sum start with any term and end with any term by changing the beginning and end of the loop. Replace 1 and 6 with variables A and B that the operator will input, as in the program in Figure 1.42. If you run this program to add up, say, the 3rd through 11th terms of the same sequence, you'd see the results in Figure 1.43.

Figure 1.42

```
ClrHome
Input "LOWER LIMIT? ",A
Input "UPPER LIMIT? ",B
0→S
For(J,A,B,1)
S+u(J)→S
End
Disp S
```

Figure 1.43

```
LOWER LIMIT
A=?3
UPPER LIMIT
B=?11
               501
              Done
```

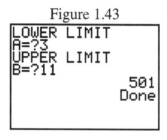

§4. Exercises

1. Modify the program FINARITH to give the sum of the first n positive integers. Input n and output the sum. [Hint: modify the formula to work specifically for this series.]

2. Write a program for the TI-83 to find the sum of a geometric series. Input the first term and the common ratio, and output the sum.

3. Write a program for the TI-83 to find the average of two numbers. Input the two numbers and output the average.

4. Write a program for the TI-83 to find (a) the midpoint and (b) the length of a segment on a Cartesian plane. Input the coordinates of the endpoints and output the coordinates of the midpoint and the length.

5. Write a program for the TI-83 to find the solutions of a quadratic equation. Input the three constants (coefficient of x^2, coefficient of x, and constant term), and output the solution(s). In this program you will have to check that the discriminant is non-negative, using the command If from the CTL menu. You can learn about the If command from the TI-83 manual.

6. Run both programs SERIES and FINARITH to add up the series $5 + 9 + 13 + \cdots + 45$. Verify that they give the same result.

7. Write a program for the TI-83 that uses a loop to print out HAVE A NICE DAY three times.

8. Write a program for the TI-83 that finds the average of five test scores. Make a loop that asks the operator for five numbers (using Input or Prompt) and keeps a running subtotal. End by computing the average and displaying the results.

9. Modify the program in Exercise 8 to allow the operator to specify the number of tests.

10. Modify the program of Exercise 8 to include a final exam in addition to five tests. The final exam is given twice as much weight as a test, so you need to find the weighted average: Multiply the exam score by 2, add it to the test subtotal, and then divide by 7.

§5. Infinite Sequences and Series

The primary focus of the last few sections has been finite sequences and series. In the study of chaos theory and fractal geometry, however, we will be investigating infinite sequences – sequences of numbers in the case of chaos, and sequences of figures in the case of fractals. In this section, we develop ways to talk about infinite sequences whose long term behavior seems predictable because they home in on a fixed point.

Limits of Sequences

Consider the sequence $1, \frac{1}{2}, \frac{1}{3}, \frac{1}{4}, \cdots, \frac{1}{n}, \cdots$. As you go further along this sequence, choosing larger values for n, the denominators regularly increase so the fractions regularly decrease, *i.e.* they get closer to 0. How close to 0? As close as you like; just make n large enough. If you want a_n to be within a billionth of 0, for example, choose n to by 1 billion and 1. You can always make $\frac{1}{n}$ as small as you want. On the other hand, note that 0 itself is not a term of the sequence. No matter how large you take n to be, $\frac{1}{n}$ is *not equal* to 0. Furthermore, the sequence never jumps over 0 to become negative; all its terms are positive. Finally, note that once the terms of the sequence get within a certain fixed distance of 0, all the terms with larger n are also within that same distance of 0.

This is an example of a predictable sequence. Though there is no end to the sequence, the terms get closer and closer to a fixed number as you go further out the sequence. In this case, 0 is the number that the terms get close to, and so we call 0 the *limit* of the sequence. In standard mathematical notation we write

$$\lim_{n \to \infty} \frac{1}{n} = 0$$

which is read "the limit of $\frac{1}{n}$ as n approaches infinity is 0." Though we are not defining *limit* formally, there are two properties that you should look for: 1) the limit is not a term of the sequence; but 2) beyond a certain integer N, all the terms are closer to the limit than whatever tolerance you specify. The integer N depends on the tolerance and can always be specified for any sequence that has a limit.

Example 1. Write a formula for the general term of the following sequence and decide whether or not it has a limit: $\frac{1}{2}, \frac{2}{3}, \frac{3}{4}, \frac{4}{5}, \cdots$.

Solution: There are a couple of different ways to look at this example. If you call the initial term a_1, then $a_1 = \dfrac{1}{2}$, $a_2 = \dfrac{2}{3}$, and there is a pattern that you could write as the closed formula:

$$a_n = \frac{n}{n+1}.$$

Or you might notice that each term of the sequence differs from 1 by the decreasing fractions of the sequence $\dfrac{1}{2}, \dfrac{1}{3}, \dfrac{1}{4}$, and so on. This insight would lead to the general formula

$$a_n = 1 - \frac{1}{n+1}.$$

A little algebra shows that these two expressions are equivalent, so either one will do. No matter how you write the general term, you probably have a pretty strong hunch that the terms of this sequence steadily approach 1, much as the sequence in the preceding example approached 0. Because a rigorous treatment of limits is inappropriate for this course, we cannot prove that your hunch is correct; but it *is* correct. In a course in analysis you could prove that

$$\lim_{n \to \infty} \frac{n}{n+1} = 1.$$

Example 2. A sequence is defined by $a_n = \dfrac{n}{(n+1)(n+2)}$ for $n = 1, 2, 3, \dots$. Write the first five terms of the sequence and decide if it has a limit.

Solution: Substituting in $n = 1, 2, 3, 4$, and 5, we have the following initial five terms of the sequence:

$$\frac{1}{6}, \frac{2}{12}, \frac{3}{20}, \frac{4}{30}, \frac{5}{42}.$$

The terms of the sequence, after the 2nd, get progressively smaller. Do they approach a limit? Clearly all the terms are positive, so if there is a limit it must be non-negative. One way to convince yourself that the sequence has a limit of 0 is to notice that the denominator of the fraction $\dfrac{n}{(n+1)(n+2)}$ is the product of two numbers a little bigger than n. Therefore the fraction is a little smaller than $\dfrac{n}{n \cdot n}$. But *this* fraction is equal to our old friend $\dfrac{1}{n}$. So each term of this new sequence is pinned between $\dfrac{1}{n}$ and 0.

Because $\lim\limits_{n\to\infty}\dfrac{1}{n} = 0$, it follows that $\lim\limits_{n\to\infty} a_n = 0$. [Note that this is not a mathematical proof, but it is a persuasive argument.]

Example 3. Write the first six terms of the sequence defined by $a_n = (-1)^n\,\dfrac{n}{n+1}$ for $n = 0, 1, 2, 3, \cdots$, and determine whether the sequence has a limit.

Solution: Substituting $n = 0, 1, 2, 3, 4, 5$ into the general formula gives the first six terms:

$$0, -\frac{1}{2}, \frac{2}{3}, -\frac{3}{4}, \frac{4}{5}, -\frac{5}{6}.$$

The factor $(-1)^n$ alternates between -1 and 1, depending on whether n is odd or even. Therefore the terms of the sequence alternate between $-\dfrac{n}{n+1}$ and $\dfrac{n}{n+1}$. Thus the even terms approach 1 and the odd terms approach -1. Mathematically speaking, we would say that the sequence has no limit because there is no single fixed number to which the terms get infinitesimally close. In chaos theory, however, we could say that the sequence approaches a *limiting cycle*, bouncing back and forth between 1 and -1, getting closer to each in turn though never equal to either.

Infinite Arithmetic and Geometric Sequences

Recall that an arithmetic sequence is one in which a common difference is added to each successive term, and a closed formula for the general term is

$$a_n = a_1 + (n-1)d\,.$$

If d is positive, then the terms of the sequence increase without bound; if d is negative, then the terms decrease without bound. We say the terms approach ∞ if d is positive and $-\infty$ if d is negative. In either case, the long term behavior is completely predictable. To describe it, you could either say that the sequence has no limit or that the limit of the sequence is infinite.

The situation with the geometric sequence is a little more complicated − and a little more interesting. Remember that a geometric sequence is constructed by multiplying successive terms by a common ratio. If the multiplier is greater than 1 (or less than −1) then the successive terms continually increase in absolute value in such a way that the sequence is unbounded. Consider, for example, the geometric sequence with $r = -2$ and $a_1 = 1$. The first five terms of the sequence are:

$$1, -2, 4, -8, 16.$$

The absolute value of the terms are doubling at each stage; the odd-numbered terms are heading toward ∞ and the even-numbered terms toward $-\infty$. This sequence is unbounded and has no limit.

On the other hand, if the common ratio is less than 1 (in absolute value), then successive terms decrease (in absolute value) and ultimately approach 0 as a limit.

Example 4. Describe the long term behavior of the geometric sequence with $a_1 = 3$ and $r = 0.1$.

Solution: To guide your intuition, write out the first few terms of the sequence. They look like this:

$$3, 0.3, 0.03, 0.003, 0.0003, \cdots.$$

At each stage, you add another zero after the decimal point, *i.e.* you divide the term by 10. By the time $n = 30$, you have 3×10^{-29}, or 28 zeroes after the decimal point followed by a 3. A mighty small number. Once again, we have a non-negative sequence that gets as close to 0 as you could want. The exponent in the general case is $-(n-1)$ or $1-n$

Therefore we could write the general term as $3 \times 10^{1-n}$ and say

$$\lim_{n \to \infty} 3 \times 10^{1-n} = 0.$$

From time to time during the study of chaos and fractals, we will have reason to find limits of geometric sequences and series. The result for the sequence in Example 4 is one instance of a more general result which we state here as follows:

If $a_1, a_2, a_3, \cdots, a_n, \cdots$ is an infinite geometric sequence with $|r| < 1$, then

$$\lim_{n \to \infty} a_n = \lim_{n \to \infty} a_1 r^n = 0$$

Limits of Series

As you know, a series is the sum of a sequence. If a sequence is infinite, then the associated series is the sum of an infinite number of numbers. Since the process never ends, you might well imagine that the result would have to end up beyond any finite number. In many cases, you'd be right; many series are unbounded. But some important infinite series are bounded and we can define a sum in terms of limits. Consider for example the series

$$\frac{1}{2}+\frac{1}{4}+\frac{1}{8}+\frac{1}{16}+\cdots.$$

To add up a long string of numbers, you'd add each new term to the subtotal you have so far. Start with $\frac{1}{2}$, then add $\frac{1}{4}$ (giving you $\frac{3}{4}$), then add $\frac{1}{8}$ (giving you $\frac{7}{8}$), and so on. You are actually defining a sequence of subtotals which you could write out as follows:

$$S_1 = \frac{1}{2}$$

$$S_2 = \frac{1}{2}+\frac{1}{4}=\frac{3}{4}$$

$$S_3 = \frac{3}{4}+\frac{1}{8}=\frac{7}{8}$$

$$S_4 = \frac{7}{8}+\frac{1}{16}=\frac{15}{16}$$

$$\vdots$$

This sequence is called a *sequence of partial sums*. Its general term is

$$S_n = 1-\frac{1}{2^n}.$$

This sequence of partial sums is an infinite sequence, but it is one *whose limit we can find*. Note that the fraction $\frac{1}{2^n}$ is the nth term of a geometric sequence with a common ratio $r=\frac{1}{2}$, so that $|r|<1$. Therefore, its limit is 0. Subtraction of each of the terms of this vanishing sequence from 1 results in our sequence of partial sums, whose terms, therefore, must approach 1. We deduce that $\lim\limits_{n\to\infty}\left(1-\frac{1}{2^n}\right)=1$.

Finally, we call this limit the sum of the original infinite series and say the series *converges* to 1. Therefore we write

$$\frac{1}{2}+\frac{1}{4}+\frac{1}{8}+\frac{1}{16}+\cdots=1.$$

In general, if $a_1+a_2+a_3+\cdots+a_n+\cdots$ is an infinite series, the sequence of partial sums is $S_1, S_2, S_3, \cdots, S_n, \cdots$ where $S_n = a_1+a_2+a_3+\cdots+a_n$. If the sequence of partial sums has a limit S, then we say the series converges to S, and S is the sum of the series.

Note that you do not get S by adding a finite number of terms of the series. If you add up the first zillion fractions of the sequence $\dfrac{1}{2}, \dfrac{1}{4}, \dfrac{1}{8}, \dfrac{1}{16}, \cdots$, the sum will not be 1; close to 1, but not exactly equal. S is the limit of the sequence of partial sums; it is not one of the partial sums (unless, of course, the series ends in an infinite string of zeroes – a finite series in disguise).

The series $\dfrac{1}{2} + \dfrac{1}{4} + \dfrac{1}{8} + \dfrac{1}{16} + \cdots$ is an infinite geometric series that converges to a finite sum because its common ratio (½) is less than 1 in absolute value. Any similar series converges and its sum is given by a formula:

If $a_1 + a_2 + \cdots + a_n + \cdots$ is an infinite geometric series with common ratio $|r| < 1$, then the series converges to the sum

$$S = \frac{a_1}{1-r}.$$

A proof would be nice here, but impossible without a rigorous definition of limit. Even though not a proof, the following argument should convince you that an infinite geometric series converges to $\dfrac{a_1}{1-r}$ whenever $|r| < 1$. Since every partial sum of a geometric series is itself a *finite* geometric series, we already have a formula for each S_n:

$$S_n = \frac{a_1(1-r^n)}{1-r}.$$

What happens to S_n as $n \to \infty$? The only expression in the formula that depends on n is r^n. And since $|r| < 1$, then r^n defines a geometric sequence that has a limit of 0. In other words, as $n \to \infty$, r^n virtually disappears, so that the numerator of S_n approaches a_1. We conclude that:

$$\lim_{n \to \infty} S_n = \frac{a_1}{1-r}.$$

Therefore, the series $a_1 + a_2 + \cdots + a_n + \cdots$ converges to the sum $\dfrac{a_1}{1-r}$.

Partial Sums using the TI-83

You have already seen that you can define more than one sequence at a time on the TI-83. This is useful for finding sums of series. You can use the u-sequence to generate your series, and then use the v-sequence as the sequence of partial sums. For example, the series whose sum we just found can be defined recursively as follows:

$$a_1 = 0.5$$
$$a_n = 0.5a_{n-1}, n = 2, 3, 4, \cdots$$

Then the sequence of partial sums would be defined recursively as follows:

$$S_0 = 0$$
$$S_n = S_{n-1} + a_n, n = 1, 2, 3, \cdots$$

You define the first partial sum to be 0 before you add the first term of the series. From then on, you add the next term of the series to the previous partial sum. The original sequence starts with $n = 1$, and the sequence of partial sums with $n = 0$. To use the u-sequence and v-sequence of the calculator, however, both must start with the same value for n. No problem; just renumber the a's:

$$a_0 = 0.5$$
$$a_n = 0.5a_{n-1}, n = 1, 2, 3, 4, \cdots$$

But now you also have to adjust the partial sum S_n to pick up the a-term that is numbered $n-1$.

$$S_0 = 0$$
$$S_n = S_{n-1} + a_{n-1}, n = 1, 2, 3, \cdots$$

Now you can let $u(n) = a_n$ and $v(n) = S_n$ in the **Y=** menu, starting nMin at 0. (see Figure 1.44.) If you press **TABLE** you would see the results in Figure 1.45. To see displayed a graph of these two sequences, make sure you have selected different graphical displays. In Figure 1.44, you'll see that the regular line is selected for the u-sequence (the sequence of a's) and the thick line selected for the v-sequence (the sequence of partial sums). The graph shown in Figure 1.46 confirms visually that the sequence of partial sums approaches 1; the sum of the infinite series is 1.

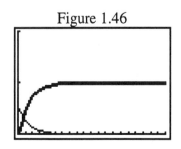

Figure 1.44	Figure 1.45	Figure 1.46

Plot1 Plot2 Plot3
nMin=0
\u(n)⊟.5*u(n−1)
u(nMin)⊟{.5}
\v(n)⊟v(n−1)+u(n −1)
v(nMin)⊟{0}
⋅.w(n)=

n	u(n)	v(n)
0	.5	0
1	.25	.5
2	.125	.75
3	.0625	.875
4	.03125	.9375
5	.01563	.96875
6	.00781	.98438

n=0

§5. Exercises

In Exercises 1-10, write a formula for the general term of the sequence and decide whether or not it has a limit. If you determine it does have a limit, state what it is and justify your reasoning.

1. $2, \dfrac{3}{2}, \dfrac{4}{3}, \dfrac{5}{4}, \cdots$

2. $\dfrac{2}{3}, \dfrac{3}{8}, \dfrac{4}{15}, \dfrac{5}{24}, \cdots$

3. 16, 20, 24, 28, ...

4. 40, −20, 10, −5, ...

5. $2, \dfrac{5}{4}, \dfrac{10}{9}, \dfrac{17}{16}, \cdots$

6. $4, 6, 9, \dfrac{27}{2}, \cdots$

7. $\dfrac{2}{3}, -\dfrac{5}{6}, \dfrac{8}{9}, -\dfrac{11}{12}, \cdots$

8. 0.6, 0.66, 0.666, 0.6666, ...

9. 0, 1, 3, 6, 10, 15, 21, ...

10. $1, \dfrac{3}{2}, \dfrac{5}{4}, \dfrac{7}{8}, \cdots$

In Exercises 11-16, find the limit.

11. $\lim\limits_{n\to\infty} \dfrac{n+2}{n}$

12. $\lim\limits_{n\to\infty} \dfrac{2n}{n+3}$

13. $\lim\limits_{n\to\infty} \dfrac{n+2}{n^2}$

14. $\lim\limits_{n\to\infty} \dfrac{3n+8}{5n+2}$

15. $\lim\limits_{n\to\infty} \dfrac{n^2-1}{n^2}$

16. $\lim\limits_{n\to\infty} \dfrac{n^2-1}{n^3}$

In Exercises 17-24, describe the long term behavior of the given sequence and justify your conclusion.

17. $1, \dfrac{4}{3}, \dfrac{9}{5}, \dfrac{16}{7}, \cdots$

18. $2, -\dfrac{2}{5}, \dfrac{2}{25}, -\dfrac{2}{125}, \cdots$

19. $\log(1), \log(1/2), \log(1/3), \log(1/4), \cdots$

20. $\dfrac{4}{\sqrt{1}}, \dfrac{5}{\sqrt{2}}, \dfrac{6}{\sqrt{3}}, \dfrac{7}{\sqrt{4}}, \cdots$

21. $\dfrac{5\sqrt{1}}{-2.5}, \dfrac{5\sqrt{2}}{-1.5}, \dfrac{5\sqrt{3}}{-0.5}, \dfrac{5\sqrt{4}}{0.5}, \cdots$

22. 0.9, 0.99, 0.999, 0.999, ...

In Exercises 23-30, find the first 5 partial sums, state whether the series converges, and if so, determine its sum.

23. $2 + \dfrac{2}{3} + \dfrac{2}{9} + \dfrac{2}{27} + \dfrac{2}{81} + \cdots$

24. $40 - 20 + 10 - 5 + 2.5 - \cdots$

25. $\dfrac{1}{2} + \dfrac{1}{8} + \dfrac{1}{32} + \dfrac{1}{128} + \dfrac{1}{512} + \cdots$

26. $1 + \dfrac{11}{10} + \dfrac{101}{100} + \dfrac{1001}{1000} + \dfrac{10001}{10000} + \cdots$

27. $\sqrt{48} + \sqrt{24} + \sqrt{12} + \sqrt{6} + \sqrt{3} + \cdots$

28. $3^{-2} + 3^{-4} + 3^{-6} + 3^{-8} + 3^{-10} + \cdots$

29. $1 - 1.2 + 1.2^2 - 1.2^3 + 1.2^4 - \cdots$

30. $27 + 36 + 48 + 64 + \dfrac{256}{3} + \cdots$

31. If an infinite geometric series whose first term is 5 has a sum of 15, what is its common ratio?

Chapter 2

FRACTALS

§1. What Is A Fractal?

Although fractals were imagined over a century ago, they were not easily seen until the a few decades ago when high speed digital computers were readily available. It was not until the late 1970s that the word *fractal* came into existence, coined by Benoit Mandelbrot. As a child in France, Mandelbrot wondered how to use the smooth regularities of Euclidean shapes to model the complexity of the world he saw around him. Where were the circles in nature? Where were the parallel lines and infinite planes? He concluded that "[c]louds are not spheres, mountains are not cones, coastlines are not circles, and bark is not smooth..." (quoted in Briggs (1992), p. 157).

If a mountain cannot be adequately understood as a cone, or as an ordered collection of Euclidean shapes, what is the geometry to describe it? Is there any kind of rational simplicity underneath the appearance of incredible complexity? One possible explanation involves the notion of iteration. A simple figure quickly becomes complex when a few simple rules of manipulation are iterated. This is *geometric* iteration, producing a sequence of geometric figures. Let's look at an example before we try to define the concept. The first example is an infinite sequence of triangles.

The Sierpinski Triangle

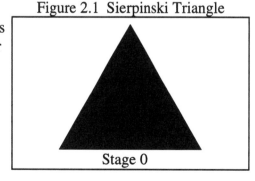

Figure 2.1 Sierpinski Triangle

Stage 0

The initial term of this sequence, Stage 0, is an equilateral triangle. The rule of iteration is: For each triangle, join the midpoints of the sides and then remove the triangle formed in the middle. After one iteration, we have three little triangles left. (See Figure 2.2.) Applying the same rules again to these triangles gives three smaller triangles in each corner, 9 in all. Iterating again produces 27 triangles, then 81, and so on.

After a relatively small number of iterations, the change in the figure at each stage will be imperceptible because the triangles will have gotten so small. But we can imagine the iteration continuing indefinitely, generating an infinite sequence which appears to approach a limit, a figure that resembles Stage *n* in Figure 2.2. This limiting figure, called the *attractor* of the sequence, is named for Waclaw Sierpinski (1882-1969), the renowned Polish mathematician who introduced it in 1916.

Figure 2.2 Sierpinski Triangle

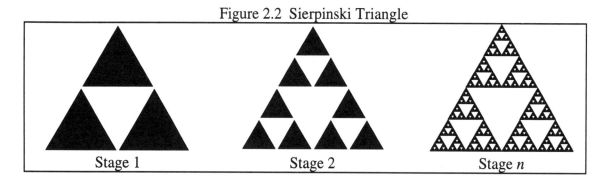

Stage 1   Stage 2   Stage *n*

Are there any triangles left in the Sierpinski triangle? Well, if there were, we'd take out the middle triangle and continue. So the attractor has no triangles, just a lot of points in a clearly recognizable pattern. The Sierpinski triangle is this limiting attractor, this pattern of points.

The Sierpinski triangle is an example of a fractal. What makes it a fractal? It would be nice to have a neat mathematical definition at this point, but none has yet been written that has the general approval of the mathematics community. Even the one proposed by Mandelbrot himself didn't stand the test of time. There are, however, five properties proposed by Falconer (1995, pp. xx-xxi) that characterize most fractals, and they will serve as our guide:

1. Fractals have a fine structure, i.e., detail on arbitrarily small scales.
2. Fractals are usually defined by simple recursive process.
3. Fractals are too irregular to be described in traditional geometric language.
4. Fractals have some form of self-similarity.
5. Fractals have fractal dimension.

The first three of these properties use language you recognize, but in properties 4 and 5 you may wonder what "self-similarity" and "fractal dimension" mean. "Self-similarity" will be explained in a moment and "fractal dimension" in the next section. First, notice how the first three properties show up in the Sierpinski triangle.

1. *Fine Structure.* The organizing structure of the Sierpinski triangle is repeated at every iteration in finer and finer detail. Computer images give an idea of the infinitesimal detail of the attractor but because printers have finite limits the detail is never visible. If you magnify any portion of the Sierpinski triangle, however, you would see more of its detail at a smaller scale. No matter how many magnifications you do, there is still finer detail to be seen.

2. *Recursive Definition.* The sequence of figures that produces the Sierpinski triangle is recursively defined. The initial term is given as a figure at Stage 0, and a recursive rule tells you how to construct the next stage. Repeated application of the same rule at every subsequent stage produces the sequence.

3. *Traditional Geometry Inadequate.* Though Stage 0 is an equilateral triangle, and the recursion rule appeals to traditional notions of midpoints of sides, the Sierpinski triangle is not a triangle nor any other traditional geometric form. We end up with a set of points that make a recognizable picture, but one which does not conform to our usual intuition about geometric objects. The next two examples show how odd the Sierpinski triangle is when described in traditional language.

Example 1. What is the total perimeter of the enclosed triangular areas at each stage of the Sierpinski process?

Solution: Let us assume that the initial triangle has a side of length 1 in some appropriate unit of measure, so that the perimeter at the initial stage is 3. After one iteration, we have three triangles whose sides are of length ½, so each has a perimeter of $\frac{3}{2}$. Since there are 3 triangles at stage 1, there is a total perimeter of $3 \cdot \frac{3}{2}$ or $\frac{9}{2}$. After two iterations, there are nine triangles with sides of length ¼, so the total perimeter is $9 \cdot \frac{3}{4}$ or $\frac{27}{4}$. The results in the next few stages are collected in the following table, along with the general result:

Stage	0	1	2	3	4	...	n
Number of triangles	1	3	9	27	81	...	3^n
Length of side	1	½	¼	$\frac{1}{8}$	$\frac{1}{16}$	...	$\frac{1}{2^n}$
Perimeter of each triangle	3	$\frac{3}{2}$	$\frac{3}{4}$	$\frac{3}{8}$	$\frac{3}{16}$	...	$\frac{3}{2^n}$
Total perimeter of bounded area	3	$\frac{9}{2}$	$\frac{27}{4}$	$\frac{81}{8}$	$\frac{243}{16}$	...	$\frac{3^{n+1}}{2^n}$

Here we see an interesting phenomenon. The total perimeter of the bounded area forms an increasing sequence

$$3, \frac{9}{2}, \frac{27}{4}, \frac{81}{8}, \frac{243}{16}, ..., \frac{3^{n+1}}{2^n}$$

which is defined recursively by

$$a_0 = 3,$$
$$a_n = \tfrac{3}{2} a_{n-1}, n = 1, 2, 3, ...$$

This is a geometric sequence where the common ratio between successive terms is greater than 1: $r = \frac{3}{2}$. So what happens as n increases without bound? The successive terms also increase without bound: As $n \to \infty$, $a_n \to \infty$. We end up with a figure having an infinite perimeter totally enclosed within the original triangle whose perimeter is 3.

Example 2. What happens to the total *area* of the triangles remaining in the construction of a Sierpinski triangle?

Solution: Again to make the numbers easy, let us assume that the area of the initial triangle is 1 in some appropriate unit of measure. The Sierpinski process splits the original triangle into 4 equal parts after the first iteration, and one of those parts is removed. Thus the total area at stage 1 is $\frac{3}{4}$ of the original area. At stage 2, each of the quarters is split into quarters and one is removed, so we end up with $\frac{3}{4}$ of each of the three quarters, for a total area of $\frac{3}{4} \cdot \frac{3}{4} = \frac{9}{16}$. Filling in the table, we have:

Stage	0	1	2	3	4	...	n
Total area	1	$\frac{3}{4}$	$\frac{9}{16}$	$\frac{27}{64}$	$\frac{81}{256}$	...	$\left(\frac{3}{4}\right)^n$

This time we have the sequence

$$a_0 = 1$$
$$a_n = \frac{3}{4}a_{n-1}, n = 1, 2, 3, \ldots$$

where the ratio between successive terms is less than 1: $r = \frac{3}{4}$. Therefore, as $n \to \infty$, $a_n \to 0$. We end up with a figure whose area at the limit is 0. Now meditate on this while you think about the results of Example 2: We have a figure with zero area and infinite perimeter, all enclosed in the original triangle!

Self-similarity

Figure 2.3

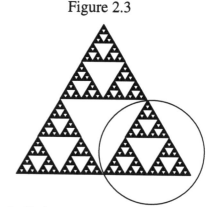

We now look at the fourth property of fractals.

4. *Self-similarity.* A figure is called *self-similar* if a part of the figure contains on a smaller scale an exact replica of the whole. In the case of the Sierpinski triangle, consider one of the three triangular corners like that enclosed in a circle in Figure 2.3. You see a half-size replica of the whole figure. If you blew it up to twice its size, you would have the original figure back again. Of course doubling the size of the particular figure in the diagram would not *exactly* replicate itself because this is a *finite* representation of the Sierpinski triangle. Exact replication happens only for the *infinite* figure that exists in your imagination.

In fact, the Sierpinski triangle is more than simply self-similar, it is amazingly self-similar. You don't have to be careful when you pick a portion to look for a small scale replica. In figure 2.3, one of the big corner triangles is circled; but if the circle had been drawn intersecting the triangle *anywhere*, it would have contained a replica of the whole. Obviously a small circle drawn completely in the white space has no replica of the triangle. But let just one piece of Sierpinski dust, one tiny black speck, inside your circle, and you've got a replica of the whole triangle on a small scale. This property is called *strict self-similarity* and defines a subset of self-similar figures.

For contrast, let's look at a figure that is self-similar but not strictly self-similar. Suppose you make a tree by taking a directed segment and at its head construct two directed segments, attached at their tail and making 120° angles with the original. Stages 0, 1, 2 and 3 are shown in Figure 2.4. If the process is iterated indefinitely, there is an attractor of the sequence which we might call a fractal tree. This fractal tree is self-similar but not *strictly* self-similar. (See Figure 2.5.)

Figure 2.4 A fractal tree

| Stage 0 | Stage 1 | Stage 2 | Stage 3 | Stage *n* |

If a circle is drawn more or less at random, including an arbitrary portion of the figure (as in the diagram on the left in Figure 2.5), it would not necessarily contain a small scale replica of the whole figure. However, if the circle is drawn with some care, including the end of one of the branches (as in the diagram on

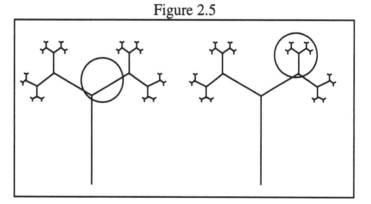

Figure 2.5

the right in Figure 2.5), then it does contain a small scale replica of the whole.

Such a fractal is an example of a self-similar figure that is not strictly self-similar. Most of what we see in nature is roughly self-similar, but not strictly self-similar. If you look at a coastline from an orbiting satellite, you will see a lot of squiggles, jigs and jags as you trace the edge of a continent with your eye. Take a normal plane ride over the same continent and you'll see a similar pattern of jigs and jags as you cross the coastline. Now stand on a rock with the ocean at your feet, and look closely at the boundary between your rock and the water: more jigs and jags. Get on your hands and knees with a magnifying glass and look at a pebble as it is washed at the ocean's edge and you see the similar jigs and jags. An electron microscope would reveal the same picture at an even smaller scale. But all this will come to a screeching halt shortly. *Matter is finite.* Molecules, quarks and photons have a small but finite diameter. The sequence does not go on indefinitely. The picture of the Sierpinski Triangle at stage *n* in Figure 2.2, was drawn by a computer that could only go so small, so the pictures, like nature, are not *strictly* self-similar. However, the notion of self-similar, even without strictness, turns out to be a useful concept to describe our world, and it is used as one of the defining qualities in fractal objects. The other defining quality, fractal dimension, will be developed in the next section.

Grid for Exercise 1, page 39

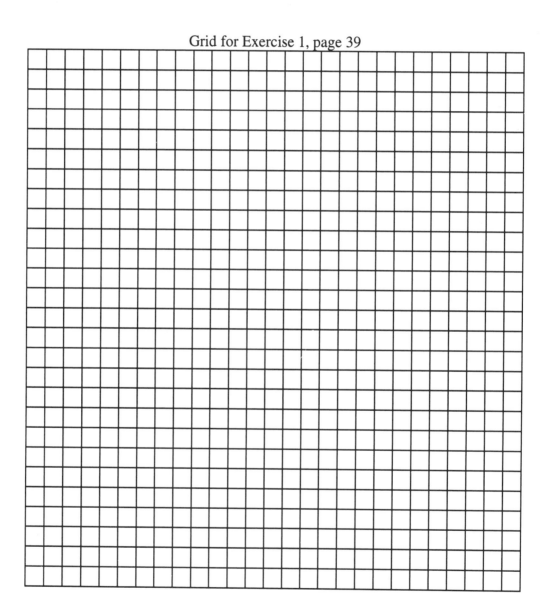

§1 Exercises

1. *The Sierpinski Carpet.* Start with a square, trisect the sides to make nine little squares, and then remove the middle square. Iterate on the remaining squares.

a) In the grid on page 38, shade the squares that show Stage 3 of the Sierpinski Carpet.
b) Count the number of shaded squares at each stage and generalize to stage n.

Stage	0	1	2	3	...	n
Number of shaded squares	1	8				

c) Suppose the shaded area at stage 0 is 1. Then the shaded area at stage 1 is 8/9. Figure out the shaded area in the next two stages and generalize to stage n.

Stage	0	1	2	3	...	n
Area of shaded squares	1	8/9				

d) What happens to the area as $n \to \infty$?
e) Is the Sierpinski Carpet self-similar? Strictly self-similar?

2. Suppose another carpet is made from an initial square by removing all but the corner and central squares after trisecting the sides. Stages 0 and 1 are shown at the right:

a) Make a grid like the one in Exercise 1 or use graph paper, and shade in squares to show the next two stages in the construction.
b) Calculate the area at stage n and determine what happens as $n \to \infty$.
c) Calculate the perimeter of the shaded area at stage n and determine what happens as $n \to \infty$.
d) Is the final figure self-similar? Strictly self-similar?

3. Suppose a strip of paper is laid flat on the table and then the left end folded over the right. Iterate the process by folding the crease (now the left end) over the right. At each stage, open up the strip of paper so the creases make a right angles. Looked at on edge, you'll see something like the following diagram on the next page.

a) Get a piece of paper and verify the results of the first two folds. Then continue for at least two more folds and draw a diagram of the strip when unfolded. Remember to fold left over right with the strip laid back down on the table in exactly the same way every time.

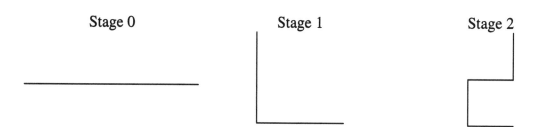

| Stage 0 | Stage 1 | Stage 2 |

b) Here is a way to model this experiment: Think of yourself as an ant walking along the edge of the paper, starting at the right-hand end. At stage 0 you walk all the way along the strip without making a turn. At stage 1, you make a right turn, so we'll model stage 1 by R. At stage 2, you make a right, then a right, then a left: RRL. Stage 3 should be RRLRRLL. What do you get for stage 4?

c) Can you see a pattern? Iterate some more and see if you can describe what is going on.

d) Find a copy of *Jurassic Park* and check out the diagrams at the beginning of each "Iteration."

e) Connect every other vertex of an unfolded strip at stage n. What do you discover?

4. Here's a way to explore self-similarity in nature. Go get a head of cauliflower and look at it. If you have a camera, take its picture. Now break off one of the main flowerets from the base of the stem and look at it. If you take its photograph, get close enough so the floweret fills up about as much of the frame as did the whole head in the first photo. Now break off one of the flowerets from the main floweret and look at it. Continue till you can't break off any more flowerets. Chop everything up and put it in a salad and meditate upon the self-similarity you are consuming. (If you don't like cauliflower, try broccoli.)

5. Find a fern and really look at it. How is it self-similar?

6. Repeat Exercise 6 with a tree, some lichen, a mountain, your bronchial tubes, your circulatory system, ...

7. In what sense could our decimal system be called self-similar? Think about a meter stick marked in decimeters, centimeters, millimeters, ...

8. You are familiar with Pascal's Triangle from previous courses. Recall that the entries are the coefficients of the terms in the binomial expansion of $(a+b)^n$, where n starts at 0 for the top row. See diagram on the next page.

a) Fill in the remaining rows. (Remember the trick? Each entry is the sum of the two entries directly above it.)

b) Now shade in all the boxes that contain an odd number, leaving the even numbered boxes white.

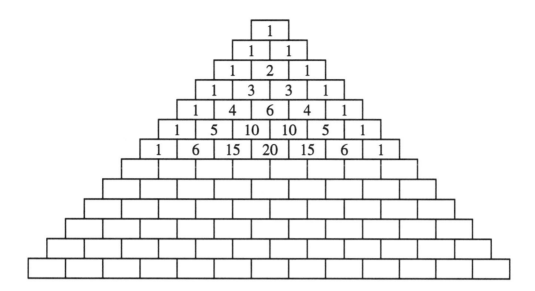

9. The pattern that emerges from the Pascal Triangle in Exercise 8 can be described as an iterative procedure for coloring in squares of a grid. Here are the rules: Two whites or two blacks give a white in the next row; one black and one white give a black in the next row.

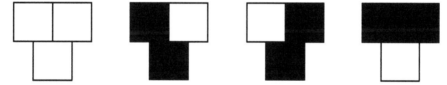

The pattern starts with one black square in the middle of the top row of the grid. Using the iterative rules, fill in the following grid:

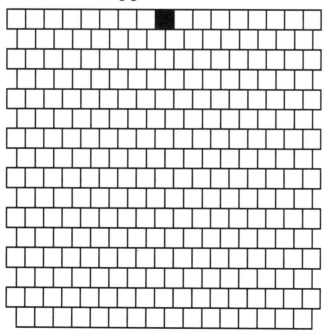

10. A computer or calculator screen can be thought of as a grid of square dots (called *pixels*) that can be made black or white, like coloring in a grid. The iterative procedure in Exercise 9 can by automated in a program. The grid of the calculator does not have alternate rows offset, so the rules would be as follows:

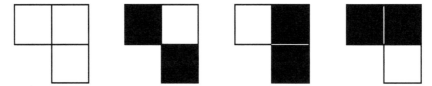

The grid is initialized by coloring the whole leftmost column black. Then rows can be colored using the iterative rules.

a) Test the rules on a piece of 32×32 graph paper.

b) Write a program to make the calculator produce an image using the same iterative rules. The calculator's screen is 63 dots high by 95 dots wide. A pixel is addressed as an ordered pair (*row*, *column*) where *row* is an integer from 0 to 62 inclusive and *column* from 0 to 94. (0, 0) is the pixel in the upper left corner of the screen and (62,94) is the pixel in the lower right. The command to turn on the pixel at the location (*row*, *column*) is Pxl-On (*row*, *column*). To turn on the pixel at *row* = 5 and *column* = 13, for example, press **2nd[DRAW] > POINTS 4: Pxl-On(5 , 1 3)**. To turn off a pixel, use **5:Pxl-Off(** using the same format as **4:Pxl-On(**. To toggle from on to off or vice versa, use **6:Pxl-Change(**. The last command, **7:pxl-Test(**, can be used to see if a pixel is on or off. The value of the pixel-test function is 1 if the pixel is on, 0 if the pixel is off. For instance, if the pixel at row 14 and column 35 were on, then pxl-Test(14,35) would have the value 1.

§2. Similarity Dimension

In everyday life, the notion of *dimension* is straightforward: a line has dimension 1, a plane 2 and physical space 3. You can think of the dimension as the number of coordinate axes needed to determine the location of a point. On a line we need just one coordinate, on a plane we need two, and in three-dimensional space we need three. We can also say that a point has zero dimension, because we need no coordinates at all to locate it when it takes up the whole space.

In short, we are comfortable talking about 0, 1, 2 and 3 dimensions. We can even generalize to *n* dimensions if we need more than 3 coordinates to specify a "point" in some "space." For example, in the inventory of pants in a men's clothing story (the "pants space"), each pair of pants might be specified by 5 coordinates: 1) waist size, 2) inseam, 3) style, 4) color, and 5) inventory number. Then (33, 30, Farmer Brown, green, 95-633) would specify a pair of green Farmer Browns with waist 33 and inseam 30, carrying the inventory number 95-633. The pants space of this store is five dimensional.

This natural way of thinking about dimension leads inevitably to integral dimensions, 0, 1, 2, 3, or higher. But the idea of dimension can get complicated. For example, think about a sheet of aluminum foil. It appears 2-dimensional when you first cut it off the roll and flatten it on the counter. But squeeze it up into a ball and what do you have? Something that looks more 3-dimensional. Now try flattening it out again. It never does quite settle back into the nice 2-dimensional form it originally had. There are ridges and valleys left over from crinkling it up. Now what would you call its dimension? It's certainly not as 3-dimensional as when it was in a ball, nor is it as 2-dimensional as when it came out of the box. It is not too far-fetched to say that it is now somewhere between 2 and 3 dimensional. If it were 2-dimensional, it would take up an area without filling up space. If it were 3-dimensional, it would completely fill up space. What we need is a number that measures the extent to which it rises up out of the plane to fill up 3-dimensional space. This number will be a number between 2 and 3 and we will call it the fractal dimension of this sheet of crumpled foil.

There are several ways to define such a number; there are many different fractal dimensions. (Remember this is still a young field, and things aren't as neat as you may be used to in math.) We'll start with the fractal dimension for self-similar figures, the *similarity dimension*, because it is relatively easy to define and because it is a prototype for several other fractal dimensions.

Figure 2.6

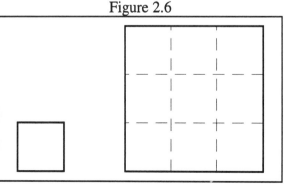

First think about a square, a

familiar object that has dimension 2. Recall that when you magnify the linear measure of a square by some number, say, 3, then the area is magnified by 3^2 or 9 (Figure 2.6). Note that the dimension is the power of 3 that gives 9.

To turn this insight into a formula, think about the process in reverse. Start with the large square on the right of Figure 2.6 (which we want to say has dimension 2), and think of reducing it to the unit square on the left. If you were using a photocopier, you'd key in a $33\frac{1}{3}\%$ reduction. That means you are reducing each linear dimension to $\frac{1}{3}$ its original length. You end up with a unit square with $\frac{1}{9}$th the original area, so you need 9 copies of the reduction to fill in the original. The relation between the reduction factor, 3, and the replacement number, 9, gives the dimension. Since $3^2 = 9$, the exponent 2 is exactly the dimension we are looking for. The dimension is the power of 3 that gives 9; the power of the reduction factor that gives the replacement number:

$$\text{Reduction factor}^{\text{Dimension}} = \text{Replacement number}.$$

You can see how this works for volumes in Figure 2.7. Reduce the large cube so that linear lengths are $\frac{1}{3}$ the original; that is, use a reduction factor of 3. Then you need 27 little cubes to replace the original. In this case, the reduction factor is cubed to equal the replacement number. The exponent is 3, and that agrees with our intuitive assignment of dimension 3 to the cube.

Figure 2.7

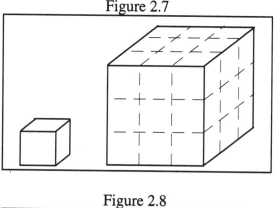

What about a line segment? If the reduction factor is 3 (as in Figure 2.8), then the replacement number is also 3, and the exponent we're calling dimension is 1: $3^1 = 3$.

Figure 2.8

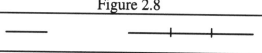

This idea works because a segment, a square and a cube are all self-similar figures. You can find parts of the figures that are reduced copies of the whole. In the case of a segment, the replacement number is equal to the reduction factor. In the case of a square, the replacement number is the square of the reduction factor. In the case of the cube, the replacement number is the cube of the reduction factor. In each case, the exponent is the natural dimension. If we let r stand for the reduction factor and n stand for the replacement number, then the dimension, D, is given by the formula:

$$r^D = n.$$

This same idea will work for *any* self-similar figure, including those that are not Euclidean, such as the Sierpinski triangle. If we identify a reduction factor and a replacement number, we can come up with an exponent that we could call "dimension" without changing our notions of dimension in the Euclidean case. One corner of the triangle (enclosed in the circle in Figure 2.9) is a 50% reduction of the whole; the linear dimensions are reduced by a factor of 2. But the original triangle is made up of 3 copies of the corner, so the replacement number is 3. Therefore, $r = 2$ and $n = 3$; and D is the exponent that works in the equation:

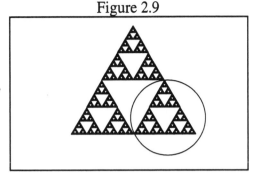

Figure 2.9

$$2^D = 3.$$

To solve the equation $2^D = 3$, you need to recall some of your previous skill with logarithms. Take the log of both sides of this equation. (You can use a log function with any base; they all give the same result here – see Exercise 1 at the end of this section.)

$$\log(2^D) = \log 3$$
$$D \log 2 = \log 3$$
$$D = \frac{\log 3}{\log 2}$$

If you use base 10, your calculator will give you the following numerical results (to four decimal places):

$$D = \frac{0.4771}{0.3010} = 1.5850...$$

Thus the fractal dimension of the Sierpinski Triangle is 1.585 – more than a line and less than a square. It seems to fill up more of an area than a line does, but there are a lot of gaps that make it less than a Euclidean area.

Now that we have used logs to solve the dimension equation for D, we see how to rewrite the equation in terms of D. If r is the reduction factor and n is the replacement number, the fractal dimension D of any self-similar figure is given by:

$$D = \frac{\log n}{\log r}.$$

To see more examples of the fractal dimension of self-similar figures, we introduce two more classical fractals, the Cantor set and the Koch curve.

The Cantor Set

Georg Cantor (1845-1918) was a German mathematician who studied fractals about 100 years before the word *fractal* existed. While most of his colleagues were studying the well-behaved sets of numbers on which the calculus is based, Cantor was drawn to think about mathematical misbehavior, and in 1883 he published a paper to present an example where calculus failed spectacularly. That example is now known as the Cantor set, and it turns out to be one of the most important fractals known.

Here is the way the Cantor set is constructed. Start with the unit interval; that is, all the numbers between 0 and 1 inclusive. (This set is called a *closed* interval because it contains its endpoints, and it is denoted [0,1]). From this set remove the middle third; that is, all the numbers between 1/3 and 2/3, leaving both 1/3 and 2/3 in the set. From the closed interval

Figure 2.10

Stage 0	0_____1	
Stage 1	0_____1/3 2/3_____1	

[0, 1] we remove the *open* interval denoted (1/3, 2/3). At this stage we are left with the numbers from 0 to 1/3 and from 2/3 to 1. In notation, [0,1/3] ∪[2/3,1].

Now you do the process again on these two subintervals. When you remove the middle third of each, you end up with four intervals: [0,1/9] ∪ [2/9,1/3] ∪ [2/3,7/9] ∪ [8/9,1]. Then you continue iterating indefinitely, and you generate something that looks like Figure 2.11.

Figure 2.11

Stage 0	————————	
Stage 1	——— ———	
Stage 2	— — — —	
Stage 3	- - - - - - - -	
Stage 4	·· ·· ·· ·· ·· ·· ·· ··	
Stage n	·· ·· ·· ·· ·· ·· ·· ··	

Obviously the intervals get smaller and smaller although there are more and more of them at each stage. How many do we end up with? Infinitely many. How big are they? Infinitely small. What's its fractal dimension? To answer that, we need to identify a reduction factor and replacement number.

First note that the Cantor set is strictly self-similar. Take the interval from 0 to 1/3, for example, and expand it by a factor of 3 as in Figure 2.12. Each of the little dots is actually the end product of an infinity of middle third removals, and when magnified by a factor of three, they reveal the same pattern as the original set. The empty interval (1/9, 2/9) becomes the empty interval (1/3, 2/3), the empty interval (7/27, 8/27) becomes the empty interval (7/9, 8/9). And so on.

Figure 2.12

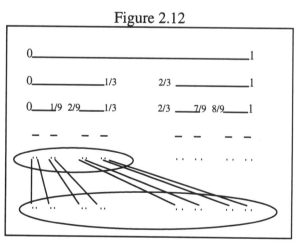

It should be clear that at every iteration, you reduce by a factor of 3 and replace with 2 copies of the reduction. Therefore, the reduction factor r is 3 and the replacement number n is 2. It follows that the dimension D is:

$$D = \frac{\log n}{\log r} = \frac{\log 2}{\log 3} = 0.6309...$$

The Cantor set has a dimension between 0 and 1, more than a point and less than a line. Does this make sense? The construction process proceeds by removing middle thirds, leaving a bunch of closed intervals at each stage. But there are *no* intervals left in the end, for if there were, you'd have to remove its middle third. There are *no intervals left!* There are only scattered points clustered in certain locations. Between every two numbers of the set there are numbers that do not lie in the set. Once again, we end up with dust.

What numbers are left in the set by this process? Well, obviously 0 and 1 are left. So are 1/3 and 2/3. And 1/9, 2/9, 7/9 and 8/9. All these numbers are in the Cantor set. In fact all the endpoints of all the removed intervals are left in the set. It looks like we could probably come up with a formula for these numbers, all being fractions with some power of 3 in the denominator. (Before going on, stop and write down the new endpoints left at stage 3. Hint: There are 8 of them and they all have 27 in the denominator.) If you think you've got it figured out now, you got fooled by the Cantor set, just like most everybody who sees this set for the first time. (Join the crowd!) It turns out that there are lots of numbers in the set that don't look anything like these nice fractions with powers of 3 in the denominator. You may be surprised to learn that $\frac{1}{4}$ is a point of the set. In fact. when you do Exercises 12-18 at the end of this section, you'll see that *most* of the Cantor points are not endpoints of removed intervals; the endpoints are only a small fraction of the numbers in the Cantor set.

The Koch Curve

In 1904, a Swedish mathematician named Helge von Koch published an article in which he introduced the curve now named for him. Little is known of von Koch beyond this one article; unlike Cantor, his seminal thoughts about fractals were not matched by other creative output in the field. His curve, however, has become an important fractal both because of its history and because its method of construction can be generalized in many interesting directions.

The process involves the replacement of a segment by several reduced copies of itself arranged in an artful way. The original segment is called the *initiator* and the first stage replacement is called the *generator*. For the Koch curve, a segment is reduced by a factor of three, then four copies are joined together to make a tent-like replacement (Figure 2.13).

At the next stage, each of the four new segments is replaced by a similar tent-like construction of 4 segments 1/3 the length of the generator's segments (or 1/9 the length of the initiator).

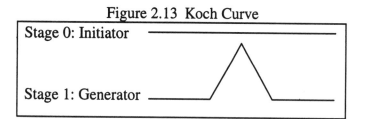

Figure 2.13 Koch Curve

Stage 0: Initiator

Stage 1: Generator

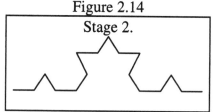

Figure 2.14

Stage 2.

Now you iterate the process indefinitely and you end up with an attractor that looks something like the diagram in Figure 2.15.

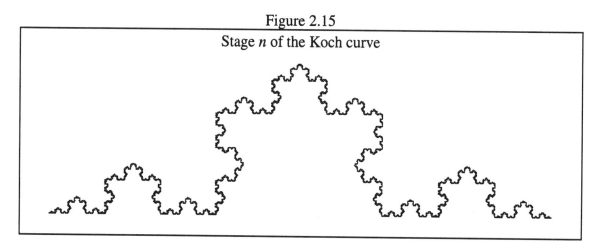

Figure 2.15

Stage *n* of the Koch curve

What about self-similarity for the Koch curve? Look at the left -hand third of the curve and magnify it by 3. The result is the same as the original. In fact, like the Sierpinski triangle and the Cantor set, if you take any little piece of the curve and magnify it enough, you will see a copy of the original curve: strict self-similarity.

From looking at the initiator and generator of the Koch curve, you can see that the replacement rule is: Reduce by 3; make 4 copies and replace. The reduction factor *r* is 3 and the replacement number *n* is 4, so the fractal dimension *D* is:

$$D = \frac{\log n}{\log r} = \frac{\log 4}{\log 3} = 1.26...$$

The Koch curve is more than a line and less than a plane. It has so many infinitely small squiggles that it "takes up more room" than a simple continuous curve; it fills up more of an area than a line but does not completely fill a plane.

The Cantor set is created by removals, replacing a segment by 2 copies of a one-third reduction; the Koch curve is created by additions, replacing a segment by 4 copies of a one-third reduction. The Cantor process moves away from a 1-dimensional figure toward a 0-dimensional figure. The Koch process moves away from a 1-dimensional figure toward a 2-dimensional figure. The fractal dimension gives us a numerical measure of where each of these figures ends up between the natural, integral dimensions.

The similarity dimension is one type of fractal dimension. In a more advanced course, you might even learn that it is a special case of the *Hausdorff dimension*, named after the great German mathematician Felix Hausdorff (1868-1942) who laid the groundwork for many of these ideas. And there are other measures of dimension. In the next section, we'll look at the *box-counting dimension* that can be used to measure the fractal dimension of non-self-similar figures.

§2. Exercises

1. Show that $\dfrac{\log_a n}{\log_a r} = \dfrac{\log_b n}{\log_b r}$ for any bases a and b.

2. Given that $r^D = n$, show that $D = \dfrac{\log n}{\log r}$.

In Exercises 3-6, an initiator and a generator are given. Draw two more stages of the iteration. If the process is continued *ad infinitum*, compute the fractal dimension of the resulting curve.

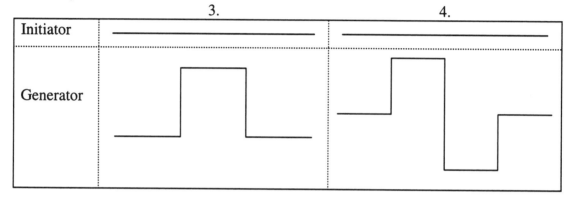

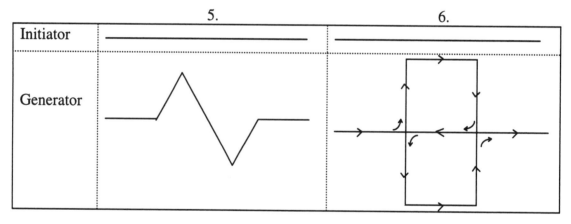

(The attractor in Exercise 6 is called the Peano Curve after the Italian mathematician Giuseppe Peano (1858-1932). It is a startling example of a space-filling curve. It covers every point in a square without intersecting itself. Though continuous, it has no line segments or smooth curves in it. It could be described as all corners.)

7. Like the Sierpinski triangle, each printed dot of the Cantor set contains an image of the whole Cantor set. For example, consider the fourth dot of the last line in Figure 2.11, reproduced in this diagram. That dot represents the interval of length

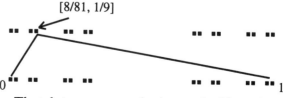

1/81, extending from 8/81 to 1/9. Define a linear function that matches every Cantor point in this interval to every point in the whole Cantor set. [Hint: First translate the interval so that its left-hand endpoint lands on the origin. Then expand the interval so that it covers the unit interval. (Remember: the speck had a length of 1/81.)]

8. Look back at the paper-folding problem in Exercise 3 of the preceding section. You can think of the initiator as a line segment, and the generator as the two legs of an isosceles right triangle built on the initiator as hypotenuse. At stage 2 and beyond, the isosceles triangles are constructed alternately on the left and right sides of the initiating segment, as shown in the diagram.

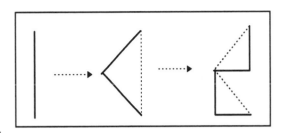

a) Continue the construction through stages 3 and 4. Verify that you derive the paper-folding curve of Exercise 3 of the last section.

b) What is the similarity dimension of its attractor?

9. A Cantor set may also be made be removing the middle fifth of the initiating interval. Start with the unit interval [0, 1]. Remove the open interval (0.4, 0.6), leaving the union of the two closed intervals [0, 0.4] ∪ [0.6, 1]. Iterate.

a) Draw stages 0, 1, 2, and 3 of the middle fifth removal, indicating the endpoints of the intervals at each stage.

b) What is the fractal dimension of the middle fifth Cantor set? How does it compare to the middle third Cantor set?

10. A two-dimensional analog of the middle third Cantor set would start with the unit square and remove middle third areas. Stages 0 and 1 are shown in the diagram. Sketch stages 2 and 3, and compute the fractal dimension of the figure that results from infinite iteration.

Stage 0　　　　　　Stage 1

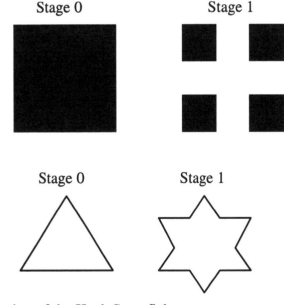

11. When the Koch construction is used with an equilateral triangle as initiator, then stage 1 looks like a Star of David. With infinite iterations, the figure is known as the Koch Snowflake. The first two stages are illustrated in the diagram.

Stage 0　　　　　Stage 1

a) Draw the next two stages in the construction of the Koch Snowflake.

b) Is the snowflake self-similar? Strictly self-similar?

c) Suppose the side of the initial triangle is 1 unit long in some measurement unit. Then the perimeter of the triangle is 3. Compute the perimeter of the figures at each stage of construction and generalize to stage n.

Stage	0	1	2	3	4	...	n
Perimeter	3						

d) What happens to the perimeter of the Koch Snowflake as $n \to \infty$?

e) If the side of the initial triangle is 1 unit, then the area is $\sqrt{3}/4$ square units (the base is 1 and the height is $\sqrt{3}/2$). At stage 1, the area is increased by 3 little equilateral triangles. At stage 2, the area is increased again, this time by 12 even smaller equilateral triangles. Continue this process, computing the area at each stage. Generalize to stage n.

Stage	0	1	2	3	4	...	n
Area	$\sqrt{3}/4$						

f) What happens to the area of the Koch Snowflake as $n \to \infty$?

Exercises 12-18 explore the Cantor set in greater depth. The question is this: What are the numbers in the Cantor set? By removing an open interval from the middle of each closed interval at each stage, some numbers are left. The numbers that are never removed constitute the Cantor set. What are they? Obviously, 0 and 1 are never removed, so they are in the Cantor set. After the first removal, the endpoints 1/3 and 2/3 are also left and they too stay in the Cantor set. After stage 2, 1/9, 2/9, 7/9 and 8/9 are also left. Clearly the endpoints of the middle thirds are left after every stage of removal.

12. What are the endpoints left after the removal of the middle third at stage 3?

13. What will be the denominators of the new endpoints created and left by the stage 4 removals?

14. How many endpoints have been left after the middle third removals at stage n?

Each point in the Cantor set can be uniquely identified by an infinite sequence of R's and L's that serve as its "address." Each time a middle third is removed, there are two subintervals left, one on the left and one on the right. At each stage, a point's location is indicated by R if it is in the right hand interval and L if it is the left hand interval. Its address, then, is given by the infinite sequence that arises by noting R or L at each state of the construction. For instance, the address for 0 is LLLLL... because it is in the left hand interval after each removal. Similarly, the address for 1/3 is LRRRR..., and for 8/9 is RRLLLL....

15. Give the addresses for: a) 1   b) 7/27   c) 20/81

16. The points you identified in Exercise 15 were all endpoints of the intervals left after each middle third removal. What is the common characteristic shared by the addresses of endpoints?

17. Give an example of an infinite string of R's and L's that does not have the characteristic you identified in Exercise 16. This must be a point in the Cantor set that is not an interval endpoint. Since most infinite strings will not have the characteristic of endpoints, we see that the endpoints make up a small subset of the Cantor set.

18. Can you tell what number you get from the address you identified in Exercise 17? Here is how you can turn addresses into numbers. If an R occurs in the nth place (counting in from the left), write $\dfrac{2}{3^n}$, otherwise write nothing; then add up all the numbers you get. For example, check that LRRRRR... $= \dfrac{1}{3}$. You ignore the L and note that the first R occurs in the 2nd place so you write $\dfrac{2}{3^2}$. The next R is $\dfrac{2}{3^3}$, and so on. Adding everything up, we have $\dfrac{2}{3^2}+\dfrac{2}{3^3}+\dfrac{2}{3^4}+\cdots=\dfrac{2}{9}+\dfrac{2}{27}+\dfrac{2}{81}+\cdots$. We recognize this as a geometric series with initial term $a_0=\dfrac{2}{9}$ and common ratio $r=\dfrac{1}{3}$. Hence the sum is $\dfrac{a_0}{1-r}=\dfrac{2/9}{1-1/3}=\dfrac{2/9}{2/3}=\dfrac{2}{9}\cdot\dfrac{3}{2}=\dfrac{1}{3}$.

a) Show that the address RRLLLL... gives the number 8/9.
b) Find the number with address LRLRRRRR....
c) Find the number with address LRLRLLLLL....
d) Find the number with address LRLRLRLRLR....

§3. Boxcount Dimension

The fractal dimension presented in the previous section works for self-similar figures. This section presents another way to measure dimension, a process that can be applied to any figure, whether it is self-similar or not. The result of this process, the *boxcount dimension*, can be applied to curlicues, coastlines and arbitrary squiggles (like the one in Figure 2.16, for instance).

Figure 2.16

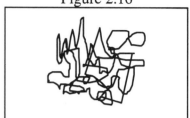

The boxcount process is simple to describe for a plane figure. You place a square *r*-by-*r* grid over the figure and count the number of boxes, *n*, that contain a portion of the figure. You then refine the grid and repeat the process, generating a sequence of ordered pairs (r, n), where the grid size *r* is the number of divisions on each edge of the grid, and *n* is the boxcount. For example, using the squiggle in Figure 2.16, and grids of size 3, 6, 8 and 12, we would have the ordered pairs (r, n) shown in Figure 2.17. All nine boxes of the 3-by-3 grid contain a piece of the figure, 20 boxes of the 6-by-6 grid, 32 boxes of the 8-by-8 grid, and 61 of the 12-by-12 grid. The corresponding ordered pairs are $(3, 9)$, $(6, 20)$, $(8, 32)$, and $(12, 61)$.

Figure 2.17

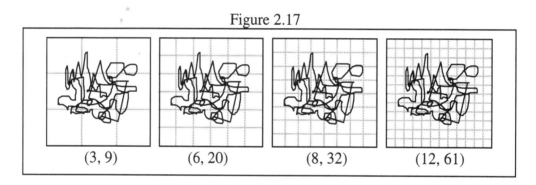

| $(3, 9)$ | $(6, 20)$ | $(8, 32)$ | $(12, 61)$ |

It turns out that *n* is roughly proportional to some power of *r*, and that power is the boxcount dimension of the figure. In other words, for some constant of proportionality *k*, it is approximately correct to say that

$$n = kr^D,$$

where the exponent *D* is the boxcount dimension. The question is: Given the specific ordered pairs in Figure 2.17, how do we find the exponent? The answer is: The calculator. Once you give the TI-83 the four points, it will plot the points, fit a function, and find the exponent. The particular kind of function we want to fit to this data is called a *power function*. Given any set of points, the calculator computes the best fitting power function, using the standard statistical measure of "best fitting." (Those who have had statistics know that the best fitting function is the one that minimizes the sum of the squared vertical distances from data points to function. But you don't need that information; you can trust the calculator on this one.) Here's how it works:

Curve fitting with the calculator

First record your points in lists as if they were statistical data. Press the **STAT** key and select the EDIT menu. When you press **ENTER**, you see three of the six lists, L1 through L6, where you can record data. You should enter the grid sizes (r) in one list and the corresponding boxcounts (n) in another. Suppose we use L1 and L2. If there is any data in those lists, you can clear them by using an up-arrow to place the cursor on the list name, L1 for example, and pressing **CLEAR** and **ENTER**. The calculator is waiting for an entry in L1(1), which in this case is the first grid size, 3.

After you enter the grid sizes in L1 and the boxcounts in L2, press **2nd[STAT PLOT]** to set up the scatter plot. (You can plot up to three sets of data points at once, but you need do only one now.) Turn on, say, Plot 1 by pressing **1:Plot1...Off** in the STAT PLOTS menu, and then select On from the first line.

Figure 2.18

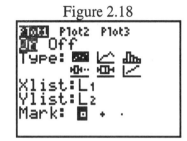

In the second line, Type, there are six icons representing different kinds of statistical graphs. The default is the first icon representing a scatter plot, and you should select it. In the Xlist you want the name of the list you used for the grid sizes, and the default is L1; in the Ylist you want the boxcounts, and the default is L2. If you have used other lists, enter their names. (Notice that the cursor is in alphabetic mode when you enter list names, because names of up to 4 letters can be given to lists. To learn how to name lists, see the TI-83 manual.) Finally, in the last line, select a little box ☐ as the Mark. You should see the screen in Figure 2.18.

Now you should set an appropriate **WINDOW**, or let the calculator set it automatically by pressing **ZOOM 9:ZoomStat**.

Finally, turn off all functions in the Y= menu so they don't get graphed when you graph the data points. To do that, press **Y=** and place your cursor over any equals-sign that is highlighted. When you press **ENTER**, you take the function out of graphing mode, indicated by an equals-sign that is not highlighted. (When you press **ENTER** again, the equals-sign is once more highlighted and the function is back in graphing mode.) Or you can take all the functions out of graphing mode at once by pressing [VARS], selecting Y-VARS, pressing 4:On/Off and then 2:FnOff. Finally, press **GRAPH** and you will see a scatter plot of your data points (Figure 2.19).

Figure 2.19

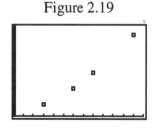

To calculate the best fitting power function, you start by pressing **STAT > CALC** and, from the CALC menu, select **A:PwrReg**. And you will see PwrReg pasted on the home screen (Figure 2.20). You can now specify the

Figure 2.20

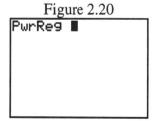

names of the lists to be used as the Xlist and Ylist, but
the default is L1 and L2. If you have used those lists, you
can now press **ENTER**. If not, enter the list names,
separated by a comma, after the expression PwrReg on
your home screen, and then press **ENTER**. You will now
see the screen in Figure 2.21 giving the values of the
constants a (our scaling factor k) and b (the boxcount

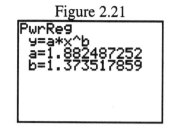

Figure 2.21

dimension D). We see that the boxcount dimension of the squiggle is about 1.37. This
tells us that the figure is more complicated than a 1-dimensional line but still leaves a lot
of the 2-dimensional space uncovered.

The process of fitting a curve to a set of data points is called *regression analysis*,
and the curve is called the *regression curve*. We have done a *power regression*, and
that's why you selected A: PwrReg to do the calculations. The word "regression" comes
from the type of data used originally when this form of analysis was developed.

The calculator automatically stores the best fitting
function and will graph it along with the data points if you
wish to see it. You give the graphing instruction at the
same time you instruct the calculator to do the power
regression by saying which function of the Y= list you want
to use as the best fitting function. If you are using the
default lists L1 and L2, you simply enter a function name,
say Y1, after the instruction PwrReg (see Figure 2.22). If
you used other lists and entered them after PwrReg, then
you add Y1 to the end of the command, separated from the
last list name by a comma. You find Y1 by pressing **VARS**
> Y-VARS 1:Function 1:Y1. Now you are almost ready to see
the graph. First make sure all other functions in whatever
mode are switched off. Second, make sure you are now in
function mode, not sequence mode as you were

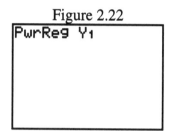

Figure 2.22

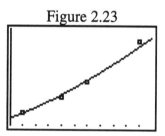

Figure 2.23

for the exercises in previous chapters. Press **MODE**, go to the fourth line, highlight Func
and press **ENTER**. Now (finally!) press **GRAPH** and you will see a screen that looks like
Figure 2.23.

The boxcount dimension for the drawing in Figure 2.16 was based on four data
points. That may seem like a rather small number of points to determine a curve and
compute a dimension. If you wanted a more refined number, you would need to continue
the process, generating a longer sequence of points as the basis for your curve. The
resulting dimension would still depend to some extent on how many points you included
in your data, how fine a grid you drew, how you placed the grid on the figure, and so on
(not to mention how much patience you have). You can perhaps imagine a succession of
computations using finer and finer grids, producing a sequence of numbers D_n, the
boxcount dimension for the nth refinement. If all goes well, this sequence will approach a
limit which should more properly be called the boxcount dimension. But for most

purposes, we stop at a reasonable point in the process and use the resulting power function exponent as the boxcount dimension.

Relating the boxcount and self-similar dimensions

We have demonstrated the boxcounting process on an arbitrary figure, but it can also be applied to self-similar figures. Will it produce the same number as the self-similar dimension? Sometimes. Remember the boxcounting process depends on personal choice and finite limitations, so it will frequently differ somewhat from the self-similarity dimension. As an example, look at the Koch Snowflake in Figure 2.24, made by doing the Koch construction on the sides of an equilateral triangle. The results of a boxcount on a 6th generation Koch Snowflake are shown in figure 2.25.

Figure 2.24 The Koch Snowflake

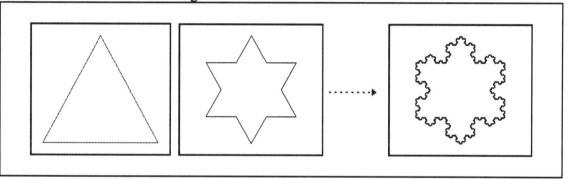

Figure 2.25 Koch Snowflake boxcount

Grid Size r	Boxcount n
4	16
8	44
16	96
32	232
64	551

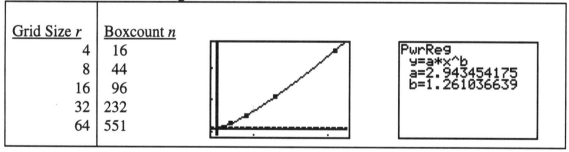

```
PwrReg
y=a*x^b
a=2.943454175
b=1.261036639
```

According to this analysis, the boxcount dimension of the Koch Snowflake is 1.2610... which compares to the self-similar dimension of $\dfrac{\log 4}{\log 3} = 1.2618...$ Not bad.

Why does boxcounting work?

You have probably already noticed that the boxcount dimension and the self-similar dimension both occur as an exponent in a formula of the form $n = r^D$. For the self-similar dimension, r was the reduction factor and n the replacement number. In the boxcount definition, *r* was the grid size and *n* the number of boxes. For non-self-similar figures, the grid size is something like the reduction number, and the number of boxes something like the replacement number. Refinement of the grid in the boxcounting process breaks the underlying figure into smaller and smaller pieces, as if the box size were the reduction factor of the whole. Then the number of boxes that cover the figure is essentially the number of reduced copies needed to replace the original figure. If you blackened the covering boxes of a very fine grid, you'd have a close approximation of the original figure, recalling the reduction-and-replacement process with self-similar figures. Because the reduction and replacement of a grid covering is not precise, and the process involves a limit, the two measures are different. But there is a similar concept underlying each, and both give useful measures of non-integral dimension.

§3. Exercises Find the boxcount dimension of the following figures.

1. A sine wave:

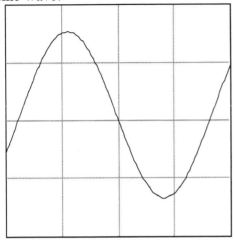 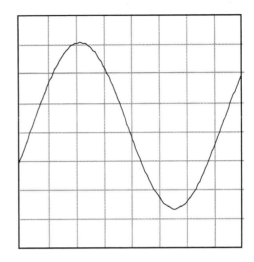

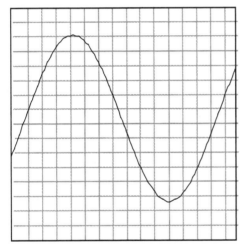 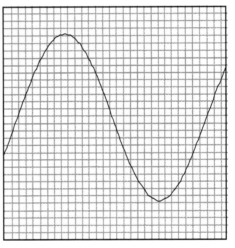

2. A line:

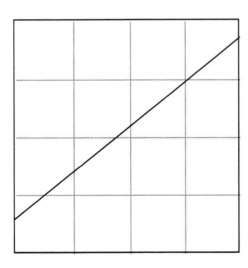 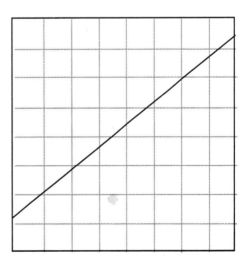

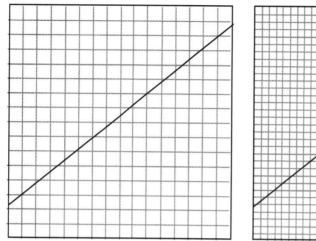 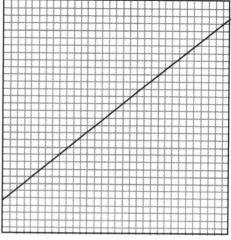

3. A filled circle:

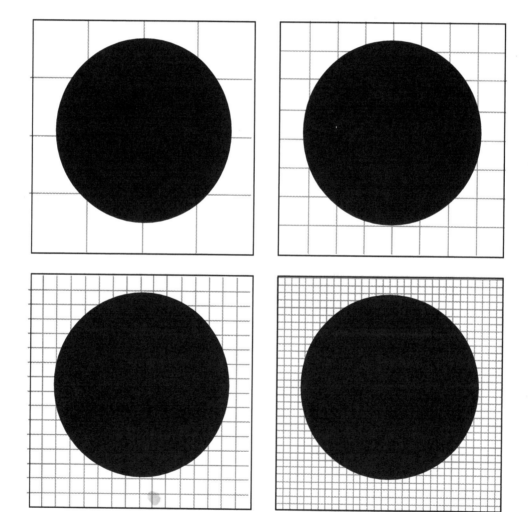

4. A rosette:

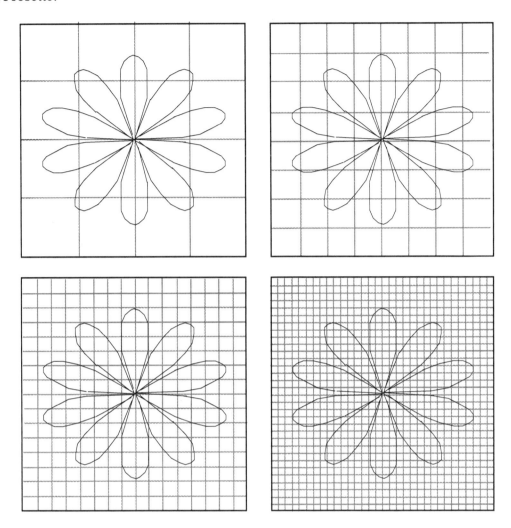

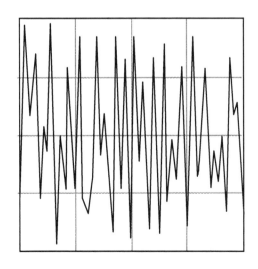

5. A rugged mountain:

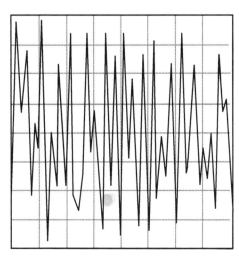

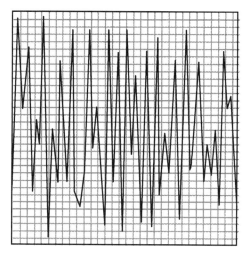 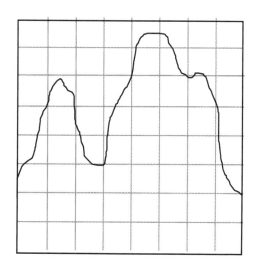

6. Hills and valleys:

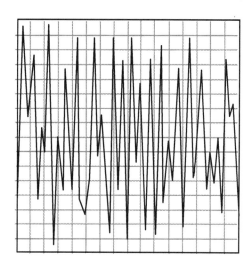 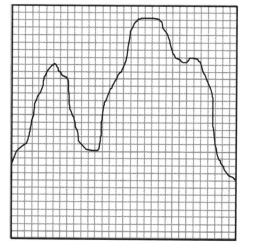

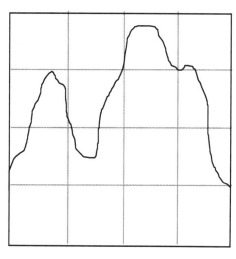 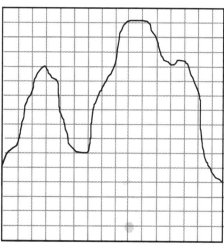

7. The coastline of an island:

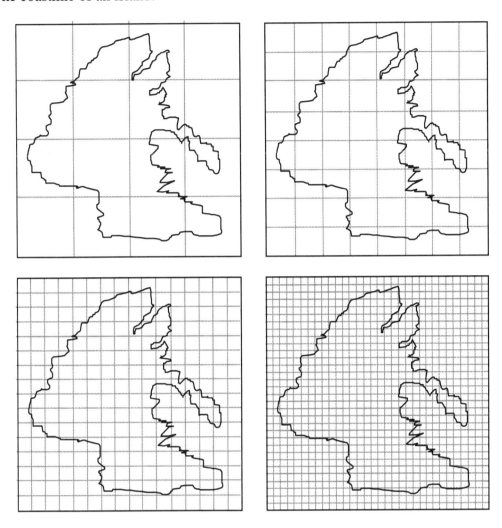

8. A Sierpinski Triangle:

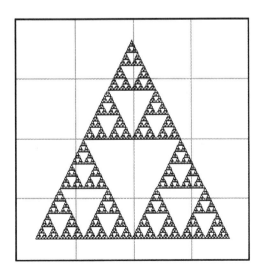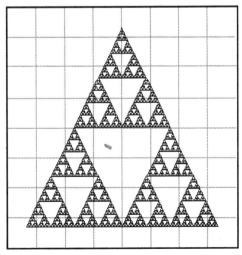

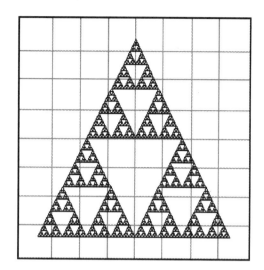 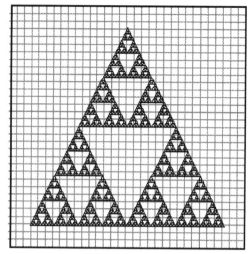

9. Compare your count for the Sierpinski Triangle using a computer and WINFEED
software (see Bibliography). Open WINFEED, select Example, and from the menu select
Fractal Curve. In the Library, select Cantor-like and then Triangle. Click Next enough
times to bring up generation 6 of the Sierpinski Triangle. Then click Boxes and then
Calculate to see a boxcount for grids from 1-by-1 through 128-by-128.
a) Using only grid sizes 4, 8, 16 and 32, compute the dimension and compare with your
   results in Exercise 8.
b) Use all eight grid sizes from WINFEED and compare again.
c) Click Boxes and Randomize corners to relocate the triangle in the grid. Recalculate
   and compare the results with the answers in parts (a) and (b).

10. Follow the procedure of Exercise 9 for the Arrowhead: From the Library, select
Cantor-like and then Arrowhead. Click Next enough times to bring up generation 8 of
the Arrowhead. Compare these results with the answers for the Sierpinski Triangle in
Exercises 8 and 9.

11. Use WINFEED to compute a boxcount dimension for the Koch Snowflake (from the
Islands submenu) using a generation 6 drawing.
a) Using only grid sizes 4, 8, 16, 32, and 64, compute the dimension and compare with
   the results in Figure 2.25.
b) Use all eight grid sizes from WINFEED and compare again.
c) Click Boxes and Randomize corners to relocate the triangle in the grid. Recalculate
   and compare the results with the answers in parts (a) and (b).

Chapter 3

ORBIT ANALYSIS

§1. Deterministic Chaos

The name Chaos Theory might seem to imply that its investigators are proponents of disorder, but a chaologist is doing much the same as other human beings: looking for order. The first step to understanding is to see and identify patterns. If you can see a relationship between two seemingly unrelated objects, then you have the beginnings of insight. If you can identify a pattern in seemingly random phenomena, you have the beginnings of understanding. Gallileo's insights into the relationship between time and distance of a falling ball set the stage for much of our contemporary understanding of the laws of motion. Students of chaos are looking inside randomness for subtle indications of pattern that will lead to deeper understanding of the order in the world around us. They are trying to make sense out of baffling data, trying to see through the chaos to an underlying order.

So how does one go about seeing patterns in random data? We start by reversing the question: How does an orderly process produce chaotic data? If we can understand how complexity arises out of simplicity, we may learn how to see simplicity hidden underneath complexity.

The chaos that we study is *deterministic chaos*, the production of unpredictable data through the iteration of a simple mathematical function. The data is the sequence of numbers that results from the iteration. The initial term of the sequence is the first number input into the function and is called the *seed*. The entire sequence is called the *orbit* of the seed.

Example 1. What is the orbit of the seed 0.2 under iteration of the function $f(x) = 2x(1-x)$?

Solution: The orbit is the sequence defined recursively by:

$$a_0 = 0.2$$
$$a_n = 2a_{n-1}(1-a_{n-1}), \text{ for } n = 1, 2, 3, ...$$

Using your calculator, press **MODE** and select Seq and G-T. In the Y= menu, set

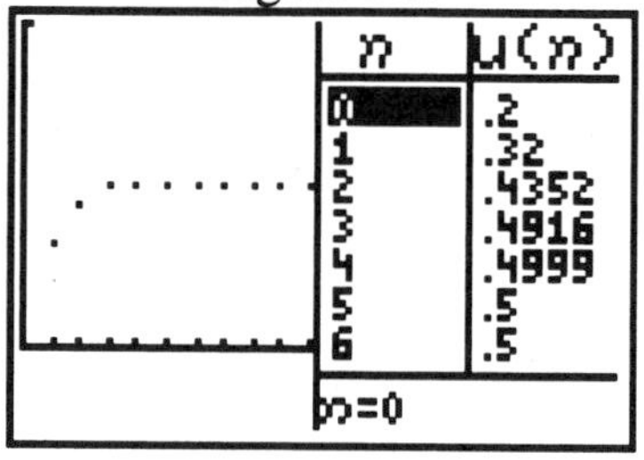

$u(n)=2u(n-1)(1-u(n-1))$. Press **WINDOW** and set nMin to **0**, nMax to **10**, Xmin to **0**, Xmax to **10**, Ymin to **0**, and Ymax to **1**. With these settings you will see the table and graph of the orbit as in Figure 3.1. It looks as if the orbit settles down on 0.5.

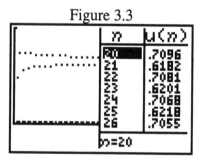
Figure 3.1

A word of caution: The calculator is doing the best it can, *but the orbit never really gets to 0.5*. It is an infinite sequence that *approaches* 0.5 as a limit. By the fifth iteration, however, the points of the orbit are closer to 0.5 than the calculator can distinguish, so it gives up and tells us, incorrectly, that 0.5 *is* a point of the orbit. You should use the calculator's results to guide you, but not fool you...

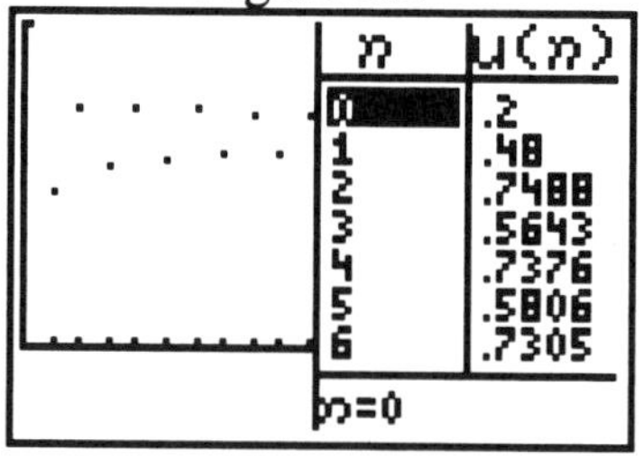

Example 2. What is the orbit of the seed 0.2 under iteration of the function $f(x) = 3x(1-x)$?

Solution: The only difference between this example and Example 1 is the constant in the function f. Make that change in the Y= menu and you will see the results in Figure 3.2. There is no clear pattern yet visible. We can take a look further along the orbit by changing TblStart to 20, nMax and Xmax both to 30. See Figure 3.3.

Figure 3.2

Figure 3.3

The numbers are still wobbling back and forth so it is hard to tell what is happening to this orbit. Maybe if we iterate enough, the orbit will settle down on one number as it did in Example 1. On the other hand, maybe it will settle down on two different numbers, jumping back and forth between them on successive iterations. Or maybe something else will happen. It's hard to say. To look further along the orbit, check $u(100)$ and $u(101)$. You'll see the results in Figure 3.4. It still hasn't settled down. Iterate 500 times and

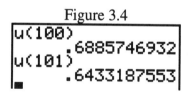
Figure 3.4

the next two points are 0.6769... and 0.6560...; still wobbling. After 1000 iterations the points are 0.6740... and 0.6591... The eventual behavior of this orbit is still questionable, and we'll leave it unanswered until a later section when we will have developed some sharper analytic tools.

Example 3. What is the orbit of the seed 0.2 under iteration of the function $f(x) = 4x(1-x)$?

Solution: If you change the constant of the sequence in the Y= menu to 4, and define the table and the window constants as in Example 1, you will see the graph and table as in Figure 3.5. The dots are all over the map and there seems to be no pattern in the first few points of the orbit. To see more of the graph, change the display back to full screen (press **MODE** and select Full), and change *n*Max and Xmax both to 40. You'll see the graph in Figure 3.6. Again, the dots seem randomly scattered, so change the graph type to a line to give the graph in Figure 3.7. Still no pattern.

Figure 3.5	Figure 3.6	Figure 3.7
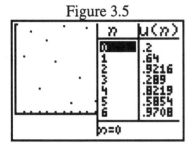	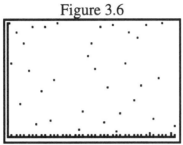	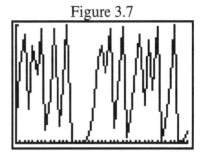

If you did 80 iterations (or 800 or 8 zillion), you'd still see no pattern. This orbit is chaotic in the sense that it is unpredictable. It does not settle down to a single value, it does not alternate periodically between two values, it doesn't end up in a cycle of any sort, and it never lands on the same point twice. It wanders around the unit interval without any order to its wandering. This is chaos, *deterministic* chaos; for, unpredictable as it is, this behavior is the result of iterating a simple algebraic function.

What is startling about this example is that a function of the form $f(x) = rx(1-x)$ produces predictable behavior when $r = 2$ and unpredictable behavior when $r = 4$. This is a simple algebraic function, in fact a *quadratic* function, the kind of function you've dealt with often in your high school years. It is more accurate to say that $f(x) = rx(1-x)$ stands for a *family* of quadratic functions, a specific function in the family determined by the choice of value for the parameter r. (The word *parameter* is used to denote a constant in the formula of a function when specification of the constant completely determines the function.) Here we have a one-parameter family of functions which have predictable orbits for some values of the parameter and unpredictable orbits for others. Where does it change? Why? What happens in between? These are questions we will want to address as this course goes on. For the moment, it is important to note that a very simple process – iteration of $f(x) = 4x(1-x)$ – produces chaotic behavior.

This is the first step toward finding simple processes that could have produced data observed to be chaotic. Ultimately we want to be able to go the other way and find the footprint of determinism underneath the appearance of chaos, but for the moment we concentrate on understanding how deterministic processes produce chaotic orbits.

The Logistic Function

In this section, we have spent a lot of time considering the dynamics of one function, $f(x) = rx(1-x)$. Why this function? Is it special? Well, yes and no.

- It has one parameter which when varied produces very different types of orbits.

Not very special; you'll see many others in the exercises.

- It is not linear.

True enough; in fact it's quadratic. But just about every other function you can think of is non-linear, and lots are at least quadratic. Again, you'll see many others in the exercises.

Still this function does have a special place in Chaos Theory because it was a function that biologists were already using to investigate the dynamics of population growth. Used as a model of population growth, the function helped ecologists address such questions as: Will the population increase without bound? Will it die out? Will it cycle periodically up and down? Will it reach a stable point and never change? Here's a bit of the history.

A first assumption about population growth is that it is proportional to the size of the present population. The bigger a population, the more babies it produces. If P_n is proportional to P_{n-1}, then for some positive parameter r we have

$$P_n = rP_{n-1}.$$

We have already seen what would happen to the orbit of an initial population P_0 under this assumption. After n iterations, we would have:

$$P_n = r^n P_0$$

The orbit is a geometric sequence. Therefore, $P_n \to 0$ if $0 < r < 1$, and $P_n \to \infty$ if $r > 1$. As a model for ecology, this function is not very realistic. It tells us that a population that cannot manage to reproduce at least one baby for each adult will die out. On the other hand, if the average population increases by just a little more than one baby per adult, the population will increase without bound. In the finite universe we inhabit, no population will increase without bound, so this first model is not very useful.

We add a second assumption to account for the counter pressure of environmental limitations to force large populations to decrease their size. As a population pushes toward the maximum the environment can nourish, more and more individuals will fail to reproduce, and the population will decline. So we assume that a population is proportional both to its present size and to the capacity of the environment to sustain it. A large population would increase the reproductive possibilities but decrease the chances for the environment to feed it.

To make these ideas concrete and keep the numbers simple, let's make an adjustment to the definition of P_n. Instead of representing the absolute numbers of a population (that is, the number of individuals), let it represent the percent of the maximum population that the environment will sustain. This keeps P_n between 0 and 1. As before, if $P_n = 0$, the population dies out. If $P_n = 1$, however, it now means the population fully occupies the space available; it is the maximum that the environment can provide for. If $P_n = 0.2$, then the population at generation n is 20% of the maximum sustainable population. If P_n represents the population at generation n, then $1 - P_n$ represents the room for growth. Therefore, to model growth that is proportional to both previous population and room for growth, we have:

$$P_n = rP_{n-1}(1 - P_{n-1}).$$

I'm sure you recognize that P_n is the nth iteration of our old friend $f(x) = rx(1-x)$. An ecologist using this model to predict the dynamics of population growth would be describing the orbit of a point under iteration of the function $f(x) = rx(1-x)$. This function (and any analogous to it) is called the *logistic function*.

Notation for Iteration

We are used to subscripts to represent successive iterates of a point. For example:

$$a_1 = f(a_0)$$
$$a_2 = f(a_1) = f(f(a_0))$$
$$a_3 = f(a_2) = f(f(a_1)) = f(f(f(a_0)))$$

and so on. To simplify the notation, we will denote the nth iterate of f by ${}^n f$. For example $f(f(f(a_0)))$ is ${}^3 f(a_0)$. Thus we have

$$a_1 = {}^1 f(a_0) \text{ or just } f(a_0)$$
$$a_2 = {}^2 f(a_0)$$
$$a_3 = {}^3 f(a_0)$$

and in general

$$a_n = {}^n f(a_0).$$

§1. Exercises

In Exercises 1-4, find the first five points in the orbit of the given seeds in the given function.
1. $f(x) = 2x + 1$ using seeds: $0, 0.5, 2, -1$
2. $f(x) = 0.5x + 1$ using seeds: $0, 2, 4, -1$
3. $f(x) = 2|x| - 1$ using seeds: $\frac{1}{3}, \frac{1}{2}, \frac{2}{5}, 1$
4. $f(x) = \sin x$ using seeds: $0, \pi, -2, 100$

5. Describe the orbit of 0.2 in the logistic function $f(x) = rx(1-x)$ for the following values of the parameter r:
a) $r = 1$ b) $r = 2.5$ c) $r = 3.5$ d) $r = 3.56$ e) $r = 3.835$

6. Describe the orbits of the following seeds in the logistic function $f(x) = 2.6x(1-x)$:
a) 0, 1   b) 0.1, 0.2, 0.3, 0.4, 0.5, 0.6, 0.7, 0.8, 0.9
c) Any seed less than 0   d) Any seed greater than 1.

7. Find $^6f(32)$ if $f(x) = \sqrt{x}$.

8. Find $^{20}f(2)$ if $f(x) = 0.8x + 1$.

9. Find $^3f(2\pi)$ if $f(x) = \cos x$.

10. Find $^{10}f(0.72)$ if $f(x) = 2|x| - 1$.

11. If $f(x) = 1 - |2x - 1|$, find $^nf(x_0)$ if
a) $n = 2$, and $x_0 = \frac{2}{3}$ b) $n = 4$, and $x_0 = \frac{1}{3}$ c) $n = 4$, and $x_0 = 0.125$
d) $n = 10$, and $x_0 = 0$ e) $n = 7$, and $x_0 = 2$ f) $n = 5$, and $x_0 = 0.9$

In Exercises 12-19, do an orbit analysis on the given function using a variety of seeds.
12. $f(x) = \sqrt{x}$ 13. $f(x) = x^2$
14. $f(x) = 1/x$ 15. $f(x) = x^2 + 1$
16. $f(x) = 2^x$ 17. $f(x) = x^2 - 1$
18. $f(x) = 2^x - 2$ 19. $f(x) = x^2 - 3$

20. This exercise is to deepen your understanding of the properties of the logistic function.
a) On the same set of axes draw graphs of $f(x) = rx(1-x)$ for $r = 1, 2, 3$, and 4.
b) Describe the graph of any member of the logistic family for $r > 0$.
c) What are the x-intercepts of a logistic function? What is its axis of symmetry?
d) If $0 < r < 4$ and the domain of $f(x) = rx(1-x)$ is restricted to the unit interval $[0, 1]$, what is its range?

§2. Fixed Points

In the last section, we began the process of analyzing an orbit in order to describe its long term behavior. The behavior of an orbit is a *qualitative* not a *quantitative* attribute. We were looking for descriptive rather than numerical answers. This may be a new tack for you to take in a math course and one that requires a new vocabulary. The goal of this section is to begin building this vocabulary.

Example 1. Describe the orbit of 0.9 in the function $f(x) = 2x(1-x)$.

Solution: Your calculator will show you the following orbit:

$$.9 \to .18 \to .2952 \to .4161... \to .4859... \to .4996... \to .4999... \to .5 \to .5 \to .5 \to \cdots$$

It appears that the orbit gradually approaches 0.5, and then, at the seventh iteration, lands on 0.5 and gets stuck there forever. But remember the calculator's limits when it deals with sequences that gradually approach limits. Actually, this orbit continues to get closer and closer to 0.5, so close in fact that the calculator can't tell the difference. Think of the calculator's result as telling you that 0.5 is the limit of the orbit. In chaos theory, a limit is called an *attractor* of the orbit, and we say that the orbit of 0.9 *is attracted to* 0.5.

The number 0.5 has a special role in Example 1 because $f(0.5) = 0.5$. Had we used 0.5 as the seed, the orbit would have had an infinite string of 0.5's. We call 0.5 a *fixed point* of *f*. In general, *x* is a *fixed point* of a function *f* if $f(x) = x$. It follows that any orbit that actually lands on a fixed point stays there forever.

Example 2. Show that 0 is a fixed point of $f(x) = 2x(1-x)$.

Solution: Substituting 0 for *x*, we have $f(0) = 2 \cdot 0 \cdot (1-0) = 0$. Therefore, 0 is a fixed point of *f*, and the orbit of 0 is an infinite string of 0's.

A seed whose orbit includes a fixed point is called an *eventually fixed point*. For example, 1 is an eventually fixed point of the function $f(x) = 2x(1-x)$ because $f(1) = 0$. After one iteration, the orbit of 1 lands on 0 and then is stuck there forever. It is important to distinguish between eventually fixed points, such as 1, and points whose orbits approach a fixed point as a limit without actually getting there, such as 0.9 in Example 1. Unfortunately, the calculator won't help here because it may not be able to distinguish. For now, use the calculator as a guide but use your knowledge of sequences too.

Example 3. Is 0.75 an eventually fixed point of $f(x) = 2x(1-x)$?

Figure 3.8

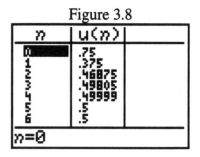

Solution: With the calculator in sequence mode, set $u(n)=2u(n-1)(1-u(n-1))$, nMin=0, and $u(nMin)=.75$. With TblStart set to 0, you can display the first 6 iterates of the function as in Figure 3.8. But is ${}^5f(0.75)$ actually equal to 0.5? The answer is No; the orbit approaches 0.5 and gets so close that once again the calculator rounds off to 0.5. So 0.75 is not an eventually fixed point; it is on an infinite journey of approach to 0.5 as a limit.

For the function $f(x) = 2x(1-x)$, you now know that there are at least two fixed points, 0 and 0.5. You might wonder if there are any others. It turns out there aren't, and you can show that fact easily by solving the equation $f(x) = x$.

Example 4. Find *all* fixed points of $f(x) = 2x(1-x)$.

Solution: We solve the equation $f(x) = x$:

$$\begin{aligned}
2x(1-x) &= x \\
2x - 2x^2 &= x \\
x - 2x^2 &= 0 \\
x(1 - 2x) &= 0
\end{aligned}$$

Therefore, $\qquad\qquad x = 0 \text{ or } x = 0.5$

It follows that 0 and 0.5 are the *only* fixed points of the function $f(x) = 2x(1-x)$.

Example 5. Show that $f(x) = x + 3$ has no fixed points and describe orbits of this function.

Solution: If we try to solve the equation $f(x) = x$, we end up with a contradiction:

$$\begin{aligned}
x + 3 &= x \\
3 &= 0
\end{aligned}$$

Hence there are no solutions, and so there are no fixed points. All orbits behave pretty much the same as you can see from considering what happens to the seeds 0, -14 and 10^9. Their orbits are:

$$0 \to 3 \to 6 \to 9 \to 12 \to \cdots$$
$$-14 \to -11 \to -8 \to -5 \to -2 \to 1 \to 4 \to \cdots$$
$$10^9 \to 10^9 + 3 \to 10^9 + 6 \to 10^9 + 9 \to \cdots$$

These orbits move slowly off to infinity, and a little thought will convince you that every other seed will follow a similar path.

Finding Fixed Points

The solutions to $f(x) = x$ can be found algebraically as in Example 4, or by using the calculator to solve the equation either graphically or numerically. The graphical technique is based on the idea that $f(x) = x$ can be thought of as the simultaneous solution of a system of equations:

$$\begin{cases} y = f(x) \\ y = x \end{cases}$$

Graphically, the solutions of this system would be the points of intersection of the two graphs $y = f(x)$ and $y = x$. For instance, using the function of Example 1, you would graph the function $y = 2x(1-x)$ with the line $y = x$. To do this, first make sure you press **MODE**, select Func in the fourth line and Full in the last line. Then press **Y=** and enter **X** for Y1, say, and **2 X (1 – X)** for Y2. A good window for this pair of functions is Xmin=–.2, Xmax=1.6, Ymin=–.2, Ymax=1. With these settings you would see a graph such as in Figure 3.9. (The window settings were chosen with a width-to-height ratio of 3:2, to match more or less the 95:63 ratio of horizontal to vertical pixels. Doing so makes a vertical unit look about the same as a horizontal unit so there is less graphical distortion. This is a matter of aesthetics; it has no effect on finding the intersection points.) To find the points of intersection, press **2nd[CALC] > 5:intersect**. You are asked to identify a "First curve" and a "Second curve." Do so by using the up or down arrows to place the flashing cursor on one of the curves and pressing **ENTER** after each request. You are then asked for a "Guess," and you can indicate a first approximation to the intersection that interests you either by keying in a numerical value (assigned by the calculator to X) or by using a left or right arrow to place the cursor near the intersection and pressing **ENTER**. If you use one of these methods near 0.5, you get the display in Figure 3.10. If you repeat the **2nd[CALC]** process and enter a number near 0 as your Guess, or trace one of the curves to the origin, and press **ENTER**,

Figure 3.9

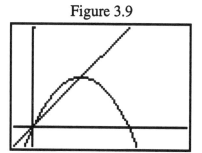

Figure 3.10

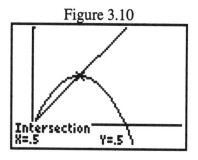

Figure 3.11

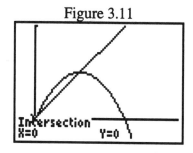

you'll see the display in Figure 3.11. Thus the graphical calculator method confirms the algebraic results of Example 4: the points of intersection are (0,0) and (0.5,0.5); the fixed points are 0 and 0.5.

The second calculator technique for finding fixed points involves a numerical solution of an equation. To start the process, press **MATH > Ø:Solver...** This brings up the Equation Solver editing screen in Figure 3.12, waiting for you to enter the equation you want solved. The calculator only handles expressions equal to 0, so to solve $2x(1-x) = x$ you would enter **2 X (1 – X) – X** after Ø= as in Figure 3.13. Alternatively, you could enter **Y2-Y1**, since you have already defined those functions in the Y= menu. Either way, when you press **ENTER**, you would see the result in Figure 3.14.

Figure 3.12

```
EQUATION SOLVER
eqn:0=
```

Figure 3.13

```
EQUATION SOLVER
eqn:0=2X(1-X)-X
```

The calculator can find only one solution at a time. You have to help it out to find the other one(s) by entering a new guess as X, or by changing the bounds within which the calculator searches (or both). The default search boundaries are from -10^{99} to 10^{99}. (To see the right hand endpoint, place the cursor on the bound= line and use the right arrow until the full number is displayed.) To initiate a new search, place the cursor in the variable line X=, enter .4 (for example) and press **ALPHA[SOLVE]**. The result would be

Figure 3.14

```
2X(1-X)-X=0
 X=0
 bound={-1ε99,1…
```

Figure 3.15

```
Y₁-Y₂=0
▪X=.5
 bound={-1ε99,1…
▪left-rt=0
```

displayed as in Figure 3.15. The last line shows the difference between the left and right approximations the calculator developed in its search. In this case, the difference is 0, indicating that the solution is reliable.

Attracting and Repelling Points

Exercise 6 of the last section asked you to investigate orbits of the function $f(x) = 2.6x(1-x)$. (If you haven't already done it, you should do it now.) The fixed points of the function are 0 and $\frac{8}{13} = 0.6153...$. But these two points have very different properties. The point 0.6153... is the limit of the orbit of virtually every seed between 0 and 1. On the other hand, 0 ends up as the final state of the orbits of just two seeds, 0 and 1. In particular, orbits of seeds near 0.6153... tend to move closer under iteration, whereas orbits of seeds near 0 tend to move away. This situation is illustrated graphically in Figure 3.16 where the light line is a graph of the first 25 iterates of $f(x) = 2.6x(1-x)$ with a seed of 0.6, and the

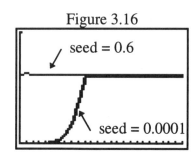

Figure 3.16

seed = 0.6

seed = 0.0001

heavy line is the first 25 iterates of 0.0001. Both orbits end up indistinguishable from 0.6513... As a result, 0.6153... is called an attracting fixed point, and 0 is called a repelling fixed point.

In general, p is called an *attracting* fixed point if there is an interval around p in which all seeds tend to p as a limit; p is called a *repelling* fixed point if there is an interval around p in which all seeds (different from p) eventually move out of the interval.

Although the idea of *attracting* and *repelling* may seem almost obvious, there are some subtle details to notice. For example, after one iteration the orbit of 1 lands precisely on 0. This does not make 0 an attractor. If the orbit of 1 had come extremely close to 0 but missed it by the tiniest fraction, the orbit would have moved away. To be an attractor, nearby seeds must orbit towards the point. Even a repelling fixed point may end up as the final state of other seeds' orbits, but only attracting fixed points gradually draw in nearby seeds.

Example 6. For the function $f(x) = \frac{1}{2}x + \frac{1}{2}$, find the fixed points, determine whether they are attracting or repelling.

Solution: As usual we solve the equation $f(x) = x$:

$$\frac{1}{2}x + \frac{1}{2} = x$$
$$\frac{1}{2} = \frac{1}{2}x$$
$$x = 1$$

Figure 3.17

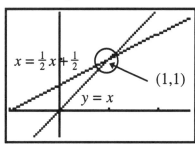

There is only one fixed point for this function (see Figure 3.17): $x = 1$. To determine if it is attracting or repelling, check a few seeds nearby, say, 1.1 and 0.9.

$1.1 \to 1.05 \to 1.025 \to 1.0125 \to 1.00625 \to 1.003125 \to 1.0015625 \to...$
$.9 \to .95 \to .975 \to .9875 \to .99375 \to .996875 \to .9984375 \to .99921875 \to ...$

Both orbits seem to tend to 1. In fact, by about the 30th iteration of both orbits, the calculator can no longer distinguish the points of the orbit from 1. It appears that 1 is an attracting fixed point.

At this point, we are doing calculator investigations of orbits without proving anything rigorously, so the best we can say is that "it appears that" 1 is an attracting point. Much of mathematics is built this way: Investigate first, follow your hunches, then try to prove you're right beyond a shadow of a doubt. In previous courses, when you have studied areas of math that have been well developed over centuries, the results were presented to you all buffed up with final proofs completely worked out. But Chaos

Theory is still young. There is still room for searching around in the dark and following your intuition. True, there are more than raw conjectures here; some results have already been proved. In section 3.4, for example, there is a more practical definition of attracting point that will give a better picture of an orbit's behavior. But for the moment, give yourself permission to take a few flyers on the basis of numerical investigations; later you can minimize doubt by doing some mathematics.

Graphical Analysis

A function is often described in terms of inputs and outputs: put in an x, get out a y. Under iteration, the output y becomes the next input x. If we add subscripts to the x's and y's, then the iteration process looks like this:

$$x_0 \xrightarrow{f} y_1 = x_1 \xrightarrow{f} y_2 = x_2 \xrightarrow{f} y_3 = x_3 \xrightarrow{f} \cdots$$

A function can be iterated geometrically with paper, pencil and ruler. First, draw the graph of the function $y = f(x)$ along with the graph of the identity function $y = x$ (Figure 3.18). Then pick a point on the x-axis as the seed x_0. To find $y_1 = f(x_0)$, draw a vertical line from x_0 to the graph of f (Figure 3.19). Now y_1 is the next input x_1. Where do you find an x_1 equal to y_1?

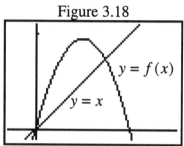

Figure 3.18

On the line $y = x$! So draw a horizontal line from the graph of f to the line (Figure 3.20). Starting from x_1, you find y_2 by drawing a vertical line to the graph (Figure 3.21). Then a horizontal line to the line $y = x$ gives x_2 (Figure 3.22). Continuing in this fashion –

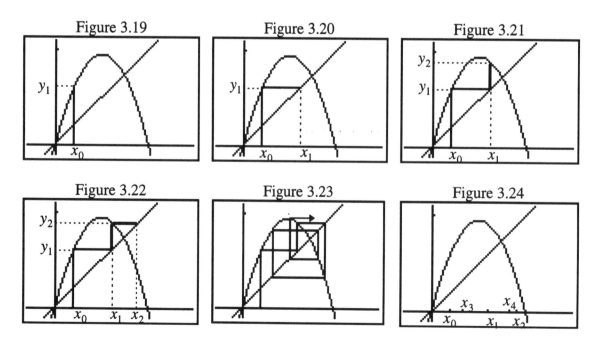

Figure 3.19   Figure 3.20   Figure 3.21

Figure 3.22   Figure 3.23   Figure 3.24

vertically to the graph, horizontally to the line – produces a web of lines that gives a geometric image of the development of the orbit (Figure 3.23). Of course the orbit itself would be simply the sequence of points $x_0, x_1, x_2, \cdots$ left along the x-axis (Figure 3.24).

This kind of graphing can be done automatically by the calculator in sequence mode. Press **2nd[FORMAT]** and select Web from the menu; press **[Y=]** and enter your function at u(n)= and your seed at u(nMin)=. If you press **TRACE**, you'll see the graph along with the line $y = x$, the values of u, n, X and Y, and a flashing cursor at the seed. Now when you press the right arrow repeatedly, you construct a web plot of the orbit as in Figure 3.23.

Example 7. Find the fixed points of $f(x) = x^3 - x$ and determine their attraction properties.

Solution:
$$x^3 - .69x = x$$
$$x^3 - 1.69x = 0$$
$$x(x^2 - 1.69) = 0$$

Therefore, $x = 0$ or $x = \pm\sqrt{1.69} = \pm 1.3$

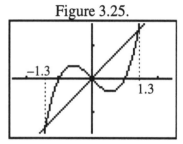

Figure 3.25.

There are three fixed points: 0, 1.3 and –1.3 (Figure 3.25). A graphical analysis shows that 0 is attracting, and both 1.3 and –1.3 are repelling. Figure 3.26, for example, shows the web plot that develops using 1.29 as a seed. At the bottom of the screen you see that both the x-coordinate and the y-coordinate of the orbital points are closing in on 0. A similar web develops for –1.29. On the other hand, a seed greater than 1.3 or smaller than –1.3 orbits off to infinity.

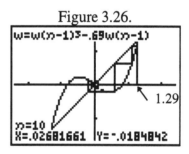

Figure 3.26.

Neutral Points

You may wonder if every fixed point is either attracting or repelling. It turns out that there are some fixed points that are neither and others that are both. Fixed points that cannot be called attracting or repelling are called *neutral*. For example, the function $f(x) = -x$ has one fixed point, $x = 0$, the only solution of $-x = x$. But 0 is neither attracting nor repelling, because every other seed ends up in a 2-cycle with its negative: $\{x_0, -x_0\}$. Therefore 0 is a neutral fixed point for the function $f(x) = -x$.

On the other hand, 0 is also a fixed point of the function $f(x) = x + x^2$ (Figure 3.27). But for this function, it is a weak attractor for nearby negative seeds (Figure 3.28) and a weak repeller for positive seeds (Figure 3.29).

Figure 3.27

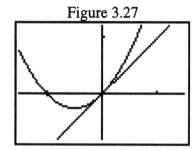

Figure 3.28

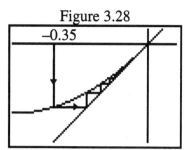

Figure 3.29

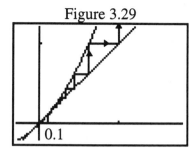

§2. Exercises

1. Find the fixed points of the following functions:
a) $f(x) = 4x - 3$ b) $f(x) = x^2$ c) $f(x) = x^2 - 0.75$
d) $f(x) = x^3 - x^2 - 5x$ e) $f(x) = |x|$ f) $f(x) = 1/x$

2. Find all fixed points of a linear function $f(x) = mx + b$ in terms of m and b. Do any values of the parameters give no fixed points?

3. Find all fixed points of a logistic function $f(x) = rx(1 - x)$ in terms of r.

4. Use the calculator's graphical or numerical equation solver to find the fixed points of the following functions:
a) $f(x) = \sqrt{x}$ b) $f(x) = \sin x$ c) $f(x) = \cos x$
d) $f(x) = 16x - 80x^2 + 128x^3 - 64x^4$ e) $f(x) = e^x - 1$ f) $f(x) = \tan^{-1} x$

5. For the following functions, write a formula for $^2f(x)$ and find the fixed points of ^2f.
a) $f(x) = 3x(1 - x)$ b) $f(x) = x^2 - 1$ c) $f(x) = x - x^3$

6. Determine the fixed points of the following functions and use graphical analysis to predict the outcome of orbits:
a) $f(x) = 3x - 1$ b) $f(x) = 1 - 3x$ c) $f(x) = 0.3x + 4$ d) $f(x) = -2.5x(1 - x)$
e) $f(x) = x^2 + 0.25$ f) $f(x) = x^3 - x$ g) $f(x) = x^{-2}$ e) $f(x) = x^{-1/2}$

7. For the following functions find the attracting fixed points:
a) $f(x) = x(1 - x)$ b) $f(x) = 2x(1 - x)$ c) $f(x) = 0.5x(1 - x)$
d) $f(x) = 2\sin x$ e) $f(x) = x^2$ f) $f(x) = x^3 - x$

8. a) Show that 0 is a fixed point of the function $f(x) = x + x^2$.
    b) Do a graphical analysis to show that nearby negative seeds are attracted to 0, and positive seeds are repelled by 0.

9. The following functions have neutral fixed points. In each case verify that the fixed points cannot be called attracting or repelling and say why.
a) $f(x) = x$ b) $f(x) = \frac{1}{x}$ c) $f(x) = |x|$ d) $f(x) = x^2 + 0.25$

10. Each member of the family of linear functions, $f(x) = mx$, has 0 as a fixed point. For some values of the parameter m, 0 is attracting, for others it is repelling, and for others it is neutral. Experiment with several different slopes and see if you can determine what values of m correspond to the three cases.

To do the next three problems, you'll need to know how to graph piecewise functions on your calculator. In case you don't, here's how. Suppose you want to graph the function:

$$f(x) = \begin{cases} 1-x^2 & \text{if } 0 \le x < 1 \\ x-1 & \text{if } x \ge 1 \end{cases}.$$

Press **Y=** and set $Y_1 = (1-X^2)(0 \le X \text{ and } X < 1) + (X-1)(1 \le X)$. The relational connectors $\le$ and $<$ are in the TEST menu when you press **2nd[TEST]**. The logical connector and is in the LOGIC menu of **2nd[TEST]**. When $0 \le x < 1$, then $(0 \le X \text{ and } X < 1)$ is TRUE, so the calculator assigns it a value of 1. At the same time, $(1 \le X)$ is FALSE, so the calculator assigns *it* a value of 0. Therefore, when $0 \le x < 1$, $Y_1 = (1-X^2) \times 1 + (X-1) \times 0$ or just $1-X^2$. Similarly, in the domain $1 \le x$, then $Y_1 = (1-X^2) \times 0 + (X-1) \times 1$ or just $X-1$. Therefore, when the first condition is true, the calculator plots the point $(x, 1-x^2)$; when the second condition is true, it plots $(x, x-1)$; when both are false, it plots $(x, 0)$. You may see some extraneous lines in the graph where the calculator tries to connect the two pieces of the function. You can clean them up if you press **MODE** and choose Dot in the 5th line.

11. For the function $f(x) = \begin{cases} -0.5x-1 & \text{if } x < 0 \\ 2x-1 & \text{if } x \ge 0 \end{cases}$, find the fixed points and determine which if any are attracting.

12. For the function $f(x) = \begin{cases} 2x & \text{if } 0 \le x < 0.5 \\ 2-2x & \text{if } 0.5 \le x \le 1 \end{cases}$, find the fixed points and determine which if any are attracting.

13. For the function $f(x) = \begin{cases} 2x & \text{if } 0 \le x < 0.5 \\ 2x-1 & \text{if } 0.5 \le x \le 1 \end{cases}$, find the fixed points and determine which if any are attracting.

§3. Periodic Points

We have seen examples of orbits that are completely predictable because they end up attracted to a fixed point. We have seen others that are predictable because they end up at infinity. For example, the function $f(x) = 2x(1-x)$ has both kinds of orbits: all the seeds in the open interval (0, 1) are attracted to 0.5, and all the seeds outside the closed interval [0, 1] are attracted to infinity. In this section, we investigate orbits that have a different kind of predictable behavior: they are *periodic*.

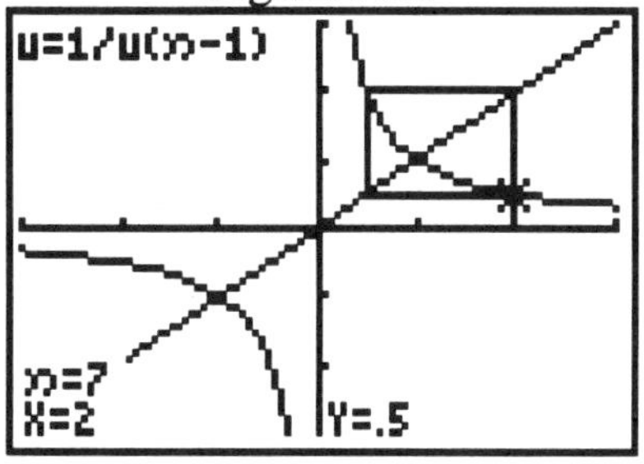

As an example, consider what happens to seeds under iteration of the function $f(x) = \dfrac{1}{x}$. Take 2, for instance. Since $f(2) = \frac{1}{2}$ and $f\left(\frac{1}{2}\right) = 2$, the orbit is

Figure 3.30

$$2 \to \frac{1}{2} \to 2 \to \frac{1}{2} \to 2 \to \frac{1}{2} \to 2 \to \cdots .$$

If you do a graphical analysis using a Web plot, as in Figure 3.30, you see the cycle {2, ½} as a closed rectangle repeatedly traced out by the cursor.

It is not hard to see that virtually every seed will have a periodic orbit under iteration of the function $f(x) = \dfrac{1}{x}$. You get the same kind of 2-cycle with the seed and its reciprocal: $\left\{ x_0, \dfrac{1}{x_0} \right\}$. Since 1 and −1 are their own reciprocals, they are both fixed points of this function and therefore trivially periodic. (Of course 0 has no orbit at all because it is not in the domain of f.)

Example 1. For the function $f(x) = 2|x| - 1$ find the periods of the points $\dfrac{1}{5}, \dfrac{1}{9}$, and $-\dfrac{1}{11}$.

Solution: A little arithmetic will reveal the following orbits:

$$\frac{1}{5} \to -\frac{3}{5} \to \frac{1}{5} \to -\frac{3}{5} \to \cdots$$

$$\frac{1}{9} \to -\frac{7}{9} \to \frac{5}{9} \to \frac{1}{9} \to -\frac{7}{9} \to \frac{5}{9} \to \cdots$$

$$-\frac{1}{11} \to -\frac{9}{11} \to \frac{7}{11} \to \frac{3}{11} \to -\frac{5}{11} \to -\frac{1}{11} \to -\frac{9}{11} \to \frac{7}{11} \to \frac{3}{11} \to -\frac{5}{11} \cdots$$

We see that $\dfrac{1}{5}$ has a 2-cycle, $\dfrac{1}{9}$ has a 3-cycle, and $-\dfrac{1}{11}$ has a 5-cycle.

In Example 1, you probably figured out that you could tell that a seed was periodic as soon as it reappeared in its own orbit. From then on, the orbit would simply trace out the same route it had just traversed. We take this property to be the definition of *periodicity* and say that an orbit is *periodic* if $^n f(x_0) = x_0$ for some n. The *primary period* of the orbit is the number of points between the seed and its first reappearance; that is, the smallest number n for which $^n f(x_0) = x_0$. In this case x_0 is called a *periodic point* and x_0 is said to have an *n*-cycle.

If in the definition of periodicity we have $n = 1$, then x_0 would be a fixed point. In a sense, then, fixed points are also periodic with any period you care to assign. For if x_0 is a fixed point of f, then $^1 f(x_0) = x_0$, $^{10} f(x_0) = x_0$, $^{327,651} f(x_0) = x_0$, and $^n f(x_0) = x_0$ for any n whatsoever. As a result, we call fixed points *trivially* periodic; the only non-trivial periodic points would be those with primary periods greater than 1. More generally, if m is a factor of n then a point whose primary period is m will also fall into an *n*-cycle. Check it out. Since 2 is a factor of 6, a point x_0 with primary period 2 will also reappear at the 6th iteration after three 2-cycles. In this case, we would say that x_0 is trivially 6-cyclic though non-trivially 2-cyclic.

The notion of *eventually periodic* is analogous to the notion of *eventually fixed*. A point would be called eventually periodic if it includes in its orbit a periodic point.

Example 2. Show that 0.1 is eventually periodic in the function $f(x) = 2|x| - 1$.

Solution: The orbit is: $.1 \rightarrow -.8 \rightarrow .6 \rightarrow .2 \rightarrow -.6 \rightarrow .2 \rightarrow \cdots$ Since the orbit of 0.1 eventually lands on 0.2 which has a 2-cycle, then 0.1 is eventually periodic.

Sometimes it's hard to tell about periodicity. In Example 2 of Section 1, we looked at an orbit of $f(x) = 3x(1-x)$ and saw it wobbling back and forth for over 1000 iterations, with the two points in the orbit approaching each other very slowly. It looked as if it was settling down, but whether to a fixed point or to a 2-cycle was hard to say. One way to investigate the situation is to look at other values of the parameter near 3. If you change the parameter to 2.8, you have the function $f(x) = 2.8x(1-x)$ which has a fixed point 0.6428...that is an attractor for the orbits of any seed in the interval (0, 1). If you change the parameter to 3.2, the orbits are all attracted to a 2-cycle, jumping back and forth between 0.5130... and 0.7994.... So somewhere between 2.8 and 3.2, the function changes from producing orbits with fixed point limits to producing orbits with periodic limits. Can we say where exactly this happens? The answer turns out to be Yes, but the explanation will have to wait until we explore the logistic function in greater depth in Chapter 4. In the meantime, we develop ways of studying cycles by understanding the connection between *n*-cycles of f and fixed points of $^n f$.

Fixed Points of $^n f$

Suppose x_0 has a 2-cycle in the function f. Then its orbit would be

$$f: \quad x_0 \to x_1 \to x_0 \to x_1 \to \cdots$$

Since $x_1 = f(x_0)$, the first reappearance of x_0 is $f(x_1)$ or $f(f(x_0))$. Thus $^2f(x_0) = x_0$. It follows that a point with a 2-cycle in f is a fixed point of ^2f. The orbit of x_0 in ^2f would be

$$^2f: \quad x_0 \longrightarrow x_0 \longrightarrow \cdots.$$

In general, points that have n-cycles in f are fixed points of $^n f$.

Example 3. Find the 2-cycles of $f(x) = 3.2x(1-x)$.

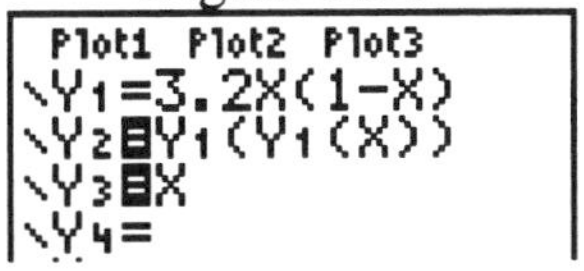

Solution: The 2-cycles of f are the fixed points of ^2f. These can by found graphically by plotting the graph of $y = {}^2f(x)$ and finding its points of intersection with the identity function $y = x$. Press **[Y=]** and set Y1=**3.2 X (1 – X)**, set Y2=**Y1 (Y1 (X)**), and set Y3=**X**. Because we are interested only in the graphs of Y2 and Y3, the graph of Y1 can be turned off. Use the arrows to place the cursor over the equals sign in Y1=, and then press **ENTER**. (See Figure 3.31.) If you use a window of $-0.1 \le x \le 1.4$ and $-0.1 \le y \le 0.9$, you will see the screen in Figure 3.32 when you press **[GRAPH]**. There are four points of intersection. One of the points is obviously 0, and you can find the other three using **2nd[CALC]**. First, zoom in on the area of interest, using a window with Xmin=**.4**, Xmax=**1**, Ymin=**.4** and Ymax=**.85** as in Figures 3.33, 3.34 and 3.35.

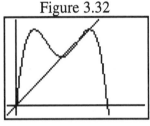

Figure 3.31

Figure 3.32

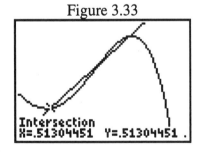

Figure 3.33

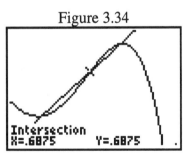

Figure 3.34

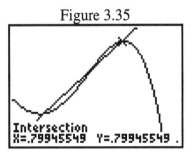

Figure 3.35

The four fixed points of ^2f are: 0, 0.5130..., 0.6875 , and 0.7994.... Only two of these turn out to be 2-cycle points of f; the other two are fixed points of f. How can you tell? By drawing a graph of f along with the graphs of ^2f and the identity function as in Figure 3.36. All three functions intersect at 0 and 0.6875 which are fixed points of both f

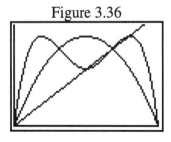

Figure 3.36

and ^2f. As fixed points of f, the points 0 and 0.6875 are trivially periodic. Therefore the other two points, 0.5130... and 0.7994..., constitute the only non-trivial 2-cycle for f.

Example 4: Find the points which have non-trivial 2-cycles in $f(x) = x^2 - 1.2$.

Solution: First determine the trivial 2-cycles by finding the fixed points of f. Graph $y = f(x)$ and $y = x$ (Figure 3.37) and use the calculator to determine the points of intersection. [2nd]CALC gives $-0.3660...$ and 1.3660... as the fixed points of f.

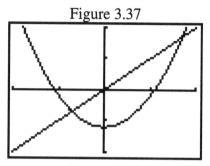

Figure 3.37

Adding a graph of $^2f(x) = (x^2 - 1.2)^2 - 1.2$ gives the diagram in Figure 3.38. There are four intersections of ^2f with $y = x$, the only new ones being 0.1708... and $-1.1708...$. Therefore, these are the only points with non-trivial 2-cycles in $f(x) = x^2 - 1.2$. You can check numerically that $f(.1708...) = -1.1708...$ and $f(-1.1708...) = .1708...$. Each is the image of the other in this function and they make up a complete 2-cycle.

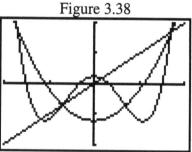

Figure 3.38

Attracting and repelling cycles

The cycles established by periodic points have the same attracting (and repelling) properties as fixed points. Suppose, for example, that a and b constitute a 2-cycle for a function f. Then $f(a) = b$ and $f(b) = a$. Suppose further that in the orbit of a seed x_0, the sub-sequence of even iterates approaches a while the sub-sequence of odd iterates approaches b. That is to say that the orbit bounces back and forth between numbers getting infinitely close to a and numbers getting infinitely close to b. Then we would call $\{a, b\}$ an *attracting 2-cycle* or a *limit cycle* for f.

Example 5. Verify that the cycle {0.5130..., 0.7994...} found in Example 3 is an attracting two cycle for the function $f(x) = 3.2x(1-x)$.

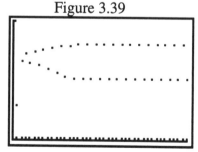

Figure 3.39

Solution: Figure 3.39 shows a graph of the first 40 iterates of f using 0.1 as a seed. The later iterates appear to be periodic. By pressing **TRACE**, you can see the value of the iterate displayed as Y at the bottom of the screen. The values of u(30), u(31), u(32), and u(33) are shown in Figure 3.40. The even iterates are close to 0.5130... and the odd iterates close to 0.71994..., so close that the calculator can't tell the difference. These points, which we found to constitute a 2-cycle, must be an attracting 2-cycle.

Figure 3.40

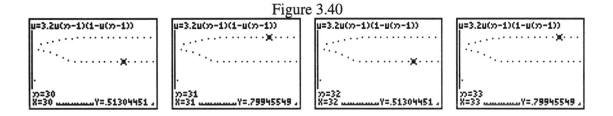

Example 6. Determine whether the cycle {0.2, –0.6} from Example 1 is an attracting or repelling cycle for the function $f(x) = 2|x| - 1$.

Solution: If you try a few one-decimal numbers, most (but not all) will end up in this cycle. For instance:

$$.1 \to -.8 \to .6 \to .2 \to -.6 \to .2 \to -.6 \to \cdots$$

or

$$.7 \to .4 \to -.2 \to -.6 \to .2 \to -.6 \to \cdots.$$

Note that these orbits happen to land on one of the cyclic points and then stay in the cycle; they are eventually periodic points. But they aren't *attracted* by the cycle because they do not have an orbit which approaches the cycle asymptotically in the same way that $1/n$ approaches 0. So we, we still cannot say whether the cycle is attracting. Instead, try some seeds close to the cycle and see what happens. If you try 0.21, for instance, you get this orbit:

$$.21 \to -.58 \to .16 \to -.68 \to .36 \to -.28 \to -.44 \to -.12 \to$$
$$-.76 \to .52 \to .04 \to -.92 \to .84 \to .68 \to .36 \to -.28 \to -.44 \to -.12 \to -.76 \to \ldots$$

So 0.21 is also eventually periodic, but its orbit ends up in a 10-cycle, not the 2-cycle of 0.2. If you try 0.201 or 0.2000001, you will find other orbits that diverge from the cycle {0.2, –0.6}. This *does* tell us about the repulsion properties of this cycle. Because nearby points move away, it is repelling.

§3. Exercises

1. In Example 2 of this section, we found that $\left\{\dfrac{1}{9}, -\dfrac{7}{9}, \dfrac{5}{9}\right\}$ constitutes a 3-cycle for the function $f(x) = 2|x| - 1$. Determine if this is an attracting or repelling cycle.

2. The function $f(x) = 2|x| - 1$ has another 3-cycle. Use your calculator to draw graphs of f, ^3f, and $y = x$ over the domain $[-2, 2]$, and find it. Is it attracting or repelling? [A little calculator hint: When you find an intersection point, it will be given in decimal form. It is easier to have it in fractional form, both to compare with the given cycle and to handle arithmetically. The intersection point is automatically stored as X. Return to your home screen by pressing **2nd[QUIT]** and enter X, then press **MATH** and select 1:▶Frac. When you press **ENTER**, you'll see the number in fractional form.]

3. The points 0 and 1 constitute a 2-cycle for the function $f(x) = x^2 - 1$. Use your calculator to determine if this is an attracting or repelling cycle.

4. Find a 2-cycle for the function $f(x) = \dfrac{1}{x}$. Is it attracting, repelling or neutral?

5. The function $f(x) = 3.84x(1 - x)$ has two 3-cycles. Use your calculator to graph f, ^3f, and $y = x$ over the domain $[0, 1]$. Find the points that belong to each cycle and determine the attraction properties of each.

6. For the function $f(x) = x^2 - 1.4$, find all the fixed points, 2-cycles and 4-cycles.

7. Use your calculator to draw graphs of f, ^2f, and ^3f along with $y = x$ if $f(x) = \pi \sin x$. Use a domain of $[0, \pi]$. How many fixed points are there of each? Make a conjecture about the number of fixed points of ^nf.

8. Given the tent-function $f(x) = \begin{cases} 2x & \text{if } 0 \le x < 0.5 \\ 2 - 2x & \text{if } 0.5 \le x \le 1 \end{cases}$
    a) Determine the piecewise definition for ^2f and ^3f.
    b) Draw the graphs of f, ^2f, and ^3f along with $y = x$ over the domain $[0, 1]$.
    c) Make a conjecture about the number of fixed points of ^nf.

9. Here is another tent-function $f(x) = \begin{cases} 3x & \text{if } 0 \le x < 0.5 \\ 3 - 3x & \text{if } 0.5 \le x \le 1 \end{cases}$.
    a) Determine the piecewise definition for ^2f and ^3f.
    b) Draw the graphs of f, ^2f, and ^3f along with $y = x$ over the domain $[0, 1]$.
    c) Make a conjecture about the number of fixed points of ^nf.

§4. The Attraction Criterion for Fixed Points

To show that a point (or cycle) is attracting (or repelling), we have relied on the use of abundant examples. After looking at the orbits of several seeds, at some point we decided we had a good enough picture to state some conclusions. Some of you may be left with a shadow of a doubt. This is, after all, mathematics. Where is the proof? How can you be 100% certain that there isn't some pathological point hiding in an otherwise domesticated domain, some seed that refuses to be attracted to the point or the cycle that draws in all its neighbors? The purpose of this section is to give you a mathematical criterion to determine without doubt whether a point or cycle is attracting or repelling.

We start by investigating the attraction properties of linear functions. These functions all have the formula $f(x) = mx$, with a slope of m and a y-intercept of 0. Whatever the slope, the graph goes through the origin where it intersects the line $y = x$. Therefore 0 is a fixed point of every linear function. Furthermore, 0 is the *only* fixed point unless $m = 1$, in which case every point is fixed.

Now consider the orbital behavior for linear functions whose slope m is positive. First, look at the three cases: $m < 1$, $m = 1$, and $m > 1$, illustrated in Figure 3.41.

Figure 3.41 Linear functions with positive slope

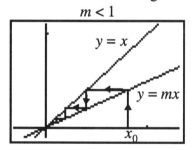 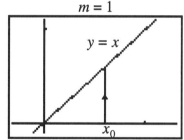 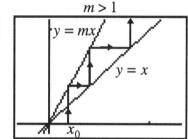

A positive slope less than 1 draws orbits into the fixed point; slopes greater than 1 send them staircasing out to infinity. When $m = 1$, every point is fixed, so 0 neither attracts nor repels orbits; in this case 0 is neutral.

When m is negative, there are again three cases: $m > -1$, $m = -1$, and $m < -1$, illustrated in Figure 3.42.

Figure 3.42 Linear functions with negative slope

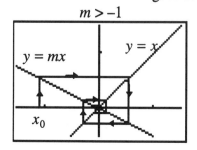 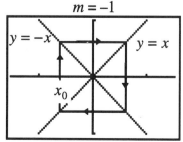 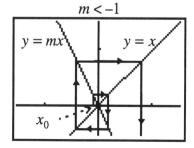

When the slope is between 0 and -1, the orbit spirals in towards 0; beyond -1, the orbit spirals out to infinity. When $m = -1$, all points fall into a 2-cycle $\{x_0, -x_0\}$, so once again, 0 neither attracts nor repels orbits; it is neutral.

To sum up, we have the following results for linear functions:

1. When $|m| < 1$, the fixed point is attracting.
2. When $|m| > 1$, the fixed point is repelling.
3. When $|m| = 1$, the fixed point is neutral.

Surprisingly, a similar situation obtains even when the function f is not linear but is continuous and smooth. For these functions, the slope of the tangent at the fixed point determines the attraction properties.

Example 1. Compare the attraction properties with the slopes of the tangents at the fixed points of $f(x) = 2x(1-x)$.

Figure 3.43

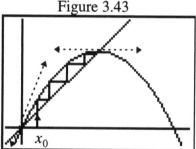

Solution: Consider the Web plot of $f(x) = 2x(1-x)$ in Figure 3.43. The slope of the line $y = x$ is 1. Where the line intersects the parabola at the origin, the curve's tangent is steeper, so its slope must be greater than 1. And notice that 0 is a repelling point.

On the other hand, the fixed point at 0.5 is the vertex of the parabola where the slope of the tangent is 0; and here the fixed point is an attractor. Both of these results agree with the results for linear functions: attraction when $|m| < 1$ and repulsion when $|m| > 1$.

Example 2. Compare the attraction properties and tangent slopes at the fixed points of $f(x) = x^2 - 0.25$.

Figure 3.44

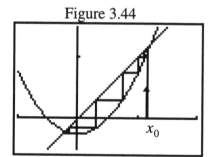

Solution: By solving $f(x) = x$, we find the fixed points are 1.2071... and -0.2071.... The graph in Figure 3.44 shows that the orbit of a seed close to 1.2071...is repelled by the positive fixed point and eventually spirals in to the negative fixed point. We can see (in Figure 3.45) that the slope of the tangent to f at 1.2071... is greater than 1 because it is steeper than the identity function there. To see what is going on at the other fixed point, we draw the line with slope −1 through (−0.2071..., −0.2071...). The graph shows that near the negative fixed point, the tangent to the parabola lies between the lines with slopes 1 and −1. Therefore at that point the slope of the tangent is between 1 and −1. Once again we see results consistent with the results for linear functions: attraction when $|m| < 1$ and repulsion when $|m| > 1$.

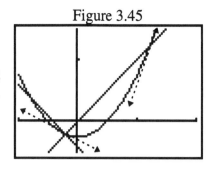

Figure 3.45

Although these two examples do not *prove* much, they are persuasive visual evidence that we are onto something here. You can probably understand why the curvilinear case is not too different from the linear case. In each case, what most influences the attraction property of a point is the shape of the graph of the function very close to the point. Functions that are smooth and continuous have a shape that is well approximated by tangents right around points of tangency. For the limited purpose of deciding about attraction, smooth curves act just like their tangents at those points.

It is not possible to prove these assertions without both a better definition of "attraction" and knowledge of calculus. Therefore, a proof is beyond the scope of this course. We will simply state without proof the following:

Attraction Criterion: If x is a fixed point of a function f, and if f has a tangent at (x, x) with slope m, then

1. x is an attractor if $|m| < 1$,
2. x is a repelling point if $|m| > 1$, and
3. x is neutral if $|m| = 1$.

The Slope of the Tangent

At this point, those of you who have had some calculus are probably feeling pretty smart. You know how to find tangents to just about any function at just about any point. That was one of the two big problems you learned how to solve in calculus. But if you haven't had calculus yet, don't worry: the calculator will give you adequate approximations for the slopes of tangents. (And you will learn how calculus students do it in Chapter 7.) Moreover, there are two ways to do it on the calculator.

First you should know the vocabulary of calculus for slopes of tangents. If a function is called f, then the slope of its tangent at the point (x, y) is called *the derivative of f at x* and denoted $f'(x)$, pronounced "eff-prime of x." It may also be denoted by y'

("y-prime") or $\dfrac{dy}{dx}$ ("dy by dx"). One way to use your calculator to find an approximation of the derivative of a function is to use nDeriv(, found by pressing **MATH 8:nDeriv**. nDeriv(takes three inputs separated by commas in the following format: nDeriv(*function*, *variable*, *value*) where *function* is the formula for the function whose tangent you are seeking, *variable* is the letter that is the variable in the function, and *value* is the value of the variable at the point where you want to find the tangent. For instance, to find the slope of the tangent to the curve $y = x^5 - 2x + \sin x$ at the point where $x = \pi$, you would evaluate the derivative of $f(x) = x^5 - 2x + \sin x$ at π. The format of the command is shown in Figure 3.46, along with the result when **ENTER** is pressed. The calculator gives 484.045554 as a numerical approximation of the derivative $f'(\pi)$. We conclude that the slope of the tangent to the curve at the point where $x = \pi$ is approximately 484.045554.

Figure 3.46

```
nDeriv(X^5-2X+si
n(X),X,π)
           484.045554
```

The second input of nDeriv(, the letter *variable*, is important if you have other letters for constants. For instance, if you are investigating the logistic function and have already stored a value for the parameter r, you could write

$$\text{nDeriv}(RX(1-X),X,1-1/R)$$

to get an approximation to the derivative at the point $1 - \dfrac{1}{r}$.

Example 3. Find the slope of the tangent to the graph of $f(x) = x^2 - 0.25$ at the negative fixed point.

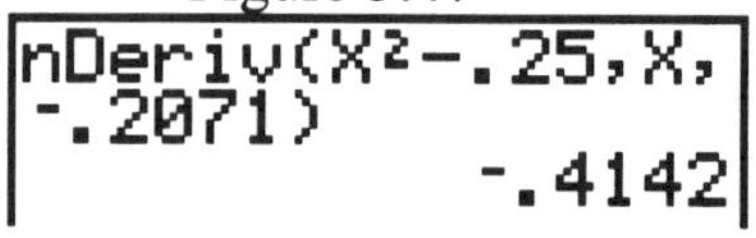

Solution: In Example 2, we found the negative fixed point at $x = -0.2071\ldots$. Using the calculator to evaluate nDeriv(X²−.25,X,−.2071), we obtain −.4142 as the

Figure 3.47

```
nDeriv(X²-.25,X,
-.2071)
              -.4142
```

approximate slope. Note that we are finding an approximate slope at an approximation of the fixed point, so don't bet your life savings on this number. If you need more accuracy, read on; but simply to decide whether the slope is between 1 and −1, the calculator result is probably good enough to confirm that the point is attracting.

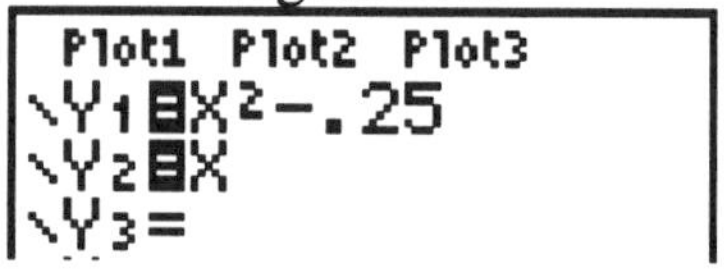

The second way your calculator finds slopes is directly from a graph, using another notation for the derivative, dy/dx, found in line 6 of the **2nd[CALC]** menu. First, put the calculator in function mode, and enter the expression for $f(x)$ as **Y1** and x as **Y2**. Using the function

Figure 3.48

```
Plot1  Plot2  Plot3
\Y1=X²-.25
\Y2=X
\Y3=
```

$f(x) = x^2 - .25$ of Example 3, you would see the screen in Figure 3.48. Then press **2nd[CALC] > 5:intersect**, and use an appropriate guess to obtain the negative fixed point as in Figure 3.49. The calculator now holds the intersection point as X. To use it in other computations, go back to the home screen and store it as another variable, say A. You do so by pressing **2nd[QUIT]**, followed by **X STO>** **ALPHA[A] ENTER** as in Figure 3.50. Now press **2nd**CALC again and select 6 : dy / dx. When you press **ENTER**, a point close to the intersection point is displayed, but when you press **ALPHA[A]** (Figure 3.51), the intersection point is once more placed in the calculator's memory as X, and the slope is calculated at that point when you press **ENTER** (Figure 3.52).

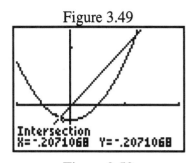

Figure 3.49

Intersection
X=˜.2071068 Y=˜.2071068

Figure 3.50

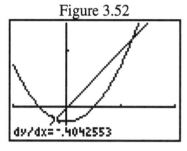

X→A
            ˜.2071067812

Note that the slope approximation by this method is different from –0.4142, the answer given by the method of Example 3. Remember that these are both approximations, and the accuracy of the results

Figure 3.51

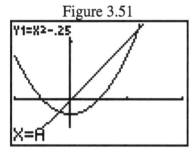

Y1=X²-.25

X=A

Figure 3.52

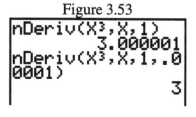

dy/dx=˜.4042553

depends both on the accuracy of the input information and the technical limitations of the calculator.

To complete this investigation of numerical differentiation on the calculator, I should mention one further detail about nDeriv(. To find the slope of a tangent to a curve at a point, you have to know the behavior of the curve not only at the point but also at points nearby. The question is: How near? The calculator is programmed to look at points 0.001 away from the point of tangency, and this tolerance limits the accuracy of the answer. If you wish to improve the accuracy, you may specify a smaller tolerance as an optional fourth input: nDeriv(*formula, variable, value, tolerance*).

Example 4. Use the calculator to find $f'(1)$ if $f(x) = x^3$.

Solution: Figure 3.53 shows that the calculator gives 3.000001 for the derivative using the pre-programmed tolerance in nDeriv(X^3 , X, 1). However, when we add the finer tolerance .0001 as the optional fourth input, the result is a derivative of exactly 3. What's the right answer? Calculus students will tell you that $f'(1) = 3$,

Figure 3.53

nDeriv(X³,X,1)
            3.000001
nDeriv(X³,X,1,.0
0001)
                    3

so the finer tolerance is more accurate for this function at this point. For our purposes in general, however, the pre-programmed tolerance will be accurate enough. If you need to increase the accuracy, include a fourth input for nDeriv.

§4. Exercises

1. Given the following functions, find the slope of the tangent to the graph of $y = f(x)$ at the given point:

    a) $f(x) = x^3 - x$, $x = 0$

    b) $f(x) = x^4 - 16$, $x = 1.5$

2. Given the following functions, find the slope of the tangent to the graph of $y = f(x)$ at the given point:

    a) $f(x) = 2x^3 + 3x^2 - 5x - 3$, $x = 0.5$

    b) $f(x) = 8x^5 + 5x^2 - 1$, $x = 0.1$

3. Given the following functions, find the slope of the tangent to the graph of $y = f(x)$ at the given point:

    a) $f(x) = 3x(1 - x)$, $x = \dfrac{2}{3}$

    b) $f(x) = \dfrac{2x - 1}{10}$, $x = -4$

4. Find the equation of the tangent to the graph of $y = f(x)$ at the given point if:

    a) $f(x) = x(x - 1)$, $x = 1$

    b) $f(x) = 4x(1 - x)$, $x = \frac{3}{4}$

    c) $f(x) = x^3 - 8x$, $x = 2$

    d) $f(x) = x^4 + 4x^3 - 5x - 1$, $x = -\frac{1}{2}$

5. Find all the fixed points of the following quadratic functions over the domain $[-2, 2]$. Use the Attraction Criterion to classify each as attracting, repelling or neutral. If the point is neutral, do a Web plot to determine what happens.

    a) $f(x) = x^2 + \frac{1}{4}$

    b) $f(x) = x^2$

    c) $f(x) = x^2 - \frac{1}{4}$

    d) $f(x) = x^2 - 1\frac{1}{4}$

6. Find all the fixed points of the following logistic functions over the domain $[0, 1]$. Use the Attraction Criterion to classify each as attracting, repelling or neutral. If the point is neutral, do a Web plot to determine what happens.

    a) $f(x) = 0.5x(1 - x)$

    b) b) $f(x) = x(1 - x)$

    c) $f(x) = 2.5x(1 - x)$

    d) $f(x) = 3.2x(1 - x)$

7. Find all the fixed points of the following functions and use the Attraction Criterion to classify each as attracting, repelling or neutral. If the point is neutral, do a Web plot to determine what happens.

    a) $f(x) = x^3 - 3x^2 + 3x$

    b) $f(x) = x^4 - 2x^2 + x$

    c) $f(x) = \dfrac{x^3 - 2x^2 + 2x + 2}{3}$

    d) $f(x) = 9x(1 - 4x + 6x^2 - 3x^3)$

8. Find the fixed points of the logistic function $f(x) = rx(1 - x)$ for the following values of the parameter r, and use the Attraction Criterion to classify each as attracting, repelling or neutral.

    a) $r = 1$

    b) $r = 2$

    c) $r = 3$

    d) $r = 4$

§5. Attraction Criterion for Cycles

In §3.3 we said that a function was periodic if $^nf(x_0) = x_0$ for some integer n. Therefore, the n-cycles of f can be found by determining the fixed points of ^nf. An n-cycle of f will be attracting if the corresponding fixed point p of ^nf is attracting; that is, if $^nf'(p)$, the slope of the tangent at p, is less than 1 in absolute value.

Example 1. Find the 2-cycles of $f(x) = x^2 - 1$ and determine if any is attracting.

Solution: If $f(x) = x^2 - 1$ then $^2f(x) = (x^2 - 1)^2 - 1 = x^4 - 2x^2$. We look for the fixed points of ^2f by solving $^2f(x) = x$.

$$x^4 - 2x^2 = x$$
$$x^4 - 2x^2 - x = 0$$

How good are you at solving fourth degree equations? One way out is to use one of the calculator methods: numerical (**MATH Ø:Solver...** and so on) or graphical (draw graphs of $y = x^4 - 2x^2$ and $y = x$, use **2nd[CALC] 5:intersect** and so on). But you could also recall some algebra from previous courses and solve it by doing some clever factoring. This method is useful in the more general cases we will look at in Chapter 7, so you'll get a head start by seeing it now:

First, notice that you already know two solutions to this equation. The fixed points also constitute trivial 2-cycles; for if $f(x) = x$, then $^2f(x) = f(f(x)) = f(x) = x$. So the first thing to do is find the fixed points of f by solving $f(x) = x$.

$$x^2 - 1 = x$$
$$x^2 - x - 1 = 0$$

The quadratic formula gives you the solutions: $x = \dfrac{1 \pm \sqrt{5}}{2}$. But you really don't need to know them; they are the trivial 2-cycles that you want to eliminate from the fourth-power equation. To do that, notice that the solutions of $x^2 - x - 1 = 0$ are the factors of $x^2 - x - 1$; and since they are also solutions of $x^4 - 2x^2 - x = 0$ then $x^2 - x - 1$ must be a factor of $x^4 - 2x^2 - x$. So divide $x^4 - 2x^2 - x$ by $x^2 - x - 1$ as shown in the diagram, and you'll get the other factor, $x^2 + x$. The quotient $x^2 + x$

$$
\begin{array}{r}
x^2 + x \\
x^2 - x - 1 \overline{\smash{\big)}\, x^4 - 0x^3 - 2x^2 - x - 0} \\
\underline{x^4 - x^3 - x^2} \\
x^3 - x^2 - x \\
\underline{x^3 - x^2 - x} \\
0
\end{array}
$$

yields the quadratic $x^2 + x = 0$, with solutions 0 and -1. And these points must constitute the only *non-trivial* 2-cycle of f. You can easily check that $f(0) = -1$ and $f(-1) = 0$.

So now we have the 2-cycle $\{0, -1\}$. To determine if it is attracting, we must check to see that the slope of the tangent to ^2f at these points is less than 1 in absolute value. It is sufficient to check just one of the points, because if one point is in an attracting 2-cycle than so is the other: it's the same cycle. So we need to find $^2f'(0)$. From the calculator we have:

$$\mathtt{NDeriv(\ X^4 - 2X^2\ ,X,\emptyset)\ =\ 0}$$

Therefore, $^2f'(0){=}^2f'(-1) = 0.$

Finally, we conclude that the 2-cycle $\{0, -1\}$ is attracting because the slope of the tangents to these points on ^2f is less than 1 in absolute value.

The 2-cycle for $f(x) = x^2 - 1$ can also be found experimentally. If you do a $\mathtt{Time}$ plot for this function and trace the orbits for a variety of seeds, you will find many attracted to a cycle. For instance, using the seed 1.5, you will see a $\mathtt{Time}$ plot like the one in Figure 3.54. The orbit starts very near one fixed point, and nearly lands on the other before being attracted to the cycle $\{0, -1\}$.

Figure 3.54

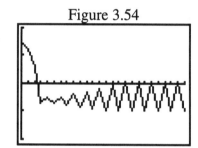

As long as fixed points or cycles are attracting, they are easy to find experimentally. If you choose at random a nearby seed, its orbit will converge to an attractor. Even a seed chosen at some distance will most likely orbit into the interval of attraction and converge to the attractor. So attracting points and cycles readily reveal themselves. On the other hand, repelling fixed points and cycles are almost impossible to find experimentally. It is extremely unlikely that a seed chosen at random would happen to land right on a repeller. Even if an orbit comes close, it will move away and not reveal the presence of a repeller.

Example 2. Find a 2-cycle for the function $f(x) = x^2 - 1.3$.

Solution: If you experiment with a few seeds, you will discover an attracting 4-cycle consisting of the points $\{0.01943..., -1.2996..., 0.3890..., -1.1486...\}$. But no 2-cycles appear. However, if you draw graphs of $y = x$, $y = f(x)$, and $y{=}^2f(x)$ you will see the diagram in Figure 3.55. Where all three graphs intersect, we have the fixed points of f, the trivial 2-cycles. But where $y = x$

Figure 3.55

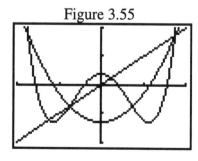

and $y{=}^2f(x)$ intersect, we have non-trivial 2-cycles. You can find those points using **2nd[CALC]**: They are $\{0.2416..., -1.2416...\}$. (Or use the methods of Example 1, dividing the fourth degree polynomial in the solution to $^2f(x) = x$ by the quadratic in the solution of $f(x) = x$ to get the quotient $x^2 + x - 0.3$. When you set the quotient equal to 0, you get a quadratic that you can solve by the formula, and you'll get two solutions, $\dfrac{-1 \pm \sqrt{2.2}}{2}$. The decimal approximations of these solutions are, of course, 0.2416... and −1.2416....) To verify that these points are repelling, check nDeriv(for one of the points as in Figure 3.56. The slope of the tangent to ^2f at 0.21416 is nearly −1.2, certainly greater than 1 in absolute value. (The slope for the other point is identical.) Therefore these points are repelling fixed points for ^2f, and they constitute a repelling 2-cycle for f.

Figure 3.56

```
nDeriv((X²-1.3)²
-1.3,X,.2416)
          -1.199909724
```

§5. Exercises

1. The quadratic $x^2 + x + 1$ is a factor of $x^4 + 4x^3 - 6x^2 - 7x - 10$.
    a) Use long division to find the other quadratic factor.
    b) Find the solutions of $x^4 + 4x^3 - 6x^2 - 7x - 10 = 0$.

2. Show that $x - 1$ is one of the factors of $3x^3 - 8x^2 + 3x + 2$ by using long division to find the other factor. Then find all the solutions of $3x^3 - 8x^2 + 3x + 2 = 0$.

3. Show that $3x^2 + 8x + 4$ is a factor of $3x^4 + 14x^3 + 14x^2 - 8x - 8$ by using long division. Then find all the solutions of $3x^4 + 14x^3 + 14x^2 - 8x - 8 = 0$.

4. Find a non-trivial 2-cycle of $f(x) = x^2 - 1.2$. Is it attracting or repelling?

5. Find a non-trivial 2-cycle of $f(x) = 3.1x(1 - x)$. Is it attracting or repelling?

6. Find a non-trivial 2-cycle of $f(x) = x^2 - 1.4$. Is it attracting or repelling?

7. Find all non-trivial 2-cycles of $f(x) = x - x^3$ and determine whether they are attracting or repelling.

8. Find non-trivial 2-cycles for $f(x) = 3.4x(1 - x)$ and $f(x) = 3.5x(1 - x)$. Are these cycles attracting or repelling? Write a few sentences to describe what happens to the 2-cycles of a logistic function as the parameter goes from 3.4 to 3.5.

9. Find a non-trivial 2-cycle of $f(x) = 2|x| - 1$. Is it attracting or repelling?

10. For the function $f(x) = x^2 - 2$,
    a) Find a non-trivial 2-cycle and determine whether it is attracting or repelling.
    b) Find a non-trivial 3-cycle and determine whether it is attracting or repelling.

11. For the function $f(x) = 4x(1 - x)$,
    a) Find a non-trivial 2-cycle and determine whether it is attracting or repelling.
    b) Find a non-trivial 3-cycle and determine whether it is attracting or repelling.

12. Does $f(x) = rx(1 - x)$ have a non-trivial 2-cycle when $r = 3$? Explain.

Chapter 4

THE ROAD TO CHAOS

§1. The Logistic Function

The use of the logistic function by biologists and ecologists in the study of population growth led to the discovery that slight changes in a single parameter could lead to wildly different behavior of a model system. This chapter will focus on the logistic function as an example of a function whose behavior changes from stable to unpredictable as a parameter is varied.

First, recall that the formula for the logistic function is $f(x) = rx(1-x)$, where r is the parameter. In our investigations we will restrict the domain to $0 \le x \le 1$ and the parameter to $0 \le r \le 4$. The domain restriction grows out of the ecological application, where x represents the size of a population as a percentage between 0% and 100%. The parameter restriction is necessary if we want all function values to fall in the range between 0 and 1, so that they are available as subsequent inputs. As long as r is between 0 and 4, the range of the logistic function is a subset of its domain, so the value after each iteration is again in the domain. (See Figure 4.1.)

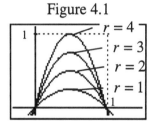

Figure 4.1

Fixed Points

To find the fixed points of f, solve the equation $f(x) = x$ in the general case:

$$rx(1-x) = x$$
$$x = 0 \quad \text{or} \quad r(1-x) = 1$$
$$x = 0 \quad \text{or} \quad 1-x = \frac{1}{r}$$
$$x = 0 \quad \text{or} \quad x = 1-\frac{1}{r}$$

Therefore, the fixed points are 0 and $1-\dfrac{1}{r}$ for every value of the parameter r (between 0 and 4).

Example 1. What are the fixed points of the logistic function $f(x) = 3.2x(1-x)$?

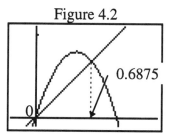

Figure 4.2

Solution: In this case, $r = 3.2$, so the two fixed points are 0 and $1 - \dfrac{1}{3.2} = 0.6875$.

0.6875

Example 2. What are the fixed points of the logistic function $f(x) = \frac{1}{2}x(1-x)$?

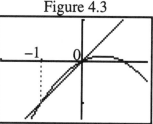

Figure 4.3

Solution: As always, 0 is one fixed point. The other is $1 - \dfrac{1}{\frac{1}{2}} = 1 - 2 = -1$. Note that when $r = \frac{1}{2}$, the second fixed point is negative, and 0 is the only fixed point in the unit interval $[0,1]$ where we are focusing our investigation.

Can we tell when both fixed points will be between 0 and 1? Yes, by doing a little algebra. When $0 \le r < 1$, then $1 < \dfrac{1}{r}$ so that $1 - \dfrac{1}{r} < 0$. Therefore, when the parameter is less than 1, the only fixed point in the unit interval is $x = 0$ (Figure 4.4a). Then, when $r = 1$, both formulas give the same fixed point, 0 (Figure 4.4b). But when $r > 1$, there are two distinct fixed points at 0 and $1 - \dfrac{1}{r}$, both in the unit interval, and that situation obtains for all values of r up to 4 (Figure 4.4c).

Figure 4.4

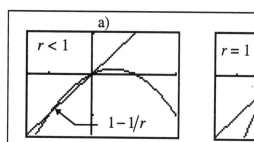
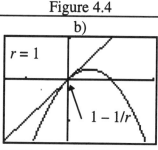
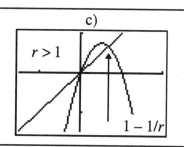

To check the attraction properties of the fixed points, we need to find the slope of the tangent at each fixed point. The calculator will help in this task. The idea is to write a program that draws the logistic function and the tangent to the curve at the fixed points, for a variety of values of r. For each value of r, we want to see the value of the parameter and the slope of the tangent along with the graph. The first program explores the attraction properties for 0 and is called TANGENT0.

Program – TANGENT0	Calculator hints	Purpose
FnOff	**VARS > Y-VARS 4:On/Off 2:FnOff**	Turns off all functions
"RX(1-X)"→Y₁	**VARS > Y-VARS 1:Function 1:Y1**	Defines Y₁ as logistic function
⁻.3→Xmin	**VARS 1:Window 1:Xmin**	Sets the window parameters
1.5→Xmax		
1→Xscl		
⁻.4→Ymin		
1.1→Ymax		
1→Yscl		
For(R,0,4,.25)	**PRGM 4:For(**	Begins loop on r, steps of ¼
0→P		Defines fixed point P as 0
Tangent(Y₁,P)	**2nd[DRAW] 5:Tangent(**	Draws tangent to Y₁ at fixed point
nDeriv(Y₁,X,P)→M	**MATH 8:nDeriv(**	Defines M as slope of tangent at P
Text(1,10,"R=",R)	**2nd[DRAW] 0:Text(**	To write "R = r-value" on screen
Text(1,70,"M=",M)		To write "M = slope" on screen
Pause	**PRGM 8:Pause**	Program waits for **ENTER**
End		Ends loop

Figure 4.5

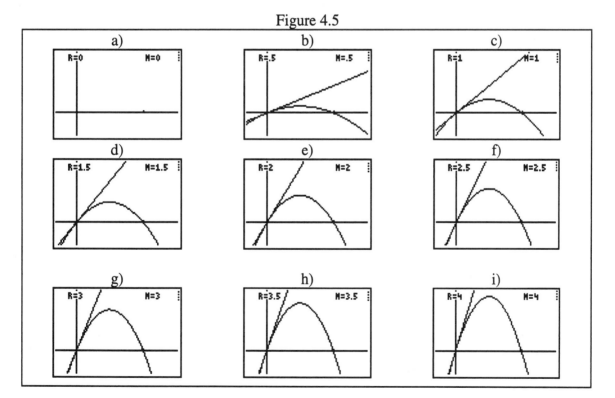

A run of TANGENT0 is shown in Figure 4.5. It is apparent that the slope of the tangent at 0 keeps increasing as r increases. In fact, the slope is the same as r (a fact we will prove in Chapter 7). Therefore, the slope is less than 1 when $r < 1$, the range where

0 is the only fixed point in the unit interval. Therefore, when $0 \leq r < 1$, 0 is an *attracting* fixed point. On the other hand, the slope of the tangent exceeds 1 when $r > 1$, so that 0 is no longer attracting. When r is exactly equal to 1, 0 is neutral.

When $r > 1$, the fixed point 0 is no longer attracting, so we need a second program to investigate the properties of the other fixed point, $1 - \dfrac{1}{r}$, when r is between 1 and 4. Much of the program is the same as TANGENT0, with some modifications to a few steps. It also helps to add the graph of $y = x$ because it clearly shows the location of $1 - \dfrac{1}{r}$ at its point of intersection with the logistic function. The modification will be called TANGENT1.

Program – TANGENT1	Modified lines	Purpose
FnOff		Turns off all functions
"RX(1-X)"→Y₁		Defines Y₁ as logistic function
"X"→Y₂	Adds the line $y = x$	Defines Y₂ as identity function
-.3→Xmin		Sets the window parameters
1.5→Xmax		
1→Xscl		
-.4→Ymin		
1.1→Ymax		
1→Yscl		
For(R,1.5,4,.5)	New starting point	Begins loop on r, steps of ½
1-1/R→P	$1-1/r$ is fixed point	Defines P as $1-1/r$
Tangent(Y₁,P)		Draws tangent to Y₁ at $1-1/r$
nDeriv(Y₁,X,P)→M		Slope of tangent at $1-1/r$ stored as M
Text(1,10,"R=",R)		To write "R = *r-value*" on screen
Text(1,70,"M=",M)		To write "M = *slope*" on screen
Pause		Program waits for **ENTER**
End		Ends loop

A run of TANGENT1 shows the tangent at $1 - \dfrac{1}{r}$ rotating around the graph of the function as the parameter increases from 1 to 4 (Figure 4.6), and its slope appears to be between −1 and 1 when r is between 1 and 3. Therefore, when $1 < r < 3$, the point $1 - \dfrac{1}{r}$ is an attractor. At the endpoints of this range, when $r = 1$ or $r = 3$, the point $1 - \dfrac{1}{r}$ is neutral.

Figure 4.6

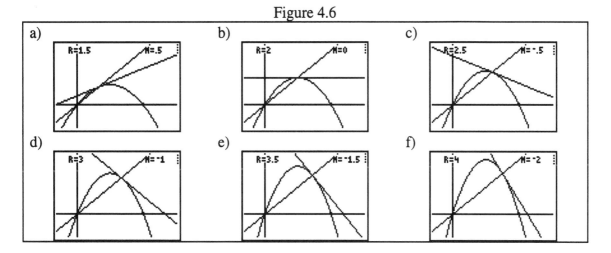

The attraction properties of both fixed points are summarized in the following table giving the absolute value of the slope of the tangent at each fixed point:

	$0 \le r < 1$	$r = 1$	$1 < r < 3$	$r = 3$	$3 < r \le 4$
$\|$ Slope of tangent at $0\|$	< 1	$= 1$	> 1	> 1	> 1
$\|$ Slope of tangent at $1 - \dfrac{1}{r} \|$		$= 1$	< 1	$= 1$	> 1

Example 3. Find the fixed points of $f(x) = rx(1-x)$ when $r = 2.5$. Find the slope of the tangent at each fixed point and verify the attraction properties given in the table.

Figure 4.7

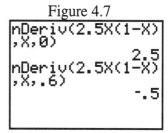

Solution: The fixed points are 0 and $1 - \dfrac{1}{r} = 1 - \dfrac{1}{2.5} = 0.6$.

The slopes of the tangents at these points can be approximated using nDeriv(. The results, in Figure 4.7, show that the slope at 0 is 2.5 and the slope at 0.6 is –0.5. Since the slope at 0 is greater than 1, 0 is a repelling point. Since the slope at 0.6 is less than 1 in absolute value, 0.6 is an attracting point. The tangent lines are shown in Figure 4.8. These results agree with the summary in the table.

Figure 4.8

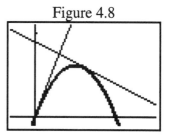

Each fixed point is neutral for a particular value of the parameter r. This happens at $r = 1$ for the fixed point 0 (and trivially for $1 - \dfrac{1}{r}$ since it is equal to 0 there), and at $r = 3$ for $1 - \dfrac{1}{r}$ (when it is different from 0). Figure 4.9 takes a closer look at what happens as r increases through the value 1, where the fixed point 0 changes from attracting to repelling, and where $1-\dfrac{1}{r}$ becomes the attracting fixed point.

Figure 4.9

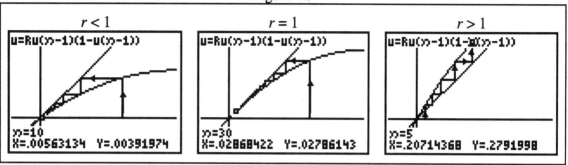

A similar abrupt change occurs to the tangent at $1-\dfrac{1}{r}$ when $r=3$ (Figure 4.10).

When r is slightly less than 3, the fixed point $1-\dfrac{1}{r}$ is attracting; the web spirals in.

When $r=3$, $1-\dfrac{1}{r}$ is neutral (but still weakly attracting). But when $r>3$, $1-\dfrac{1}{r}$ is suddenly repelling, and the web spirals away from the fixed point.

Figure 4.10

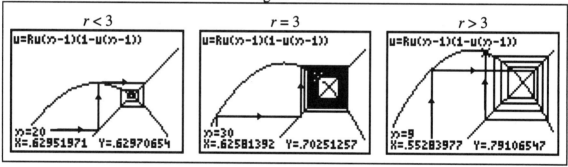

Birth of cycles

As r passes through 1, we saw that one fixed point (0) stops being an attractor and the other starts attracting. As r passes through 3, the second fixed point stops being an attractor, and ... and then what happens to the orbits after $r=3$? A 2-cycle is born!

To understand better how a 2-cycle is born when r passes through 3, we need to look at the function ${}^{2}f$. (Recall that a 2-cycle of f occurs at the fixed points of ${}^{2}f$.) When $r=3$, $f(x)=3x(1-x)$. Therefore:

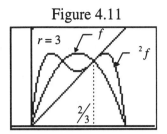

$$\begin{aligned} {}^2f(x) &= f(f(x)) \\ &= 3(3x(1-x))(1-3x(1-x)) \\ &= 9x(1-x)(1-3x+3x^2) \\ &= 9x - 36x^2 + 54x^3 - 27x^4 \end{aligned}$$

Figure 4.11

r = 3
f
^2f
2/3

The graph of ${}^2f$ is shown in Figure 4.11 along with the graph of *f* and $y = x$. The fixed point of interest is $1 - \frac{1}{r} = 1 - \frac{1}{3} = \frac{2}{3}$. It looks as if both *f* and ${}^2f$ have $\frac{2}{3}$ as a fixed point, and it also looks as if ${}^2f$ is tangent to the line $y = x$ at $\frac{2}{3}$. With a little help from the calculator, you can show that ${}^2f\left(\frac{2}{3}\right) = \frac{2}{3}$, and that the slope of the tangent to ${}^2f$ at $\frac{2}{3}$ is 1 (Figure 4.12). Thus there are no non-trivial 2-cycles with $r = 3$, and even the trivial one at 2/3 is neutral. To gain some insight into the question of 2-cycles for values of the parameter *r* near 3, you could zoom in on ${}^2f$ right around the point $\frac{2}{3}$ as in Figure 4.13. You can see that a 2-cycle is born when $r > 3$ because there are three fixed points for ${}^2f$ in the right-hand graph: one is also the fixed point of *f*, but the other two constitute a non-trivial 2-cycle for *f*.

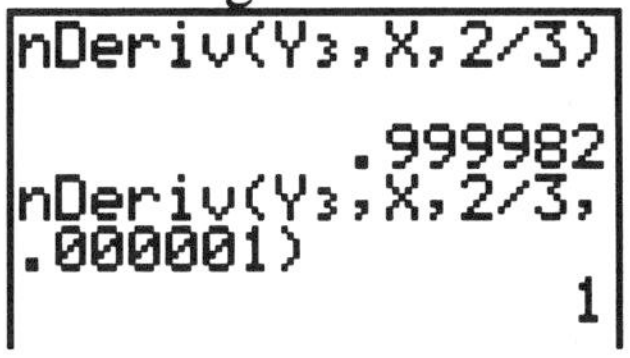

Figure 4.12

nDeriv(Y3,X,2/3)
.999982
nDeriv(Y3,X,2/3,
.000001)
1

Figure 4.13

r < 3
r = 3
r > 3
f
^2f
y = x

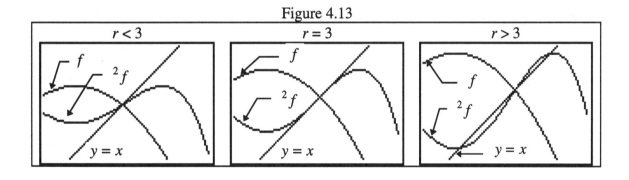

All fixed points of ${}^2f$ must satisfy the equation ${}^2f(x) = x$, and by doing a little algebra we can find formulas for the points in the non-trivial 2-cycles born at $r = 3$. Given

$$f(x) = rx(1-x)$$

then

$${}^2f(x) = r[rx(1-x)](1-[rx(1-x)]) = r^2x - r^2(r+1)x^2 + 2r^3x^3 - r^3x^4.$$

Then to solve ${}^2f(x) = x$, we would have:

$$r^2 x - r^2(r+1)x^2 + 2r^3 x^3 - r^3 x^4 = x$$
$$(r^2 - 1)x - r^2(r+1)x^2 + 2r^3 x^3 - r^3 x^4 = 0$$

There are two trivial solutions of this equation that can be identified because they are the fixed points of f. We have already used this idea in §3.5: The fixed points are solutions of $f(x) = x$ (or $f(x) - x = 0$); therefore the quadratic $f(x) - x$ is a factor of the fourth-power polynomial $^2f(x) - x$ (that we just worked out); divide the quadratic into the fourth-power polynomial, and the quotient is a quadratic with the 2-cycle points as solutions. So we now need to find the quadratic $f(x) - x$:

$$f(x) - x = 0$$
$$rx(1 - x) - x = 0$$
$$rx - rx^2 - x = 0$$
$$(r - 1)x - rx^2 = 0$$

Therefore, $(r-1)x - rx^2$ is a factor of $(r^2 - 1)x - r^2(r+1)x^2 + 2r^3 x^3 - r^3 x^4$. If you do the division (very carefully!) you'll get the other factor $r^2 x^2 - r(r+1)x + (r+1)$. Hence, the non-trivial solutions of $^2f(x) = x$ are solutions of

$$r^2 x^2 - r(r+1)x + (r+1) = 0.$$

Using the quadratic formula, you'll find the solutions:

$$x = \frac{(r+1) \pm \sqrt{r^2 - 2r - 3}}{2r}.$$

Granted, this is not the simplest formula in the world, but it has some important information. For what values of r does the formula give real solutions? When the expression under the radical sign is non-negative:

$$r^2 - 2r - 3 \geq 0$$
$$(r - 3)(r + 1) \geq 0$$
$$r \leq -1 \text{ or } r \geq 3$$

Since r is never negative, we learn that there are real solutions when $r \geq 3$. But when $r = 3$, we get the double root $\frac{2}{3}$ which we already know is a trivial 2-cycle. When $r > 3$, there are *two distinct* solutions which give two distinct *non-trivial* fixed points of ^2f.

Thus, as soon as r passes through 3, a non-trivial 2-cycle for f is born. The point $1 - \frac{1}{r}$ switches from attracting to repelling, and all orbits are instead attracted to a 2-

cycle consisting of the two points:

$$\frac{(r+1)+\sqrt{r^2-2r-3}}{2r} \text{ and } \frac{(r+1)-\sqrt{r^2-2r-3}}{2r}.$$

For example, when $r = 3.1$ as in Figure 4.14, the 2-cycle is $\{0.7645..., 0.5580...\}$.

Figure 4.14

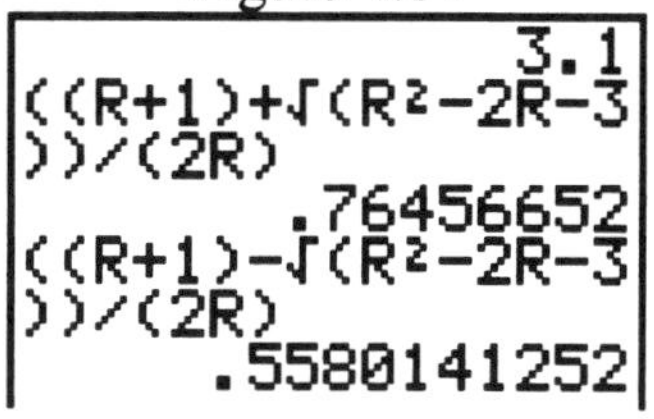

```
                          3.1
((R+1)+√(R²-2R-3
))/(2R)
                   .76456652
((R+1)-√(R²-2R-3
))/(2R)
                  .5580141252
```

But wait a minute: How can we be sure that the 2-cycles are attractors when $r > 3$? Either by doing the orbit analysis of several seeds to see what happens, or by checking the slopes of the tangents at the fixed points of ^2f for several values of r, just as we checked the tangents of f around 0 and $1 - \dfrac{1}{r}$. Checking slopes of tangents is a little easier, especially if we use a calculator program like TANGENT1. We'll need to modify the program TANGENT1 so that it draws tangents to ^2f at a non-trivial fixed point when $r > 3$. Suppose we call the modification TANGENT2. The modification is shown in the following table.

Program – TANGENT2	Modified lines	Purpose
FnOff		Turns off all functions
"R²X(1-X)(1-RX(1-X))"→Y₁	Formula for ^2f	Defines Y₁ as logistic function
"X"→Y₂		Defines Y₂ as identity function
.2→Xmin	New window	Sets the window parameters
1.1→Xmax	Ditto	
1→Xscl		
.4→Ymin	Ditto	
1→Ymax	Ditto	
1→Yscl		
For(R,3,3.5,.1)	New range for r	Begins loop on r, steps of ½
((R+1)+(√(R²-2R-3))/(2R)→P	New Fixed point	
Tangent(Y₁,P)		Draws tangent to Y₁ at P
nDeriv(Y₁,X,P)→M		Slope of tangent at P stored as M
Text(1,10,"R=",R)		To write "R = *r-value*" on screen
Text(1,70,"M=",M)		To write "M = *slope*" on screen
Pause		Program waits for **ENTER**
End		Ends loop

When TANGENT2 is run, the result will be the series of screens in Figure 4.15. The tangent rotates around the graph of ^2f, decreasing from a slope of 1 to a slope of -1.2 as r goes from 3 to 3.5. The absolute value of the slope exceeds 1 somewhere between 3.4 and 3.5. By letting r run from 3.4 to 3.5 in steps of 0.01, you could refine the estimate of where the switch occurs, and you could repeat the process as long as you wish, to pinpoint the switch as accurately as you care to. Or you could turn to Chapter 7 where you'll find the algebra showing that the switch occurs exactly at $r = 1 + \sqrt{6} \approx 3.45$.

Figure 4.15

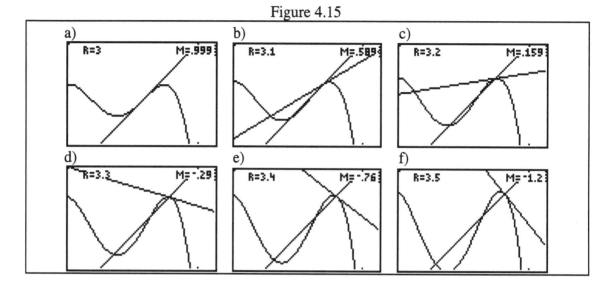

To sum up, when r is between 0 and $1 + \sqrt{6}$, the 2-cycles of $f(x) = rx(1-x)$ are attracting. What happens beyond $1 + \sqrt{6}$ will be answered in the next section.

Example 4. Find a 2-cycle for the logistic function $f(x) = 3.6x(1-x)$ and determine whether it is attracting, repelling or neutral by finding the slope of the tangent to ^2f at these points.

Solution: First find the 2 cycle by finding the nontrivial intersections of ^2f with $y = x$. Press **MODE** and select Func. Press **Y=** and set Y1=RX(1-X), Y2=R²X(1-X)(1-RX(1-X)), and Y3=X. Choose a window that includes the unit interval on both horizontal and vertical axes. Press **2nd[QUIT]** to return to the home screen and store 3.6 as R. Press **GRAPH** to see the screen of Figure 4.16. To find the intersection points, press **2nd[CALC]** and choose **5:intersect**. Use the down arrow to place the cursor on Y2, then select it by pressing **ENTER**. The cursor automatically jumps to Y3, and you select it as the second curve by pressing **ENTER**. Using the left or right arrow, place the cursor on one of the intersection points not shared by Y1 and press **ENTER**. You'll see the intersection given in Figure 4.17. Return to the home screen and store X as A by typing **ALPHA[X] STO> ALPHA[A]**. This records the intersection point as the constant A and makes it available for other uses. You can go through this same procedure with the

Figure 4.16

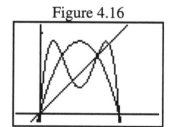

Figure 4.17

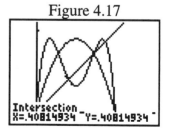

other non-trivial point of intersection but you could also simply
evaluate Y1 at A: press **2nd[CALC] 1:value**. The graph is
displayed again along with a flashing cursor where you can
enter a value for X. Press **ALPHA[A]** and **ENTER**, and you'll see
Figure 4.18 with the value of Y1 given as Y at the bottom of the
screen. To store the second point of the 2-cycle, return to the
home screen and store Y as B. Finally, to determine whether
the cycle is attracting, find the slope of ^2f at one of the points
of intersection by pressing **2nd[CALC] 6:dy/dx**. Use the up or
down arrow to place the cursor on Y2 and then press **ALPHA[A]**
to find the slope at the point you have stored as A. The slope
shown in Figure 4.19 is greater than 1 in absolute value and
tells us that the 2-cycle {A,B} is repelling. You can verify this
result by checking a web diagram, if you like. If you choose a
seed near A, you will see a web that fills in an area around the 2-cycle but never is
attracted to it.

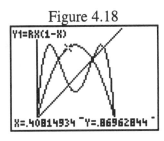

Figure 4.18

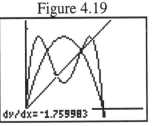

Figure 4.19

§1. Exercises

1. Determine the fixed points of the logistic function in the interval [0, 1] for the following values of r:

a) 0.5   b) 1.6   c) 2.4   d) 3.1   e) 3.5

2. Check the boxes in the following table where your answer is Yes:

	$0 \le r < 1$	$r = 1$	$1 < r \le 4$
Is 0 a fixed point?			
Is $1 - \frac{1}{r}$ a fixed point?			

3. Determine whether the fixed point 0 is attracting, repelling or neutral for the logistic function with $r =$:

a) 0.3   b) 0.9   c) 1   d) 2.8   f) 3.1

4. Determine whether the non-zero fixed point is attracting, repelling or neutral for the logistic function with $r =$:

a) 0.8   b) 1.7   c) 2.9   d) 3   e) 3.1

5. Find the fixed points for the logistic function in [0, 1] and determine whether they are attracting, repelling or neutral if $r =$:

a) 0.2   b) 0.75   c) 1.75   d) 2.2   e) 2.8

6. Use your calculator to draw graphs of the logistic function and its tangent lines at the fixed points if $r =$:

a) 1   b) 1.5   c) 2.4   d) 3.865   e) 4

7. Fill in the table on the next page for the logistic function, giving the fixed points in the interval [0, 1], along with the slope of the tangent to the curve at those points, for the given values of the parameter r.

8. This exercise explores the logistic function for $r > 4$.

a) Draw a graph of $f(x) = 5x(1 - x)$ over the domain $0 \le x \le 1$. What is the range of the function over this domain? Is the range a subset of the domain?

b) Analyze and describe the orbits of the following seeds: 0.1, 0.3, 0.75, 0.99, 1.

c) What are the fixed points of this function? Are they attracting, repelling or neutral?

d) Find two seeds other than the fixed points whose orbits do not escape to infinity.

9. Find the non-trivial 2-cycle when $r = 3.3$.

a) Verify that this 2-cycle attracts the orbit of 0.5.

b) Find the slope of the tangent to the graph of ^2f at both points in the 2-cycle and verify that its absolute value is less than 1.

10. Find a 2-cycle for the logistic function $f(x) = 3.8x(1-x)$ and determine whether it is attracting, repelling or neutral by finding the slope of the tangent to ^2f at these points.

11. Choose a value of r a little bit bigger than $1 + \sqrt{6}$ and investigate the orbit of 0.5.
a) What do you discover? Make a conjecture.
b) Find a 2-cycle for your parameter and verify that the slope of the tangent to ^2f at these points is greater than 1 in absolute value.

Table for Exercise 7, page 108.

$r =$	Fixed Points	Slope of Tangent	Attracting, Repelling or Neutral
0.5			
1.0			
1.5			
2.0			
2.5			
2.9			
3.1			
3.4			
3.5			

§2. Period Doubling

In the last section, we found attracting fixed points and 2-cycles of the logistic function when $0 \leq r < 1 + \sqrt{6}$, and we derived formulas for these points and cycles in terms of r. For every value of r between 0 and 3, there was one attracting point; for r between 3 and $1 + \sqrt{6}$, there was one attracting 2-cycle. Any seed x_0 between 0 and 1 would eventually be attracted to the limiting point or cycle.

But the algebra was already getting complicated. We needed a fourth-power polynomial to study ^2f. To continue an investigation of orbital behavior, we will turn to the calculator for help.

The Feigenbaum plot

For each value of the parameter r, we want to explore the eventual behavior of orbits to find out if there is an attracting point or cycle. Does it make a difference which seed we pick? Would different seeds give different answers? It turns out that if there is an attractor, there is only one, and most seeds will head toward it. One representative seed that *always* finds attractors for the logistic function is 0.5. The reason that 0.5 works so well has to do with the fact that it is the vertex of the parabolic arch of the logistic function, but the details are beyond the scope of this course; please take it on faith that it will work.

What happens if there isn't an attractor? In most cases 0.5 is still a good representative in the sense that its orbit will wander unpredictably around the unit interval as will most other seeds' orbits. There are special values of r where 0.5 is eventually fixed while most other orbits wander, and some times when 0.5 wanders though other seeds are eventually fixed. But the important thing is what happens when there *is* an attractor; and for those r-values, 0.5 is an impeccable representative: it finds the attractor every time.

So here's the plan: For every parameter r between 0 and 4, we record the eventual behavior of the orbit of 0.5 by looking at some sufficiently large number of iterations, say 200. Because the orbit may jump around for a while before settling down into a clear pattern, we will ignore the first 50 iterations and record only the points in the orbit between 51 and 200 iterations. We will make a graphical record by plotting r on the horizontal axis and the orbit points vertically over the r-value. Thus we need a horizontal axis running from 0 to 4 and a vertical axis from 0 to 1.

Remember that the calculator usually tells us (incorrectly) that an orbit attracted to a limit actually lands on the limit. This error is useful now because it reveals the limiting point or cycle we want to see. If the orbit is attracted to a fixed point, the calculator will plot its approximation of that point (over and over again). If it is attracted to a cycle, the calculator will plot its approximation of the points in the cycle (several times). If the orbit wanders around the unit interval, the calculator will plot a scattering of dots between 0 and 1.

As an example, consider the orbit of 0.5 when $r = 3.2$. The first few iterations are shown in Figure 4.20, and the iterations from $n = 50$ to $n = 56$ in Figure 4.21. The orbit is attracted to a 2-cycle consisting of the points 0.5130... and 0.7994... Without the first

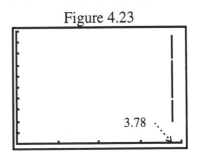

Figure 4.20

n	$u(n)$
0	.5
1	.8
2	.512
3	.79954
4	.51288
5	.79947
6	.51302

$n=0$

Figure 4.21

n	$u(n)$
50	.51304
51	.79946
52	.51304
53	.79946
54	.51304
55	.79946
56	.51304

$n=50$

Figure 4.22

(3.2,0.79946)

(3.2,0.51304)

fifty iterations, the plot would consist of the two dots shown in Figure 4.22, (3.2, 0.51304...) and (3.2, 0.79946...).

As another example, when $r = 3.78$, the orbit wanders around without being attracted to any cycle. Therefore, the graph would be a smear of points vertically above $r = 3.78$, as in Figure 4.23.

Figure 4.23

3.78

Now we're ready for the whole picture. Obviously we can't use *every* value of r because the calculator is finite, and its screen is only 95 pixels wide. The best we can do is break up the interval [0, 4] into subintervals of uniform length, with 0 being the left endpoint of the first subinterval, and 4 the right endpoint of the last subinterval. There are 94 subintervals of length $\dfrac{4}{94}$. Unfortunately, when $r = 4$, the seed 0.5 loses its representative status; it is eventually fixed while most other orbits are chaotic. (See Exercise 1.) To make the final graph a little more realistic, we stop r at 3.999 instead of 4, and therefore make the step size $\dfrac{3.999}{94}$. At each step we run the orbit of 0.5, throw out the first 50 iterations, and plot the points corresponding to iterations 51 through 200. The graph, called the *orbit diagram*, is generated by the program ORBDIAG.

Program – ORBDIAG	Calculator hints	Purpose
ClrDraw	2nd[DRAW] 1:ClrDraw	Clears the decks
ClrHome	PRGM > I/O 8:ClrHome	
FnOff		
0→Xmin		Sets the window
3.999→Xmax		

`1→Xscl`		
`0→Ymin`		
`1→Ymax`		
`.1→Yscl`		
`3.999/94→S`		Step size
`For(R,0,3.999,S)`		95 values of r from 0 to 3.999
`.5→X`		0.5 is the seed
`For(J,1,200,1)`		Inner loop: J counts 200 iterations
`RX(1-X)→X`		Logistic formula: output becomes next input
`If J>50`	**PRGM 1:If ALPHA[J] 2nd[TEST] 3:>**	If true, do next step; if false, skip next step
`Pt-On(R,X)`	**2nd[DRAW] > POINTS 1:Pt-On(**	Plots (*parameter*, *orbit point*)
`End`		Ends J-loop
`End`		Ends r-loop

The graph drawn by ORBDIAG is shown in Figure 4.24. The orbit diagram is also called the *Feigenbaum plot* for Mitchell Feigenbaum (b. 1945), one of the pioneers of Chaos Theory, who is credited with discovering and explaining the universality of this graph. More about that later. Even with the low resolution of a graphing calculator, you can see some stunning patterns in the orbit diagram. More details emerge if you use a computer with finer pixels and more points. (See Figure 4.25.)

Figure 4.24

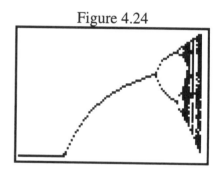

Figure 4.25

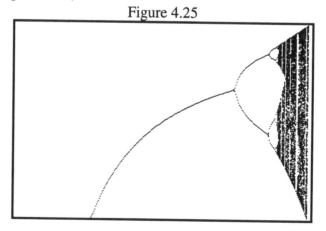

The Feigenbaum plot gives a graphical picture of information about the logistic function. At the left, the graph stays along the horizontal r-axis from 0 to 1. Why? Because 0 is the attractor for orbits when r is between 0 and 1. At 1, the picture changes:

The fixed point attractor is no longer 0; it is now $1-\dfrac{1}{r}$ and rises steadily as r goes from 1 to 3. Then the graph branches into two lines as r passes through 3, where both fixed points become repelling and orbits are attracted to a 2-cycle. This branching is called *bifurcation* (a two-tined fork).

So Figures 4.24 and 4.25 give graphical confirmation of the algebraic facts we deduced in that last section. But now what happens in this graph? There seems to be another bifurcation at about $r = 3.4$, where each of the branches forks into two more branches. We can get a better picture by zooming in on the right-hand portion of the graph. We can do so by changing Xmin to 3 and running the program again. Because we will want to make other adjustments to the window in the future, we first modify the program to make changes easy. Call the modified program ORBDIAG1.

Program – ORBDIAG1	Modifications	Purpose
`ClrDraw`		
`ClrHome`		
`FnOff`		
`Disp "WINDOW"`		Alerts user to input window parameters
`Prompt Xmin`	Input left limit	
`Prompt Xmax`	Input right limit	
`Prompt Ymin`	Input bottom limit	
`Prompt Ymax`	Input top limit	
`1→Xscl`		
`.1→Yscl`		
`(Xmax-Xmin)/94→S`	New step size	
`For(R,Xmin,Xmax,S)`	New limits for r	
`.5→X`		
`For(J,1,200,1)`		
`RX(1-X)→X`		
`If J>50`		
`Pt-On(R,X)`		
`End`		
`End`		

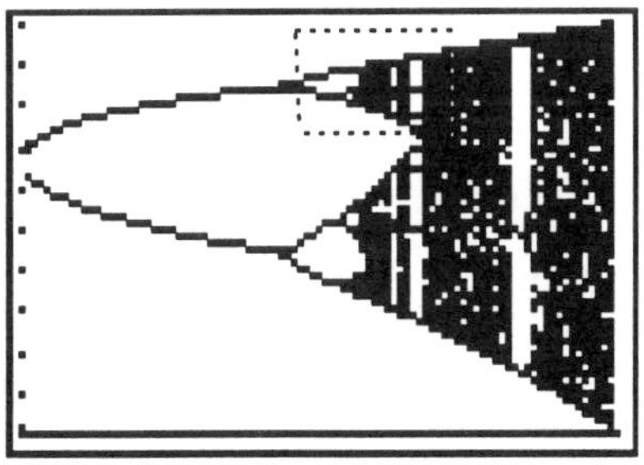

A run of ORBDIAG1 using Xmin=3, Xmax=3.999, Ymin=0, Ymax=1 would give the graph in Figure 4.26. Now the second bifurcation is clearly visible, and from the last section, we know that it occurs when the value of the parameter is $1+\sqrt{6} \approx 3.45$.

Figure 4.26

But now it looks as if there is yet another bifurcation at the end of these four branches at about 3.55. We can clarify the picture by zooming in on the graph again, this time focusing in on the bifurcation of the top branch, marked in Figure 4.26 by the dotted rectangle. Figure 4.27 shows a run of ORBDIAG1 with the *r*-axis going from 3.44 to 3.66 and the *y*-axis from 0.76 to 0.91.

Figure 4.27

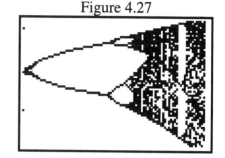

Figure 4.27 shows that there is indeed another bifurcation, and you could check that there are similar bifurcations on the lower branch. Thus *f* erupts into an 8-cycle around the middle of the screen, the point being about 3.5441....

The Feigenbaum Number: The end of order

Look at Figure 4.27 and you can see more bifurcations piling up in the middle of the graph. Bifurcations on top of bifurcations giving cycles of period 2, 4, 8, 16, 32, and so on, the so-called *period-doubling route to chaos*. As the period doubling cascade continues through all the powers of 2, the branches become shorter and shorter. Peitgen, Jürgens and Saupe (1992) suggest, it is "tempting ... to imagine that the lengths of the branches might decrease according to some law, perhaps a geometric law." Feigenbaum has shown that there is indeed such a decreasing sequence of lengths, and he found a limiting point that marks the end of the period-doubling cascade: 3.5699456.... That point is now called the *Feigenbaum point*. To the left of this point attracting periods double themselves into the chaos that appears on the right.

But order does not end with the Feigenbaum point. There are a lot of patterns visible in the Feigenbaum plot. First, you must have been struck by the similarity of the last two graphs. The Feignbaum plot is in fact self-similar. Little pieces of the graph contain miniature copies of the whole. *It is a fractal.* Here we see one manifestation of the intimate connection between chaotic dynamics and fractal geometry.

All these graphs have another feature in common: a window of periodicity that appears in a sea of chaos. In Figure 4.26, there is a band of white at about *r* = 3.8. If you check the orbit of 0.5 for *r* = 3.83, you discover it is quickly attracted to a 3-cycle (Figure 4.28). There is a similar band of white in Figure 4.27. Since this is a magnification of the upper branch of Figure 4.26, you might guess that the lower branch would look the same and that the attractor in this area would be a 6-cycle. With a little bit of effort, you can show that 0.5 is attracted to a 6-cycle when *r* = 3.627. Now if you look back at Figure 4.26, you will notice there are

Figure 4.28

n	u(n)
20	.1561
21	.5047
22	.9574
23	.1561
24	.5047
25	.9574
26	.1561

n=20

actually several narrow bands of white, one of which occurs around 3.627 where we find this 6-cycle. The others represent other windows of order in the midst of the chaotic regime beyond the Feigenbaum Point.

How does the organization of the 3-cycle window end? If you zoom in on the lower branch of the Feigenbaum plot at r = 3.83, you see another period doubling cascade collapsing into chaos at another Feigenbaum point. Figure 4.29 shows this result in a graph produced by ORBDIAG1 with the r-axis going from 3.826 to 3.852 and the y- axis from 0.135 to 0.165.

Figure 4.29

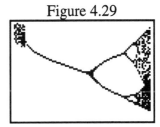

§2. Exercises

1. When $r = 4$, show that 0.5 is eventually fixed. Pick three other seeds at random and describe their orbits.

2. The orbit of 0.5 eventually lands on 0. Does this make 0 an attractor? Explain.

3. Copy the program ORBDIAG1 and use it to reproduce Figures 4.25 and 4.26.

4. The graph of the Feigenbaum plot is the graph of a function for $0 \leq r \leq 3$; that is, for each value of r there is one and only one value of y.
a) Give a formula for y in terms of r when $0 \leq r \leq 1$. What kind of a function is this?
b) Give a formula for y in terms of r when $1 \leq r \leq 3$. What kind of a function is this?

5. The third bifurcation point, where 8 branches start, occurs at about 3.54. Run the program ORBDIAG1 to zoom in on the bifurcation process at this point, letting the r-axis run from 3.54 to 3.59, and the y-axis from 0.44 to 0.58.
a) Move your cursor to the new bifurcation point in the middle of the screen and record the value of r. What kind of cycle does the orbit of 0.5 develop at this point?
b) Pick a value of r just beyond this point and verify that it has the cyclic behavior you predicted.

6. Use the program ORBDIAG1 to show that the 6-cycle window identified in this section around $r = 3.627$ ends with a period-doubling cascade. Size the window so that you zoom in on one of the six branches showing both the beginning and the end of the bifurcation. For example, let the r-axis run from 3.626 to 3.636, and y-axis from 0.30 to 0.31

7. Use your calculator to draw a graph of ${}^3f$ when $r = 3.84$. Show that there are two 3-cycles and determine which is attracting.

8. In Exercise 7, you discovered one attracting and one repelling 3-cycle.
a) Verify numerically that the orbit of 0.5 is attracted to the attracting cycle.
b) Observe that none of the points in the repelling cycle follows the example of the orbit of 0.5. Find two other seeds that do not behave like 0.5.
c) From parts (a) and (b), you know five seeds that behave differently from 0.5. Find one more.

§3. Universality

In 1975, Mitchell Feigenbaum was studying the period doubling cascade much as you are, using a hand-held calculator. He applied the same process to a whole range of functions, and made a stunning discovery: The route to chaos is the same for a whole class of similar but unrelated functions. In this section we take a closer look at two of those functions, one quadratic, one trigonometric.

The Quadratic Family

The first type of function we will consider is quadratic, like the logistic function, but one whose algebra is even easier. The function has the form $f(x) = x^2 + c$, and the graph is the familiar parabola $y = x^2$ translated up (or down) by the value of the parameter c (Figure 4.30).

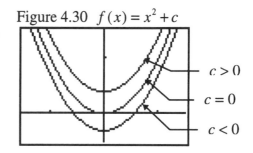

Figure 4.30 $f(x) = x^2 + c$

The first task is to find the fixed points by solving the familiar equation $f(x) = x$. If you set up the equation in terms of $x^2 + c$ and solve it using the quadratic formula, your answer should be $x = \dfrac{1 \pm \sqrt{1 - 4c}}{2}$. It follows that there are real fixed points when the discriminant, $1 - 4c$, is nonnegative. Solving this inequality we have:

$$1 - 4c \geq 0$$
$$-4c \geq -1$$
$$c \leq \frac{1}{4}$$

When $c > \frac{1}{4}$, there are no fixed points; when $c = \frac{1}{4}$, there is one fixed point at $x = \frac{1}{2}$; and when $c < \frac{1}{4}$, there are two distinct fixed points. Graphically, this means the quadratic does not intersect the identity function when $c > \frac{1}{4}$; it has one point of intersection at a point of tangency when $c = \frac{1}{4}$; and it intersects twice when $c < \frac{1}{4}$. (See Figure 4.31.)

Figure 4.31

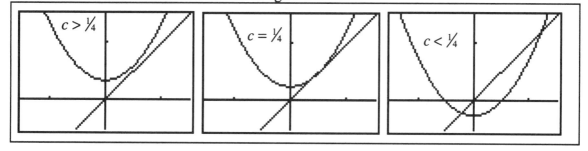

The web plot in Figure 4.32 reveals that the dynamics of all orbits for $c > \frac{1}{4}$ are completely predictable: Everything escapes to infinity. When $c = \frac{1}{4}$, the fixed point is the point of tangency with the identity function whose slope is 1. Therefore, the point is neutral. As Figure 4.33 shows, the neutral fixed point is weakly attracting on the left and weakly repelling on the right.

Figure 4.32

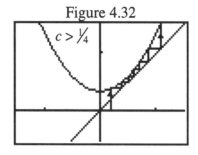

Figure 4.33

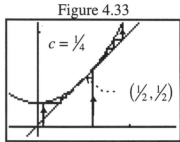

Things are more interesting when $c < \frac{1}{4}$. For example, the graphs in Figures 4.34 and 4.35 show web plots for $c = -0.6$ using as seeds both 1.15 and -1.15. Both orbits spiral in towards the leftmost fixed point.

Figure 4.34

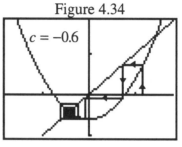

Figure 4.35

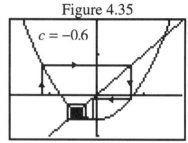

If we call the left-hand fixed point p_{left} and the right-hand fixed point p_{right}, then p_{left} appears to be an attractor and p_{right} a repeller when $c = -0.6$. By substituting $c = -0.6$ you can check that

$$p_{left} = \frac{1 - \sqrt{1 - 4c}}{2} = -0.4219... \qquad \text{and} \qquad p_{right} = \frac{1 + \sqrt{1 - 4c}}{2} = 1.4219...$$

Furthermore, the calculator will give $-0.8439...$ as the slope of the tangent at p_{left} and $2.8439...$ as the slope of the tangent to p_{right}, confirming the graphical results in Figures 4.34 and 4.35.

p_{right} is a fixed point, so that $f(p_{right}) = p_{right}$. From the symmetry of the quadratic function, it is clear that $f(-p_{right}) = f(p_{right})$, so that $-p_{right}$ is an eventually fixed point. In between these two extremes, however, all seeds are attracted to p_{left}, and outside this interval all points are attracted to infinity. (See Figures 4.36 and 4.37.) To simplify the notation, let $b^+ = p_{right}$

Figure 4.36

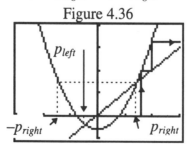

Figure 4.37

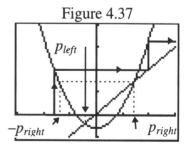

and $b^- = -p_{right}$. With this notation, we have

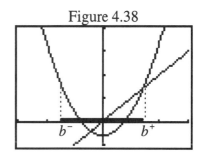

Figure 4.38

$$b^+ = p_{right} = \frac{1-\sqrt{1-4c}}{2}$$

and

$$b^- = -p_{right} = -\frac{1-\sqrt{1-4c}}{2}$$

By restricting the domain to the interval $\left(b^-, b^+\right)$, we insure that the range is a subset of the domain, so that function values can be used as subsequent inputs. You can see that fact graphically if you draw a square outlining the domain and including the range (Figure 4.39).

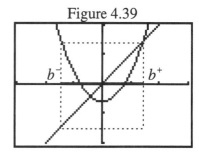

Figure 4.39

Notice what happens, however, when c is close to −2 as shown in Figure 4.40: When $c > -2$, the vertex of the graph is contained within the box, so the range is a subset of the domain. When $c = -2$, the vertex of the graph rests on the bottom of the box, so the range and domain are identical. When $c < -2$, the graph extends beyond the bottom of the box, so for these values of c, the range exceeds the domain. Some function values will escape the interval of attraction to p_{left} and orbit out to infinity. Therefore, the range is a subset of the domain only when $c \geq -2$.

Figure 4.40

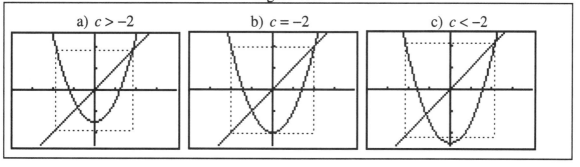

The moral of the story so far is that the parameter c is restricted to the interval from −2 to +0.25. In that interval, we are interested in the orbit of a representative point. Once again we use the vertex of the parabola which, in this case, is 0. We want to investigate details about fixed points, cycles and attraction properties, but we start with an overall picture by modifying the program ORBDIAG1 to adapt it to the new representative seed 0, the new parameter c, and the new formula $x^2 + c \to x$. The modification is left as an exercise. Once again you must be cautious of 0 as a representative when the parameter gets to the extreme of its range, *i.e.* when $c = -2$. In your modification of ORBDIAG1, let c run from −1.999 to 0.25, set the window bottom to −2 and the window top to 2. You will see the graph shown in Figure 4.41.

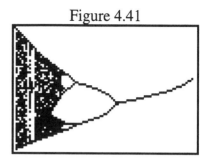

Figure 4.41

The Trigonometric Family

The Feigenbaum plot for the quadratic family in Figure 4.41 shows a period doubling route to chaos that is startlingly similar to the logistic function in Figure 4.24. Even more startling is the similarity with a family of trigonometric functions. The family is $f(x) = k \sin \pi x$ with the parameter k. You will have a chance to explore this family and the quadratic family in greater depth in the exercises at the end of this section. For this function, the domain of x is restricted to the unit interval [0,1]. If $0 \le x \le 1$, then $0 \le \pi x \le \pi$, so that $\sin(\pi x)$ produces one arch over this domain (see Figure 4.42). The vertex of the arch occurs at $x = \frac{1}{2}$, and we use that value for the representative seed. Furthermore, the maximum value of the sine function occurs at that point so that

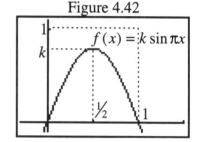

Figure 4.42

$f\left(\frac{1}{2}\right) = k \sin \frac{\pi}{2} = k$. Therefore, if the range of f is to be a subset of its domain, k must not exceed 1. If you modify ORBDIAG1 again using 0.5 as the representative seed, the formula for the trigonometric family as an iterator, and the restriction $0 \le k < 1$ for the parameter, you will see another Feigenbaum plot shown in Figure 4.43.

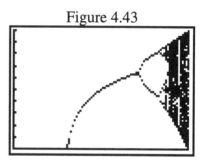

Figure 4.43

These orbit diagrams created considerable excitement when they were first viewed in the 1970s. The period doubling route to chaos appeared not to be the exclusive property of the logistic function or even of polynomials. It might in fact be a universal property (Gulick, 1992, p. 50; Peitgen, 1992, p. 616). Shortly after Feigenbaum's article was published, several researchers in different parts of the world discovered some physical evidence supporting this radical hypothesis (Pietgen, 1992, p. 618; Briggs, 1990, pp. 64-65). Both in America and in Canada, it was confirmed that the onset of a heart attack is signaled by period doubling behavior that ends in chaos. In Italy and in France, researchers into fluid turbulence discovered that liquid also follows a period doubling route to chaos when subjected to heat or other disturbance. Research continues to confirm these results in all kinds of turbulent behavior, physical, social and psychological.

The Feigenbaum Constant

In all these orbit diagrams, Feigenbaum noted that branches shorten as the periods double, and the rate of shortening seemed similar for all functions. To investigate the rates, Feigenbaum looked at lengths of successive branches and computed their ratio. For example, in Figure 4.25, notice that the branches in one level of bifurcation are about four times as long as those in the next level. Feigenbaum conjectured that this ratio of successive branches is constant. When he computed the ratio of lengths of successive branches, he discovered not a constant, but a sequence that converged rapidly to a constant. The limit turns out to be 4.6692...and is now called the *Feigenbaum constant*. This constant turned up in the physical experiments that confirmed the universality of period doubling. Like the constant π, it seems to be one of the numerical constants embedded in the heart of this universe, appearing in theoretical and natural settings with uncanny frequency.

To see how the Feigenbaum constant is developed in the logistic function, we start by measuring a sequence of r's, the values of r where the bifurcation points occur. From this sequence, we can construct a second sequence of lengths of bifurcation branches, and then finally we can construct the sequence of ratios of successive branches.

The first bifurcation occurs at $r = 1$ when 0 becomes repelling and orbits are attracted to the fixed point $1 - \dfrac{1}{r}$. The second bifurcation occurs at $r = 3$ when $1 - \dfrac{1}{r}$ becomes repelling and orbits are attracted to a 2-cycle around it. In sequence notation we have $r_0 = 1$ and $r_1 = 3$. In general, r_k is the value of the parameter where the orbits start being attracted to a 2^k-cycle. The next point in the sequence would be r_2 where orbits fall into a 2^2-cycle. We know that point is $r_2 = 1 + \sqrt{6} = 3.4494....$ After some more experimentation, you can add a few numbers to this sequence. If you carry out decimals to 7 places and round, you'll get 10^{-6} accuracy and see the following seven points in the sequence:

$$
\begin{aligned}
r_0 &= 1.000000 \\
r_1 &= 3.000000 \\
r_2 &= 3.449489 \\
r_3 &= 3.544090 \\
r_4 &= 3.564407 \\
r_5 &= 3.568759 \\
r_6 &= 3.569692
\end{aligned}
$$

The length of the branches would be the difference between successive terms of the r-sequence. The length of the first branch is $r_1 - r_0$; the length of the second branch is $r_2 - r_1$; and their ratio is

$$
f_1 = \frac{r_1 - r_0}{r_2 - r_1}.
$$

In general, the ratio of the kth branch to the $k + 1$st branch is

$$f_k = \frac{r_k - r_{k-1}}{r_{k+1} - r_k}.$$

Working out the ratios for the bifurcation points yields the following sequence (rounded to 6 decimal places):

$$f_1 = 4.449497$$
$$f_2 = 4.751429$$
$$f_3 = 4.656248$$
$$f_4 = 4.668428$$
$$f_5 = 4.664523$$

This is the beginning of a sequence that Feigenbaum discovered converged to the limit 4.6692.... You might well have a question about what happened to f_5 here; it appears to be headed in the wrong direction. The reason is round-off error. Using the rounded numbers for r_k, we get 4.664523 for f_5. Had we carried more decimal places, f_5 would have been 4.6687..., continuing on toward the Feigenbaum constant. A more accurate sequence would require computing equipment more sophisticated than the TI-83, but even with these few points we can see some of the same numbers that led Feigenbaum to conjecture, and then to confirm, the existence of the limit 4.6692...

Round-off error is just one of the reasons that it is very difficult to reproduce Feigenbaum's research. Another is that it is hard to decide exactly where a bifurcation occurs experimentally. (How many iterations do you look at before you decide? How many decimal places do you want and can your computer accurately provide?) Feigenbaum himself used more sophisticated mathematics that is beyond the scope of this course (and is described in Peitgen, 1992, pp. 613-616). As a project, you may want to try finding the bifurcation points for the quadratic or trigonometric functions with a calculator or computer and see how close you come to producing a sequence that approaches the Feigenbaum constant.

§3. Exercises

1. Using the domain $-2 \le x \le 2$, determine the fixed points of the quadratic function $f(x) = x^2 + c$ for the following values of c:

a)   0.1   b)   –0.5   c)   –1   d)   –1.5   e)   –2

2. Determine whether the fixed point $p_{left} = \dfrac{1 - \sqrt{1 - 4c}}{2}$ is attracting or repelling for the quadratic function with $c =$:

a)   0.2   b)   –0.4   c)   –0.7   d)   –0.8   e)   –1

3. Determine the endpoints of the interval within which seeds' orbits approach the attracting fixed points in Exercise 2.

4. Modify the program TANGENT1 to plot tangents to the quadratic functions $f(x) = x^2 + c$ at the fixed point $p_{right} = \dfrac{1 + \sqrt{1 - 4c}}{2}$ letting c run through several values in the interval $[-2, 0.25]$. What do you conclude about p_{right}?

5. Modify the program TANGENT1 to plot tangents to the quadratic function $f(x) = x^2 + c$ at the fixed point $p_{left} = \dfrac{1 - \sqrt{1 - 4c}}{2}$ letting c run through several values in the interval $[-2, 0.25]$. For what values of c is p_{left} attracting?

6. Do web plots of the quadratic function for $c = 0, -0.5, -1.0, -1.5, -1.999$, and -2, using the seed 0 in each case. Describe the orbits.

7. Determine whether there is a nontrivial 2-cycle for the quadratic function $f(x) = x^2 + c$ with the following values of c. If so, specify the points in the cycle and determine whether it is attracting.

a)   0.1   b)   –0.2   c)   –0.9   d)   –1.2   e)   –1.5

8. A mathematical exploration of the 2-cycles of the quadratic function is postponed until Chapter 7. There you will learn that non-trivial 2-cycles consist of the points $\dfrac{-1 \pm \sqrt{-3 - 4c}}{2}$. (The method is the same as used for the logistic function in §4.1, but the algebra is easier.)

a)   Use the formula to find the 2-cycles for $c = -1.1$, and use your calculator to verify that the orbit of 0 is attracted to this cycle.

b)   If the points in the 2-cycle of part (a) are called p_1 and p_2, show that $f(p_1) = p_2$ and $f(p_2) = p_1$.

c) Show algebraically that if $f(x) = x^2 + c$, then $f\left(\dfrac{-1+\sqrt{-3-4c}}{2}\right) = \dfrac{-1-\sqrt{-3-4c}}{2}$ and vice versa.

d) Use the formula to determine the range of values of c for which there are non-trivial 2-cycles. [Hint: The expression under the radical sign must be positive.]

9. Modify the program TANGENT2 to plot tangents to ^2f, the second iterate of the quadratic function, using the formula given in Exercise 8 for the point of tangency. Let c range from –2 to –0.75 in steps of 0.25 or smaller. For what range of values of c are the 2-cycles attracting? Verify by checking the orbit of 0 for a value of c chosen at random from that range.

10. Make a conjecture about the white band visible in Figure 4.41 near the left end of the Feigenbaum plot for the quadratic function. Verify your conjecture.

11. Find (a) an attracting (b) a repelling 3-cycle for the quadratic function. In your answer include both the value of c and the points in the cycle.

12. In the Y= menu of your calculator, write in formulas for the quadratic function f and its iterates ^2f and ^4f, along with the identity function $y = x$. Plot the graphs for $c = -1.35$. Determine the fixed points, 2-cycles and 4-cycles for f with this parameter. Is any attracting?

13. Modify ORBDIAG1 to draw the Feigenbaum plot for
a) the quadratic function $f(x) = x^2 + c$ shown in Figure 4.41. For the window, use $-2 < c \le 0.25$ and $-2 \le y \le 2$. The representative seed is 0.
b) the trigonometric function $f(x) = k \sin \pi x$ shown in Figure 4.43. For the window, use $0 \le k < 1$ and $0 \le y \le 1$. The representative seed is 0.5.

§4. The Properties of Chaos

Although the study of chaos is really a search for order, the last two chapters have been an investigation into the way order becomes chaos. But was it really *chaos*? In everyday life we use that word to mean *randomness* or *confusion* or *turmoil* or *disorder*. Certainly these words would describe orbits of the logistic function when the parameter approaches 4. But the randomness is generated in a very ordered way, with each point in an orbit produced from its predecessor by a simple quadratic formula. This chaos is called *deterministic chaos*, and may be different from the general disorder and confusion of everyday life. Deterministic chaos can even be characterized by three properties.

Sensitivity, Mixing, Periodicity

A function is called *chaotic* if it has the following three properties when iterated:

1. *It is sensitive to initial conditions*: Arbitrarily close to every seed is another whose orbit moves far away.

2. *It mixes the domain*: If you specify any two subintervals of the domain, you can always find a seed in the first interval whose orbit gets into the second.

3. *Periodic points are dense in its domain*: Any point of the domain is arbitrarily close to a periodic point.

The first property ("sensitivity") is a hallmark of unstable systems, in which small initial differences lead to vastly different final states. In stable, predictable systems, small errors in initial information correspond to small errors in the final result. In unstable, chaotic systems, a tiny error in the umpteenth decimal point eventually becomes large enough to make the orbit wander off unpredictably.

The second property ("mixing") implies that you can get practically everywhere from practically anywhere. If you pick a tiny subinterval at the left end of the domain as a starting place and a tiny subinterval at the right end of the domain as an ending place, you can always find a point in the first interval that iterates into the second interval. Since this is true about any two intervals you pick, it means that a chaotic function thoroughly mixes up its domain.

The third property ("periodicity") means that periodic points are just about everywhere, scattered densely among non-periodic points like the rational numbers are scattered among the irrationals. You can always approximate a non-periodic point by a periodic point to any degree of accuracy you require. No matter how small a circle you draw around a point in the domain, there will always be a periodic point inside the circle.

Stephen Smale (b. 1930), one of the pioneers of Chaos Theory, saw this complicated definition in terms of a simple stretching-and-folding process. Think of kneading bread. To mix the yeast thoroughly into the dough, you can iterate the following process: First stretch the dough to twice its length, then fold it over on itself; repeat for about 10 minutes. In Figure 4.44, you see the length of dough stretched up in the middle till each half is the same length as the original. Then the two halves are folded together, and the dough is laid back down on the table, ready for the next iteration.

Figure 4.44

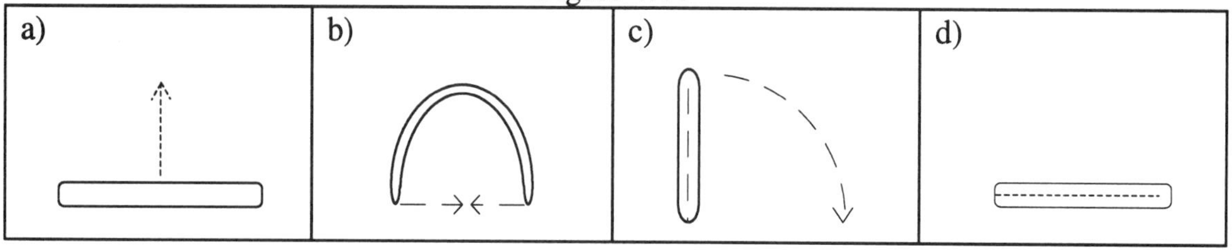

a)	b)	c)	d)

If the kneading is thorough, molecules of bread that start close to each other move far apart, and those that start far apart pass close to each other at some point, a good example of the sensitivity and mixing properties of chaos.

Leaving the bread behind, notice that the stretch-and-fold process is precisely what the logistic function $f(x) = 4x(1-x)$ does to its domain. First, recall that the domain and range are identical, both being the unit interval $[0,1]$. Now think of x chugging along uniformly from 0 to 1, and watch what happens to y in your mind's eye. As x goes from 0 to ½, y goes from 0 to 1 (Figure 4.45); as x continues from ½ to 1, y reverses itself and goes from 1 back to 0 (Figure 4.46). By mapping $[0, ½]$ onto $[0, 1]$, and $[½, 1]$ onto $[0, 1]$, f doubles the length of each half of its domain. By inverting the map of the second half of the domain, it effectively folds the stretched domain over onto itself. Thus when $r = 4$, the logistic function stretches the unit interval and folds it over onto itself with each iteration, a perfect bread-kneading function – even better than your normal bread kneader because the stretch is non-linear.

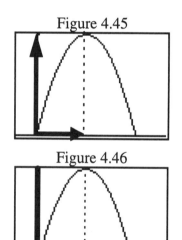

Figure 4.45

Figure 4.46

$f(x) = 4x(1-x)$ is Chaotic

Because we don't have a mathematical definition yet, we can't *prove* anything is chaotic. But we can investigate a few examples that will demonstrate that $f(x) = 4x(1-x)$ has the three properties: sensitivity, mixing, and periodicity.

Sensitivity

A function is sensitive if small initial differences get magnified under iteration to the point that orbits become unrecognizably different. One way of demonstrating that $f(x) = 4x(1-x)$ is sensitive is to observe a time sequence of the first few iterations of the function using two different but nearby seeds. In Figure 4.47, for example, both the u and v sequences are defined as the logistic function with $r = 4$. But u(*n*Min)=.2 and v(*n*Min)=.201, a difference of 0.001. The first 20 iterations of both orbits are shown in Figure 4.48, with the graph of u a heavy line and the graph of v a light line. You see only the heavy line for the first six iterations, but by the seventh the two graphs are beginning to separate. Three iterations later they are in opposite halves of the unit interval, and from then on the orbits bear no resemblance to one another as can be seen in the table in Figure 4.49. Of course there is nothing special about the seeds. 0.2 and 0.201. If you change v(*n*Min) to 0.20001 it takes a little longer to see the divergence, about 16 iterations. If you choose any other pair of seeds, no matter how close, you will observe the same kind of divergence. Well ..., you *could* make them so close that you exceed the calculator's power to discriminate. In that case, you would not see any divergence. For the moment you will have to take it on faith that even orbits of infinitesimally close seeds diverge.

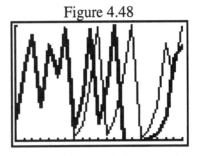

Figure 4.47

Figure 4.48

Figure 4.49

n	u(*n*)	v(*n*)
10	.14784	.9895
11	.50392	.04157
12	.99994	.15938
13	2.5E-4	.53592
14	9.8E-4	.99484
15	.00394	.02053
16	.01568	.08045

n=10

Mixing

To illustrate the mixing property, we need to specify two intervals, and then find a seed in one of them (the "pool") whose orbit eventually passes through the other (the "target"). For example, suppose the pool is [0.1, 0.101] and the target is [0.9, 0.901]. Now if $f(x) = 4x(1-x)$ is really chaotic, we should be able to find in the pool a seed that orbits into the target. But that's not easy. You could try picking a seed at random out of the pool, say the midpoint 0.1005, and just start iterating. The TI-83 would tell you that the 847th iteration of 0.1005 is 0.9000417895, and therefore in the target. Do you believe that? I'm skeptical. Remember that this function is sensitive, so a slightly different seed will have a totally different orbit. And remember also that the calculator has to round numbers to a finite number of decimal places. How many decimal places would you need before you could be sure that $^{847}f(0.1005)$ is exactly 0.9000417895? Rounding errors of the calculator and sensitivity of the function mean that we cannot really trust these results. Again the lack of real proof means you have to make a leap of faith after seeing a few examples.

Another way to see the mixing property is to ask how thoroughly a seed from the pool explores the unit interval. Does it wander all over, poking into every nook and cranny? Or are there gaps in its orbit where a target interval could hide untouched? The following program ("MIXING") is a way of answering these questions. It picks a seed at random and follows its orbit for 1000 iterations. The unit interval is divided up into 20 subintervals, each having length 0.05, and the program counts the number of times the orbit is in each subinterval. The subintervals are numbered from 1 to 20, and those numbers are stored in list $L1$. The number of orbital passes through an interval is stored at the corresponding place in list $L2$. That is, $L2(J)$ is the number of times the orbit lands in the interval number J. Finally, the results are displayed as a histogram.

Program – MIXING	Calculator Hints	Purpose
ClrHome		Clears the decks
ClrAllLists	2nd[MEM] 4:ClrAllLists	
FnOff	VARS > Y-VARS 4:On/Off 2:FnOff	
PlotsOff	2nd[STATPLOT] 4:PlotsOff	
rand→X	MATH >>> PRB 1:rand	$0 \le \text{rand} < 1$ is the seed
Disp "SEED"		Displays the seed while the rest of
Disp X		the program runs
For(J,1,20,1)		Starts loop to initialize lists
J→L1(J)		$L1$ stores subinterval numbers 1-20
0→L2(J)		$L2$ stores tally of points in each subinterval; initialized at 0
End		
For(K,1,1000,1)		Loop to iterate 1000 times
4X(1-X)→X		Iteration step
int(20X)+1→A	MATH > NUM 5:int(	A is the number of the subinterval in which X lands
L2(A)+1→L2(A)		Adds 1 to the tally of orbit passes in the Ath subinterval
End		
Plot1(Histogram, L1,L2)	2nd[STATPLOT] 1:Plot1(2nd[STAT PLOT] > TYPE 3:Histogram ...	Defines Plot 1 as a histogram with abscissas in $L1$ and ordinates in $L2$.
PlotsOn 1	2nd[STATPLOT] 5:PlotsOn	Turns on Plot 1
0→Xmin		Sizes the window
21→Xmax		
1→Xscl		
0→Ymin		
max(L2)→Ymax	2nd[LIST] >> MATH 2:max(	
0→Yscl		
DispGraph		Displays the graph

A run of MIXING starts with a display of the seed, as in Figure 4.50, while the iteration is performed 1000 times. The graph in Figure 4.51 is displayed when the program ends. You can see that the orbit spent more time at each end of the interval but otherwise hit every other subinterval about the same number of times. In 1000 iterations, the function sent the seed just about everywhere around the domain in a relatively unbiased fashion, except for its obvious preference for intervals close to the endpoints. While this does not prove that a seed from any pool eventually iterates into any target, it does show that a random seed makes a reasonably uniform exploration of the entire unit interval.

Figure 4.50

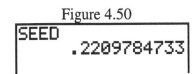

Figure 4.51

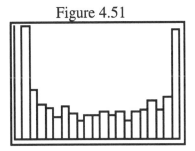

Periodicity

Finally, there's the periodicity property. If you pick a seed at random out of the unit interval, the chances are very slim that it's periodic or even eventually periodic. If f is chaotic, however, there must be a periodic point that lives arbitrarily close to this seed. "Arbitrarily close" means "as close as you want to specify." You want it within one billionth? There's one there. A trillionth? Still no problem. A zillionth? Whatever you want.

Now *finding* that periodic point is another story. Knowing it exists and producing it for the world to admire are two different things. In general, it can't be done for the logistic function. (In Chapter 7, you will see how to do it for a linear relative of the logistic function; and when you're in graduate school, you'll be able to prove that the relationship is close enough to conclude that both have the mixing property.)

You can, of course, find *some* periodic points by solving $f(x) = x$, $^2f(x) = x$, $^3f(x) = x$, and so on. But since the nth iterate of the logistic function is a polynomial of degree 2^n, things get out of hand very quickly, long before you would find the periodic points supposedly scattered densely throughout the unit interval. If they were only *attracting*, the task would be easy. But they're not. And repelling periodic points are impossible to find experimentally. Furthermore, if it takes more decimal points to specify a periodic point than your calculator handles, then you cannot test the exact point: Since it's a repelling point, and since the function is sensitive, your calculator will soon wander away from the period and miss it completely.

Though it is hard to find the periodic points guaranteed by the periodicity property, it is not hard to see why they contribute to the random behavior characteristic of chaotic functions. It's like entering a crowded dance floor with a lot of different groups whirling around and holding on for dear life. You can't break into any of the groups (they repel you) but as you get close to one you tend more or less to follow in their pattern. Since the dance floor is so crowded, you are immediately pulled away from one group and start following another group's pattern. But you have no better luck with them and are whirled off in another direction by a third group. And so on. Pretty soon you've covered the whole dance floor, and you're still dancing by yourself in an infinite unstable orbit.

§4. Exercises

1. Investigate the orbits of 0.7 and 0.70001 under iteration of the function $f(x) = 4x(1-x)$. With the calculator in sequence mode, set both the u-sequence and v-sequence equal to the logistic function. Let u(nMin)=.7 and v(nMin)=.70001.
   a) For how many iterations do the orbits stay within 0.1 of each other?
   b) When is the first time that u(n) and v(n) are in opposite halves of the domain?
   c) What is the farthest apart the orbits get in the first 20 iterations?

2. Investigate the orbits of the following pairs of points, and note the number of the iteration when the orbits first differ by at least 0.5.
   a) 0.6, 0.60001   b) 0.987534, 0.987533   c) 0.25, 0.249999

3. Investigate the orbits of 0.2 and 0.200000000001. Write a sentence or two to describe the results.

4. Run MIXING three times. Compare the graphs with each other and with the one in Figure 4.51. Write a sentence or two to describe what you observe.

5. Modify MIXING to allow a seed to be specified. Run your program with the following seeds and compare the histograms with Figure 4.51.
   a) 0.2   b) 0.928   c) $\sqrt{2}/2$

6. Write a calculator program to trace the orbit of a seed and to notify you when it is in a specified target interval. There will be three inputs: the seed, and the left and right endpoints of the target interval. If the orbit lands in the target interval, the program should stop and output the orbit point and the number of the iteration.
   a) Try your program with a seed of 0.4999 and a target interval of [0.2, 0.2001].
   b) Find by trial and error a number within 0.0005 of 0.8 whose orbit enters the target interval [0.4999, .5001].
   c) Write a few sentences to describe your confidence in the results of (a) or (b). What are the factors affecting your confidence?
   d) If you know someone with a different brand of programmable calculator, try your program for Exercise 6 on it and compare answers. Describe and explain the results.

7. Find a 2-cycle of $f(x) = 4x(1-x)$. Express your answer in radical form and as a decimal approximation.
   a) Use your calculator to verify numerically that the decimal approximations do constitute a 2-cycle.
   b) If you continue iterating this 2-cycle, what happens? Explain.

8. To explore graphically the periodicity property of $f(x) = 4x(1-x)$:

a) Graph $y = x$ and $y = f(x)$, and count the number of intersections between 0 and 1 (inclusive). How many fixed points are there in [0, 1]?

b) Graph $y = x$ and $y = {}^2f(x)$, and count the number of intersections between 0 and 1 (inclusive). How many points of period 2 are there (including trivial and non-trivial)?

c) Repeat (b) for $y = {}^3f(x)$.

d) Make a conjecture about the number of points of period 4 (trivial and non-trivial) you will find in [0, 1]. Graph $y = x$ and $y = {}^4f(x)$, and verify your conjecture.

e) Make a conjecture about the number of points of period n you will find in [0, 1] and describe how they will be distributed in the interval.

9. The fixed points of $f(x) = 4x(1 - x)$ are 0 and 0.75, and both are repelling. This exercise explores points that are eventually fixed on 0.

a) Show that $a_1 = 1$ is an eventually fixed point.

b) Show that $a_2 = 0.5$ is an eventually fixed point.

c) Find the smallest positive point a_3 such that $f(a_3) = 0.5$. Explain why a_3 is an eventually fixed point.

d) Find the smallest positive point a_4 such that $f(a_4) = a_3$. Explain why a_4 is an eventually fixed point.

e) Describe the sequence $a_1, a_2, a_3, \cdots$.

f) Write a paragraph describing what additional exploration you might do to find other eventually fixed points and eventually periodic points, and make a conjecture about what is happening. Relate your thoughts to the periodicity property.

10. Draw a graph of the following function over the domain [0, 1]:

$$f(x) = \begin{cases} 2x & \text{if } 0 \le x < \frac{1}{2} \\ 2 - 2x & \text{if } \frac{1}{2} \le x \le 1 \end{cases}.$$

Describe the stretch-and-fold characteristics of f. Compare and contrast with the logistic function.

11. Draw a graph of the following function over the domain [0, 1]:

$$f(x) = \begin{cases} 2x & \text{if } 0 \le x < \frac{1}{2} \\ 2x - 1 & \text{if } \frac{1}{2} \le x \le 1 \end{cases}.$$

Describe the stretch-and-fold characteristics of f. Compare and contrast with the logistic function.

12. Exercise 1 asked you to use the calculator in sequence mode to investigate the sensitivity of the logistic function. Modify the settings to permit an investigation of the quadratic function $f(x) = x^2 - 2$ over the domain [–2, 2]. Use your program to compare the obits of three pairs of points that are within 0.0001 of each other. Does the quadratic function appear sensitive when $c = -2$?

13. Modify MIXING to investigate the quadratic function $f(x) = x^2 - 2$. Run your program three times and compare with the histograms you saw for the logistic function.

16. Repeat Exercise 8 for the quadratic function $f(x) = x^2 - 2$ to investigate its periodicity property.

17. Think of your life as a dynamical system. Can you see examples of sensitivity, mixing and/or periodicity in your life? Is your life a chaotic system?

Chapter 5

COMPLEX NUMBERS

§1. A Review of the Basics

All the orbits we have studied so far have been modeled by sequences of real numbers. Therefore, the geometric trace of an orbit's path would be a series of dots on the number line (as in Figure 5.1).

Figure 5.1

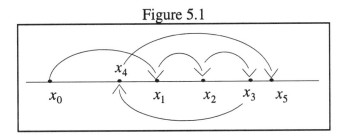

The complex and beautiful images associated with chaos theory, such as the Julia Sets and the Mandelbrot Set, are not confined to a line. These images reside on a 2-dimensional plane. To study them we will need to follow the orbits of 2-dimensional numbers: the complex numbers. The purpose of this chapter is to review the definitions and arithmetic of complex numbers, and then to extend the investigation to functions of complex numbers. This will lay the groundwork necessary to understand the Julia and Mandelbrot Sets in Chapter 6.

The Complex Number System

The number i was invented in the 16th century to solve the equation $x^2 + 1 = 0$. Thus the square of i is –1. Of course the square of any *real* number is positive, so i is a different kind of number, called *imaginary*. The smallest set containing all the real numbers and the imaginary number i is called the *complex number system*. It consists of all numbers of the form $a + bi$ where a and b are real numbers. If $z = a + bi$, then a is called the *real part* of z and b the *imaginary part*. The *conjugate* of z is $a - bi$ and is denoted by $\overline{z}$.

Because complex numbers are specified by pairs of real numbers, their geometric representation is a plane, called the *complex plane*. The number $z = a + bi$ is represented by the point (a,b). Since the real part of z is the abscissa and the imaginary part is the ordinate, the horizontal axis of the complex plane is called the *real axis* and the vertical axis the *imaginary axis*. (See Figure 5.2.)

Figure 5.2

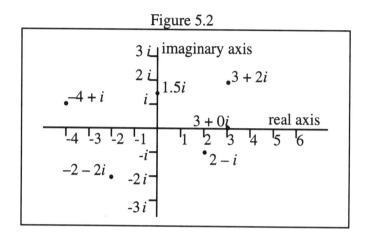

Example 1. If $z = 5 + 2i$, graph z and its conjugate $\overline{z}$.

Solution: If $z = 5 + 2i$, then $\overline{z} = 5 - 2i$. The number $5 + 2i$ is graphed at $(5,2)$, and $5 - 2i$ at $(5,-2)$ as shown in Figure 5.3. We note in passing that $\overline{z}$ is the mirror image of z across the real axis.

Figure 5.3

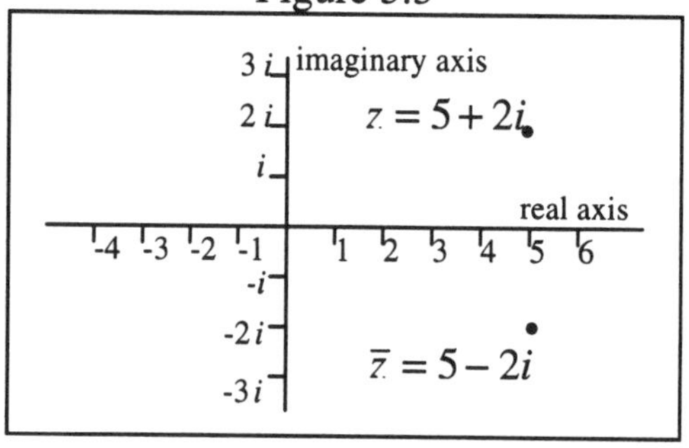

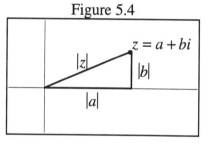

The *absolute value* of a complex number z, denoted by $|z|$, is its distance to the origin. If $z = a + bi$, then its graph is the point (a,b), and its distance to the origin is the length of the hypotenuse of a right triangle whose legs are $|a|$ and $|b|$ as shown in Figure 5.4. It follows that

$$|z| = \sqrt{a^2 + b^2}.$$

Figure 5.4

Note that the absolute value of a *complex* number is a *real* number, and moreover it is always positive. Thus the algebraic definition is consistent with the geometric notion of *distance to the origin*.

Example 2. Find the absolute value of $-3 + 4i$.

Solution: $|-3 + 4i| = \sqrt{(-3)^2 + 4^2} = \sqrt{9 + 16} = \sqrt{25} = 5$. The point $z = -3 + 4i$ lies at a distance of 5 units from the origin. Draw its graph and note that you have a familiar 3-4-5 right triangle.

Complex Number Arithmetic

Addition, subtraction and multiplication of complex numbers can be done by thinking of $a + bi$ as a binomial in i, and replacing i^2 by -1 wherever it occurs.

Addition: $(a+bi)+(c+di) = (a+c)+(b+d)i$
Subtraction: $(a+bi)-(c+di) = (a-c)+(b-d)i$
Multiplication: $(a+bi)(c+di) = ac+bci+adi+bdi^2 = (ac-bd)+(bc+ad)i$

Division is complicated by the need to express the answer in $a + bi$ form. The trick is to multiply the numerator and denominator by the denominator's conjugate.

Division: $$\frac{a+bi}{c+di} = \frac{(a+bi)(c-di)}{(c+di)(c-di)} = \frac{(ac+bd)+(bc-ad)i}{c^2+d^2} = \frac{ac+bd}{c^2+d^2} + \frac{bc-ad}{c^2+d^2}i$$

Example 3. Express $\dfrac{2-5i}{3+4i}$ in $a + bi$ form.

Solution:
$$\frac{2-5i}{3+4i} = \frac{(2-5i)(3-4i)}{(3+4i)(3-4i)}$$
$$= \frac{6-23i+20i^2}{9-16i^2}$$
$$= \frac{6-23i-20}{9+16}$$
$$= \frac{-14-23i}{25}$$
$$= -\frac{14}{25} - \frac{23}{25}i$$

Complex Arithmetic with the TI-83

The TI-83 can do computations with complex numbers if you give it advance notice. Press **MODE**, and in the seventh line select a+b i (Figure 5.5). All the arithmetic operations on complex numbers are then available using the **+, –,** ×, and ÷ keys. For instance, the division in Example 2 would appear as in Figure 5.6. (The *i* key is the second function of the decimal point: **2nd[i]**.) Note in Figure 5.6 that the conversion to a fraction is still accomplished for the real numbers 0.56 and 0.92.

Operations specific to complex numbers are found by pressing **MATH > > CPX**. The menu is shown in Figure 5.7.

Figure 5.5   Figure 5.6   Figure 5.7

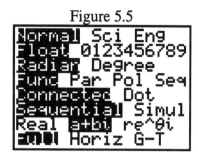

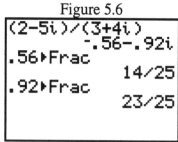

Example 4. Evaluate $\left| (2 - 5i)^3 \right|$ using the TI-83.

Solution: For the absolute value of a complex number, press **MATH > > CPX 5:abs(**. If you then key in **(2 – 5 2nd[i]) ^ 3)**, you should see the results in Figure 5.8.

Figure 5.8

```
abs((2-5i)^3)
            156.1697794
```

§1. Exercises

Simplify the expressions in exercises 1-20 and express answers in the form $a + bi$.

1. $(4+3i)-(2-5i)$

2. $(1+i)(2+3i)$

3. $(1+3i)^2$

4. $i^3 + i^4$

5. $(1+i\sqrt{3})^3$

6. $\left(\dfrac{1}{2}+\dfrac{\sqrt{3}}{2}i\right)^2$

7. $\dfrac{2}{3-2i}$

8. $\dfrac{2+i}{2i}$

9. $\dfrac{1+2i}{3-4i}$

10. $\dfrac{(2+i)^2}{3-2i}$

11. $\sqrt{-1}\cdot\sqrt{-4}\cdot\sqrt{-9}$

12. $(3+i\sqrt{5})(3-i\sqrt{5})$

13. $(4-3i)+(-2-9i)$

14. $(2-3i)^2$

15. $(7-8i)-(6+2i)$

16. $(8+3i)(2+5i)$

17. $\dfrac{1}{2+5i}$

18. $\dfrac{4-i}{2+3i}$

19. $\dfrac{5+i}{5-i}$

20. $\dfrac{2+i\sqrt{5}}{3-i\sqrt{5}}$

In Exercises 21-29, plot the graph of each complex number and compute its absolute value.

21. $3+i$

22. $2-2i$

23. $\dfrac{1}{2}+\dfrac{\sqrt{3}}{2}i$

24. $-4-3i$

25. $(1-2i)+(5i-2)$

26. $\dfrac{1}{i}$

27. i^7+i^{10}

28. $(3+7i)(3-7i)$

29. $\dfrac{1+i}{1-i}$

30. a) Calculate i^n for $n = 1, 2, 3, 4, 5, 6, 7, 8, 23, 92$, and 105.

    b) State in words the pattern you discover in part (a).

31. Show that $-1+i\sqrt{2}$ and its conjugate are solutions of $z^2+2z+3=0$.

32. Show that $3+5i$ and its conjugate are solutions to $z^2-6z+34=0$.

Find all complex number solutions to the equations in Exercises 33-38 and express the answers in the form $a + bi$.

33. $(3+5i)+2z=4-3i$

34. $3iz=4$

35. $z^2-z+1=0$

36. $3z^2-4z+7=0$

37. $i^5z=i^2+2i^3$

38. $(z-2)(z-3)=-1$

39. If $z=4-2i$, sketch a graph of z and $\bar{z}$. Then find $|\bar{z}|$.

40. Show that the sum of a complex number and its conjugate is a real number.

41. Show that the product of a complex number and its conjugate is a real number.

42. If z and w are complex numbers, show that $\overline{z+w} = \overline{z} + \overline{w}$.

43. If z and w are complex numbers, show that $\overline{z \cdot w} = \overline{z} \cdot \overline{w}$.

§2. Graphing Complex Numbers

Geometry of Absolute Value

We have defined the absolute value of a complex number geometrically as the distance to the origin, and as a result we have the algebraic formula $|a+bi| = \sqrt{a^2 + b^2}$. The geometric notion of absolute value can be extended to the distance between *any* two points on the complex plane using the Pythagorean Theorem.

Example 1. Find the distance between $z = -4 - 2i$ and $w = -1 + 2i$.

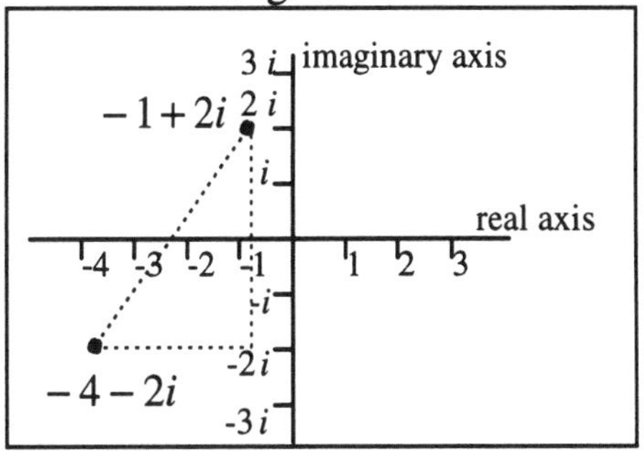

Solution: The line joining z and w forms the hypotenuse of a right triangle whose legs are parallel to the real and imaginary axes. The horizontal leg is $|(-4) - (-1)| = 3$ units long and the vertical leg is $|(-2) - 2| = 4$ units long. From the Pythagorean Theorem we conclude that the hypotenuse is

Figure 5.9

$\sqrt{3^2 + 4^2} = 5$ units long. Therefore the distance from z to w is 5.

The result of Example 1 can be generalized to any complex numbers z and w. Suppose that $z = x + yi$ and $w = u + vi$. Then

$$|z - w| = |(x - u) + (y - v)i|$$

by the definition of complex number subtraction. Therefore,

$$|z - w| = \sqrt{(x - u)^2 + (y - v)^2} .$$

by the formula for absolute value. But this is just the familiar distance formula for the segment joining the two points (x, y) and (u, v) on a coordinate plane. Hence, $|z - w|$ is the distance between the points $z = x + yi$ and $w = u + vi$ on the complex plane.

Example 2. Sketch a graph of the set of all complex numbers z that satisfy the equation $|z - 2| = 3$.

Solution: This is the set of points z whose distance to the point $2 + 0i$ is 3. Therefore all these points

Figure 5.10

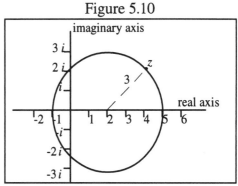

lie on a circle centered at $2 + 0i$ with a radius of 3. (See Figure 5.10.)

Example 3. Describe the set of complex numbers z that satisfy $|z + 3| \leq 2$.

Solution: This is the set of points z whose distance from $-3 + 0i$ is less than or equal to 2 units. Hence it is the interior and the boundary of the circle whose center is $-3 + 0i$ and whose radius is 2. (See Figure 5.11.)

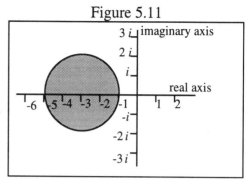

Figure 5.11

Geometry of Addition

The graph of the complex number $a + bi$ is the point (a, b), but sometimes it is convenient to identify it with the arrow whose tail is at the origin and whose head is on the point (a, b), as shown in Figure 5.12.

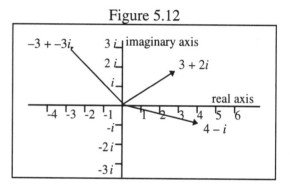

Figure 5.12

Thinking in terms of arrows gives us a geometric model for addition of complex numbers. For example, the algebraic sum of $3 + 2i$ and $2 - i$ is:

$$(3 + 2i) + (2 - i) = (3 + 2) + (2 - 1)i = 5 + i.$$

If we first draw an arrow graph of $3 + 2i$, and then use its head as an origin to add on the arrow graph of $2 - i$, as in Figure 5.13, we end up on the point $(5, 1)$, the point that represents the sum $5 + i$.

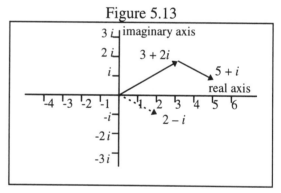

Figure 5.13

Another way to use the arrow model of addition is to draw the arrows representing the two addends, complete the parallelogram they define, as in Figure 5.14. If you then draw the diagonal from the origin, you have the arrow graph of the sum. In general, if you draw arrow graphs of $x + yi$ and $u + vi$ and complete the parallelogram they form, the fourth vertex of the parallelogram is a graph of the sum $(x + u) + (y + v)i$.

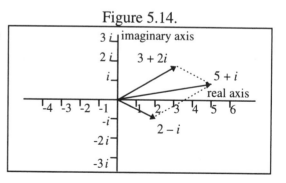

Figure 5.14.

Example 4. Draw an arrow graph of the sum of $-3+i$ and $4+2i$.

Solution: First draw the two arrows representing $-3+i$ and $4+2i$. Then complete the parallelogram (dotted lines in Figure 5.15). Finally draw in the diagonal to the fourth vertex from the origin, and you obtain the sum: $1+3i$.

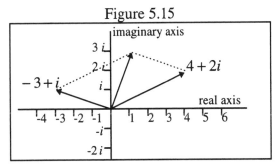

Figure 5.15

Of course, if the two points z and w are collinear with the origin. Then the parallelogram ploy will not work: there is no fourth vertex. In this case, you can still draw in the arrow for z, use its tip as the origin for another arrow with the same length and direction as w, and you end up on the point (or arrow head) that represents $z + w$.

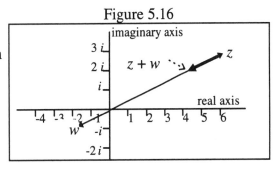

Figure 5.16

Triangle inequality

You are familiar with the triangle inequality for real numbers: $|x+y| \le |x|+|y|$ for any real numbers x and y. This property generalizes to complex numbers.

> **Theorem:** For any complex numbers z and w, $|z+w| \le |z|+|w|$.

The proof of this theorem is algebraically tedious, but its truth can be grasped intuitively by a geometric argument. If you draw an arrow graph of the sum of z and w, you see that $|z|$, $|w|$, and $|z+w|$ are three sides of a triangle. Since the length of one side of a triangle must be less than the sum of the other two sides, we see that

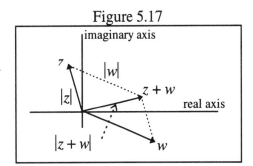

Figure 5.17

$$|z+w| < |z|+|w|.$$

If the graphs of z and w happen to be collinear with the origin, then either

$$|z+w| = |z|+|w| \text{ or } |z+w| = |z|-|w|.$$

Putting it all together, we conclude that in all cases

$$|z+w| \leq |z| + |w|.$$

There is an extension of the triangle inequality that we will need in our study of Julia sets.

Theorem: For any complex numbers z and w, $|z - w| \geq |z| - |w|$.

Proof: Notice that $|z| = |z - w + w|$. Then if you use the regular triangle inequality on $|(z-w)+w|$, you get

$$|z| = |(z-w)+w| \leq |z-w| + |w|.$$

Subtracting $|w|$ from both sides of the inequality gives the result

$$|z| - |w| \leq |z-w|.$$

§2. Exercises

1. Given the following pairs of complex numbers, z and w, find the distance between them:

a) $z = 2 + 3i, \quad w = -1 - i$ b) $z = -5 + 2i, \quad w = 7 - 3i$ c) $z = -3 + i, \quad w = 1 + 5i$

2. Given the following pairs of complex numbers, z and w, find the distance between them:

a) $z = -4 + 2i, \quad w = 2 - 6i$ b) $z = 2 + i, \quad w = 6 + 9i$ c) $z = -2, \quad w = 2 + 4i\sqrt{3}$

3. The vertices of a triangle in the complex plane are the graphs of $-4 + 14i$, $1 + 2i$, and $4 + 6i$. Find the perimeter of the triangle.

4. Describe the set of points z in the complex plane such that:

a) $|z| = 6$ b) $|z - i| = 5$ c) $|z + 2| = 5$

5. Describe the set of points z in the complex plane such that:

a) $|z| > 2$ b) $|z| \le 5$ c) $|z - 3| < 4$

6. Describe the set of points z in the complex plane such that $1 < |z - 3| < 2$.

7. Describe the set of points z in the complex plane such that:

a) $z = |z|$ b) $z + \overline{z} = 4$ c) $|z - \overline{z}| = 2$

8. Draw arrow graphs of z, w, and $z + w$ given:

a) $z = 4 + i, \quad w = 2 + 5i$ b) $z = -3 + 2i, \quad w = 5 + 3i$ c) $z = -3 - i, \quad w = 5$

9. Draw arrow graphs of z, w, and $z + w$ given:

a) $z = -4 + 2i, \quad w = 2 - 5i$ b) $z = -2 - i, \quad w = 6 + 3i$ c) $z = 2i, \quad w = 5 - 4i$

10. Show that $|z| = |-z| = |\overline{z}|$ for all complex numbers z.

11. Show that $|zw| = |z| \cdot |w|$ for all complex numbers z and w.

12. If $z = 3 - 4i$ and $w = 5 + 12i$, then the triangle inequality guarantees that

a) $|z + w|$ is at most how big?   b) $|z - w|$ is at least how big?

13. If $z = 3 - 2i$ and $w = 1 + 3i$, sketch a graph of z, w, $z + w$, and $z - w$ on the complex plane.

a) Find $|z + w|$ and compare to $|z| + |w|$.   b) Find $|z - w|$ and compare to $|z| - |w|$.

§3. Polar Form

A complex number can always be represented in the form $x + yi$ and associated with the ordered pair of real numbers (x,y). For some purposes it is more convenient to represent the number in terms of two other real numbers: r, its distance from the origin and θ, the angle made with the positive real axis by the ray joining the origin to the graph of the number. (See Figure 5.18.) Of course, r is the absolute value of $x + yi$, and it is also called the *modulus* θ is called the *angle* or *argument* of $x + yi$.

Figure 5.18

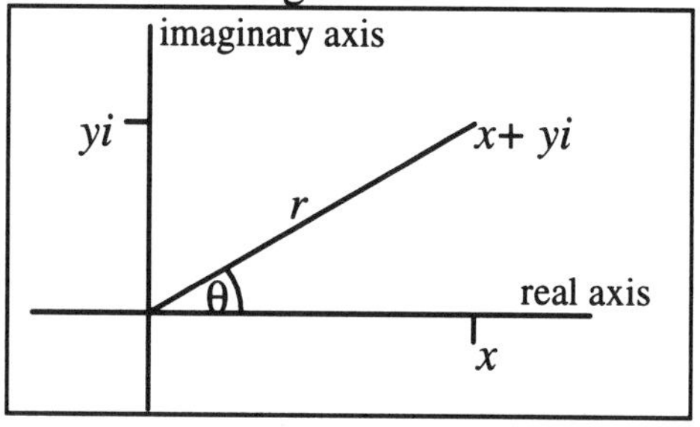

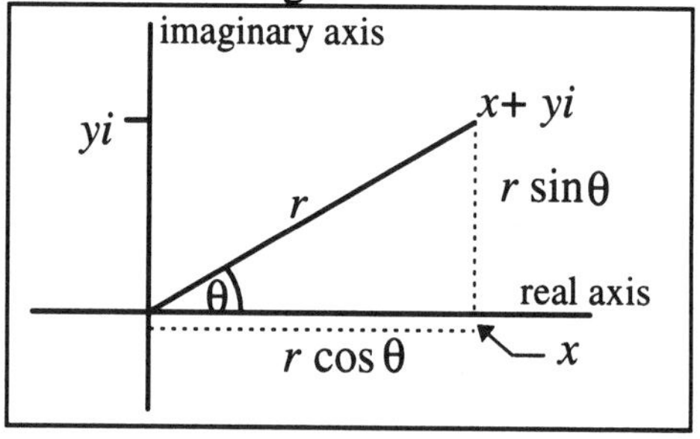

The angle θ is connected to x and y by the trigonometry of the right triangle formed by the perpendicular to the real axis from the point $x + yi$, as shown in Figure 5.19. Because $\cos\theta = \dfrac{x}{r}$ and $\sin\theta = \dfrac{y}{r}$, we see that $x = r\cos\theta$ and $y = r\sin\theta$. Therefore,

Figure 5.19

$$x + yi = r\cos\theta + (r\sin\theta)i = r(\cos\theta + i\sin\theta)$$

The expression $\cos\theta + i\sin\theta$ is usually denoted by $e^{\theta i}$ using Euler's Formula

$$e^{\theta i} = \cos\theta + i\sin\theta.$$

Using this notation we have

$$x + yi = re^{\theta i}.$$

If a complex number z is written as $x + yi$ we say it is in *rectangular form*; if it is written as $re^{\theta i}$, we say it is in *polar form*.

You may wonder how a sum of trigonometric functions can be converted to an exponential function. Not just any old exponential function, but the one with base e. Moreover, an exponential function with complex numbers as a power! Seems a bit arbitrary. There *is* an explanation, of course, but it is beyond the scope of this course. What you will see shortly is that $\cos\theta + i\sin\theta$ can be proved to have some familiar exponential properties, so this formula is not as farfetched as it may appear at first glance. For the moment, however, the next few examples will familiarize you with the notation.

Example 1. Express $z = 4e^{45°i}$ in rectangular form.

Solution: Using Euler's formula, you can replace $4e^{45°i}$ by $\cos 45° + i\sin 45°$. Therefore the rectangular form of z is

$$z = 4e^{45°i} = 4(\cos 45° + i\sin 45°) = 4\left(\frac{\sqrt{2}}{2} + i\frac{\sqrt{2}}{2}\right) = 2\sqrt{2} + 2i\sqrt{2}.$$

Example 2. Express $z = \sqrt{3} - i$ in polar form.

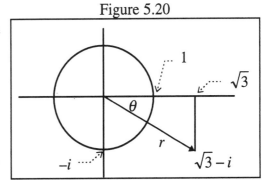

Figure 5.20

Solution: We need to find the modulus r and the argument θ. First draw the arrow graph of $\sqrt{3} - i$. Then draw the right triangle formed by dropping a perpendicular to the real axis, as in Figure 5.20. The hypotenuse is the modulus r and the central angle is the argument θ. You probably recognize this as a 30-60-90 triangle and can read off the length r and the angle θ. If not, you can find r by using the formula for absolute value:

$$r = |z| = \sqrt{\left(\sqrt{3}\right)^2 + 1^2} = 2$$

and

$$\theta = \tan^{-1}\frac{-1}{\sqrt{3}} = -\frac{\pi}{6}.$$

With the modulus 2 and the argument $-\dfrac{\pi}{6}$, the polar form is:

$$z = 2e^{(-\pi/6)i}.$$

Of course you can express the angle in any form you'd like: $-\dfrac{\pi}{6}, \dfrac{11\pi}{6}, -30°, 330°$, or whatever.

Rectangular and Polar Form with the TI-83

As you might have guessed, the calculator can help with Examples 1 and 2. In the seventh line of the **MODE** menu, you have your choice of rectangular form $a+bi$ or polar form $re^{\wedge}\theta i$. For Example 1, select $a+bi$ and then key in **4 2nd[e^x] 2nd[i] 4 5 2nd[ANGLE] 1:°)** When you press enter, you will see the screen in Figure 5.21. (The calculator interprets angle inputs in polar form as radian measure regardless of your selection in the

Figure 5.21.

```
4e^(i45°)
2.828427125+2.8…
```

second line of the **MODE** menu. Consequently you must indicate any input in degrees with the degree sign, though you could input $\pi/4$ with no indication that it was radians.)

To do Example 2 with the calculator, you can change the seventh line of the **MODE** menu to re^θi and imitate the procedure for Example 1. Or you can leave the **MODE** as a+bi and use the **MATH > > CPX** menu. Here's how the second method works. First key in **2nd[√] 3) – 2nd[i]** and then press **MATH > > CPX 7: ▸Polar**, as in Figure 5.22. You may not recognize–.523598775... as $-\pi/6$, the answer given in Example 2, but you can easily verify that it is indeed the calculator's best approximation. If you return to the **MODE** menu, change the third line from Radian to Degree, and do this problem again, you will see the result in Figure 5.23, showing the angle as –30°.

Figure 5.22

```
√(3)-i▸Polar
2e^(-.523598775...
```

Figure 5.23

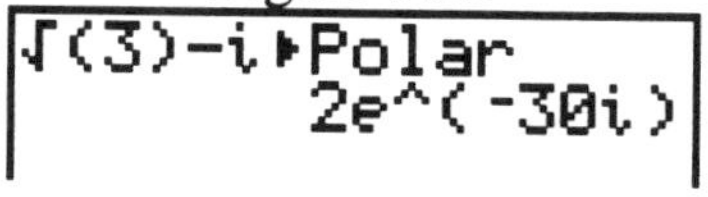

```
√(3)-i▸Polar
        2e^(-30i)
```

Converting Between Polar and Rectangular Forms

Examples 1 and 2 along with Figure 5.19 suggest simple conversion formulas for polar and rectangular form:

If $z = re^{\theta i}$, then the rectangular form of z is $x + yi$ where $x = r\cos\theta$ and $y = r\sin\theta$.

If $z = x + yi$, then the polar form of z is $re^{\theta i}$ where $r = \sqrt{x^2 + y^2}$, and $\theta = \tan^{-1}\dfrac{y}{x}$.

The first formulas, from polar to rectangular, work fine; but there are problems with the second formulas: they don't work for points that lie in the second or third quadrants or on the imaginary axis. The problem is that the inverse tangent function returns angles between $-\dfrac{\pi}{2}$ and $\dfrac{\pi}{2}$. So for the problem cases, you'll have to be more careful. The next two examples show you what to do.

Example 3. Express $-\sqrt{3} - i$ in polar form.

Solution: This is nearly the same problem as Example 2, except here the real part, $-\sqrt{3}$, is negative so that $-\sqrt{3} - i$ is in the third quadrant. The diagram in Figure 5.24 shows that you still have a 30-60-90 triangle with a hypotenuse of 2. But to get the correct value of θ in the third quadrant, you have to add (or subtract) π (or 180°) to the central angle of the triangle. Therefore,

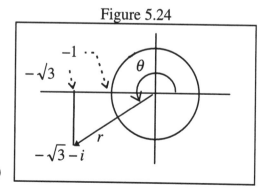

Figure 5.24

$$\theta = \pi + \tan^{-1} \frac{-1}{-\sqrt{3}} = \pi + \frac{\pi}{6} = \frac{7\pi}{6} \text{ or } 210°.$$

The polar form for $-\sqrt{3} - i$ is $2e^{(7\pi/6)i}$.

Figure 5.25

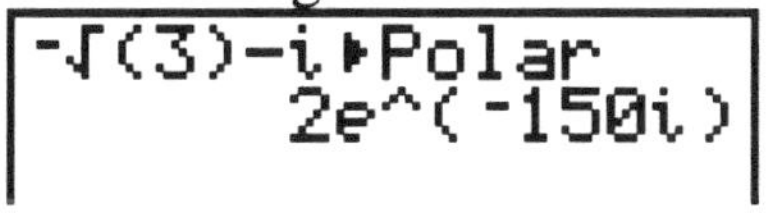

The calculator has a built in correction factor for angles in the second or third quadrant. It adds π (or 180°) for angles in the second quadrant and subtracts π (or 180°) for angles in the third quadrant. Its answer in degree mode for Example 3 is shown in Figure 5.25.

```
-√(3)-i▶Polar
         2e^(-150i)
```

If the real part of a complex number is 0, then the $\tan^{-1}$ formula will once again be useless. For if $z = x + yi$ with $x = 0$, then $\tan^{-1} \frac{y}{x}$ cannot be computed because of the zero in the denominator. But if the real part is 0, then the number is the pure imaginary yi whose graph lies on the imaginary axis. In that case, the argument θ is $\pi/2$ or $-\pi/2$, depending on whether y is positive or negative.

Example 4. Convert $-2i$ to polar form.

Figure 5.26

Solution: From the diagram in Figure 5.26, you can read off the values of r and θ. Clearly $r = 2$ and $\theta = -\frac{\pi}{2}$.

Therefore the polar form is $2e^{(-\pi/2)i}$. The calculator gives the same result, –90° in degree mode, as shown in Figure 5.27.

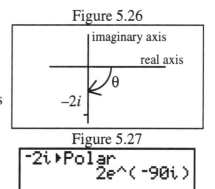

Figure 5.27

```
-2i▶Polar
       2e^(-90i)
```

To summarize the conversion formulas:

If $z = re^{\theta i}$, then the rectangular form of z is $x + yi$ where $x = r\cos\theta$ and $y = r\sin\theta$.

If $z = x + yi$, then the polar form of z is $re^{\theta i}$ where $r = \sqrt{x^2 + y^2}$ and

$$\theta = \begin{cases} \tan^{-1} \dfrac{y}{x} & \text{if } x > 0 \\[2mm] \pi + \tan^{-1} \dfrac{y}{x} & \text{if } x < 0 \\[2mm] \dfrac{\pi}{2} & \text{if } x = 0 \text{ and } y > 0 \\[2mm] -\dfrac{\pi}{2} & \text{if } x = 0 \text{ and } y < 0 \end{cases}$$

When both x and y are 0, then $z = 0$ and it has no polar form because the angle is indeterminate.

Multiplication in Polar Form

Polar form provides a surprising simplification of the multiplication process. the rule is: Multiply the moduli and add the arguments:

> **Theorem:** If $z = ae^{\alpha i}$ and $w = be^{\beta i}$ then $zw = abe^{(\alpha+\beta)i}$.

Proof: $zw = ae^{\alpha i} \cdot be^{\beta i}$

$$= a(\cos\alpha + i\sin\alpha) \cdot b(\cos\beta + i\sin\beta)$$

$$= ab(\cos\alpha\cos\beta + i\cos\alpha\sin\beta + i\sin\alpha\cos\beta + i^2\sin\alpha\sin\beta)$$

$$= ab\left[(\cos\alpha\cos\beta - \sin\alpha\sin\beta) + i(\sin\alpha\cos\beta + \sin\beta\cos\alpha)\right]$$

$$= ab\left[\cos(\alpha+\beta) + i\sin(\alpha+\beta)\right]$$

$$= abe^{(\alpha+\beta)i}$$

This result shows one of the exponential properties of polar form. As you know, when you multiply powers of real numbers, you add exponents. We just proved it's still true with complex exponents. If you use your old exponential habits on $e^{\alpha i} \cdot e^{\beta i}$, you'd get the right answer: $e^{\alpha i+\beta i}$ or $e^{(\alpha+\beta)i}$. This is at least a beginning of a justification for Euler's formula.

Example 5. Sketch a graph of $2e^{240°i}$, $3e^{145°i}$, and their product.

Solution: Using the theorem we have:

$$2e^{240°i} \cdot 3e^{145°i} = 6e^{385°i} = 6e^{25°i}.$$

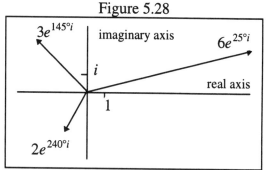
Figure 5.28

Example 7. What is the geometric effect of multiplying a complex number by i?

Solution: In polar form, $i = e^{90°i}$. If $z = re^{\theta i}$, then $iz = e^{90°i} \cdot re^{\theta i} = e^{(\theta+90°)i}$. Hence the geometric result is a

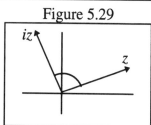
Figure 5.29

counterclockwise rotation of z through an angle of $90°$.

Powers and Roots

The multiplication theorem is also an implication for raising complex numbers to integral powers using polar form. For example, to square a complex number:

$$\left(re^{\theta i}\right)^2 = re^{\theta i} \cdot re^{\theta i} = r^2 e^{2\theta i}.$$

Multiplying again would give the cube of a complex number:

$$\left(re^{\theta i}\right)^3 = re^{\theta i} \cdot \left(re^{\theta i}\right)^2 = re^{\theta i}\left(r^2 e^{2\theta i}\right) = r^3 e^{3\theta i}.$$

And in general, the nth power of a complex number is given by:

$$\left(re^{\theta i}\right)^n = r^n e^{n\theta i}.$$

This result is known as de Moivre's Theorem, named for Abraham de Moivre (1667-1754), the person credited with its proof.

Example 7. Express $\left(2e^{30°i}\right)^4$ in rectangular form.

Solution:

$$
\begin{aligned}
\left(2e^{30°i}\right)^4 &= 2^4 e^{4\cdot30°i} \\
&= 16e^{120°i} \\
&= 16(\cos 120° + i\sin 120°) \\
&= 16\left(-\frac{1}{2} + i\frac{\sqrt{3}}{2}\right) \\
&= -8 + 8i\sqrt{3}
\end{aligned}
$$

If we ask what numbers raised to the nth power equal a given complex number z, we are essentially reversing the operations of de Moivre's theorem.

Example 8. Find the cube roots of $8e^{120°i}$.

Solution: We need to find a positive real number r such that $r^3 = 8$, and an angle θ such that $3\theta = 120°$. Obviously $r = 2$ and $\theta = 40°$ will do the trick. But we're not done. Because cosine and sine are both periodic with a period of 2π or $360°$, then so is $e^{\theta i}$; and there are more solutions for θ. We need to solve

$$3\theta = 120° + k360°, \text{ for } k = 0, 1, 2.$$

This yields the solutions:

$$\theta = 40° + k120°, \text{ for } k = 0, 1, 2.$$

In other words,
$$\theta = 40°, 160°, 280°.$$

So the cube roots of $8e^{120°i}$ are $2e^{40°i}$, $2e^{160°i}$, and $2e^{280°i}$. The graphs appear in Figure 5.30.

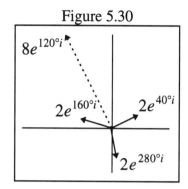

Figure 5.30

§3. Exercises

1. Sketch a graph of the given number and express in rectangular form:

a) e^{0i} b) $e^{(\pi/2)i}$ c) $e^{(2\pi/3)i}$

d) $e^{225°i}$ e) $e^{300°i}$ f) $e^{-150°i}$

2. Sketch a graph of the given number and express in rectangular form:

a) $5e^{\pi i}$ b) $2e^{(-\pi/6)i}$ c) $4e^{(5\pi/3)i}$

d) $\sqrt{2}e^{135°i}$ e) $7e^{270°i}$ f) $6e^{-45°i}$

3. Express in polar form:

a) $2 - 2i$ b) -5 c) $4 + 4i\sqrt{3}$

d) 10 e) i^3 f) $(1-i)^2$

4. Compute and express your answer in rectangular form:

a) $e^{(\pi/2)i} \cdot e^{(\pi/2)i}$ b) $2e^{(\pi/5)i} \cdot 3e^{(4\pi/5)i}$ c) $2e^{20°i} \cdot 4e^{40°i}$

d) $(2 + 2i\sqrt{3})^2$ e) the square roots of i f) the cube roots of -1

Solve the equations in Exercises 5-10.

5. $z = (1+i)^4$ 6. $z^2 = -1 + i\sqrt{3}$

7. $z^2 + 4 = 0$ 8. $x = \left(2e^{108°i}\right)^5$

9. $z^3 = -i$ 10. $z^3 = 8 + 8i$

11. a) If θ is any real number, what is the rectangular form of $e^{\theta i}$?

    b) Show that $\left|e^{\theta i}\right| = 1$.

    c) If θ is any real number, what is the set of all points z such that $z = e^{\theta i}$?

12. Show that $e^{x+\pi} = -e^x$ for all real numbers x.

13. Show that $\dfrac{1}{e^{\alpha i}} = e^{-\alpha i} = \overline{e^{\alpha i}}$ for all real numbers α.

14. If $z = e^{ti}$, show that $\bar{z} = e^{-ti}$.

15. Let f be the function defined by $f(x) = e^{xi}$ for all real numbers x.

a) Show that $f(0) = 1$.   b) Show that f is periodic with a period of 2π.

c) Describe the range of f.   d) Show that $f(a) \cdot f(b) = f(a+b)$.

§4. Complex Functions

So far in this course, the focus has been on the dynamics of functions of real numbers. The logistic function, for instance, had a real number domain and a real number range. Through iteration, we generated sequences of real numbers whose graphs we could plot on two dimensional graph paper. Now we are going to look at the dynamics of functions of complex numbers, and this study poses a special problem. If we iterate a function with complex number inputs and complex number outputs, we have a two-dimensional domain and a two dimensional range. A graph would require four dimensions. Can't do that ... so we improvise. One way to "see" a complex function is to draw before-and-after figures.

Example 1. Given the function $f(z) = -iz$, compute the values the function relates to the arguments $-2+i, -3+i,$ and $-2+4i$. Describe geometrically what effect f has on the plane.

Solution:
$$f(-2+i) \quad = -i \cdot (-2+i) = 2i - i^2 = 1 + 2i$$
$$f(-3+i) \quad = -i \cdot (-3+i) = 3i - i^2 = 1 + 3i$$
$$f(-2+4i) \quad = -i \cdot (-2+4i) = 2i - 4i^2 = 4 + 2i$$

Figure 5.31

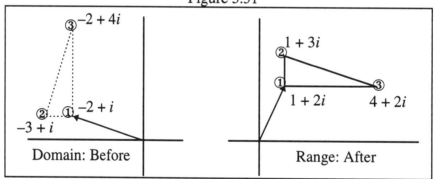

Domain: Before   Range: After

The geometric effect of f is to rotate the plane 90° clockwise around the origin. The result is more obvious when graphed on a single set of axes.

Figure 5.32

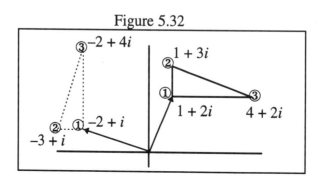

Example 2. Describe the geometric effect of $f(z) = 2iz$ on the complex plane.

Figure 5.33

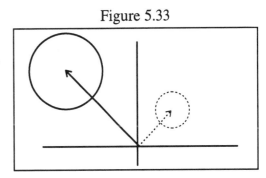

Solution: In polar form, if $z = re^{\theta i}$, then $f(z) = 2re^{(\theta + 90°)i}$. Geometrically f doubles the distance from the origin and rotates the plane 90° in a counterclockwise direction. For example, if the numbers z lie on a circle in the first quadrant (dotted in Figure 5.33), then the numbers $f(z)$ lie on a circle with twice the diameter, twice the distance from the origin and rotated 90° into the second quadrant (solid in Figure 5.33).

Figure 5.34

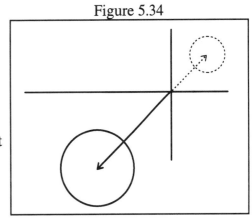

Example 3. Describe the geometric effect of $f(z) = -2z$.

Solution: In polar form, $z = re^{\theta i}$ and $-2 = 2e^{\pi i}$, so $f(z) = -2z = 2e^{\pi i} \cdot re^{\theta i} = 2re^{(\theta + \pi)i}$. Thus f doubles the modulus and adds 180° to the angle. It stretches and rotates the plane.

Example 4. Sketch the polygon joining the graphs of 0, $1 + 3i$, $-3 - i$, and $-4 + i$. Show that the geometric effect of applying the function $f(z) = z + (3 + 2i)$ is to translate the plane 3 units to the right and 2 units up.

Figure 5.35

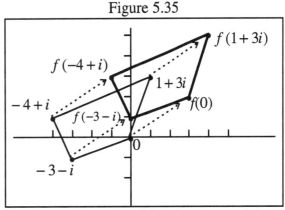

Solution: Applying the function f to each point, we have
$$f(0) = 3 + 2i$$
$$f(1 + 3i) = 4 + 5i$$
$$f(-3 - i) = i$$
$$f(-4 + i) = -1 + 4i$$

Clearly the polygon (and every other point on the plane) is translated 3 units right and 2 units up.

Example 5. Describe the geometric effect of $f(z) = z^2$.

Solution: Converting to polar form, we have $f(re^{\theta i}) = r^2 e^{2\theta i}$. The effect of this function is more complicated than the other examples, and we need to consider three cases: $r < 1$, $r = 1$, and $r > 1$. (See Figure 5.36.)

Case I: $r < 1$. In this case, $r^2 < r$ so that f moves points closer to the origin while it rotates them by doubling the polar angle.

Case II: $r = 1$. In this case, $r^2 = 1$, so that $z = e^{\theta i}$ and $f(z) = e^{2\theta i}$. Since z is on the unit circle, so is $f(z)$. The function simply rotates z by doubling its polar angle.

Case III: $r > 1$. In this case, $r^2 > r$, so that f expands points away from the origin at the same time as it doubles the polar angle.

Figure 5.36

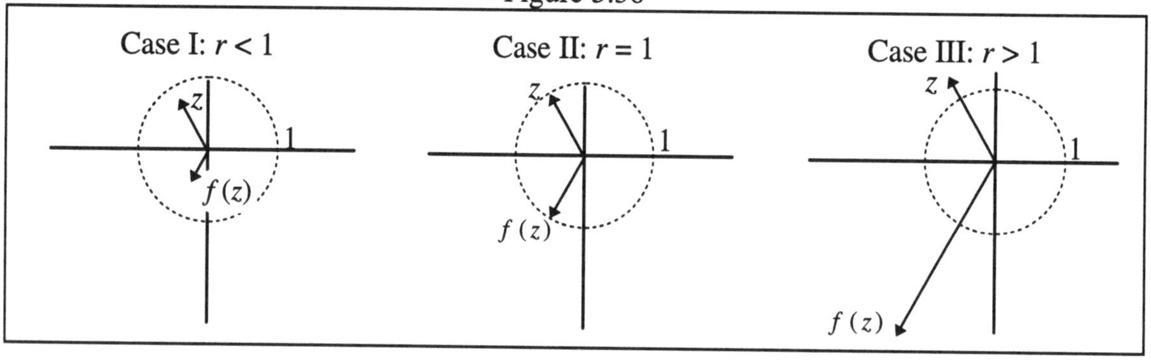

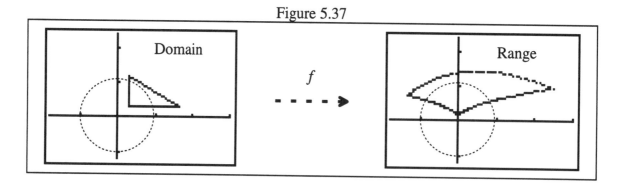

The function $f(z) = z^2$ transforms the plane in a non-linear way that is considerably more complicated than the functions in Examples 1-4. To get a better idea of the geometric effect of f, consider the diagram in Figure 5.37. In the left-hand image, you see a set of complex numbers whose graph is the triangle with vertices at $0.3 + 0.3i$, $0.3 + 1.2i$, and $1.6 + 0.3i$. In the right-hand image, you see how the triangle is distorted by f. Each image is superimposed on the unit circle which is not changed by f.

Figure 5.37

§4. Exercises

In Exercises 1-12, describe the geometric effect of f on the complex plane by doing the following for each problem:
a) Plot the triangle with vertices $0, 2,$ and $-i$.   b) Plot $f(0), f(2),$ and $f(-i)$.

1. $f(z) = z+5-i$ 5. $f(z) = -2iz$ 9. $f(z) = \bar{z}e^{240°i}$

2. $f(z) = -z$ 6. $f(z) = ze^{(\pi/3)i}$ 10. $f(z) = 2ze^{-90°i}$

3. $f(z) = \bar{z}$ 7. $f(z) = \bar{z}e^{(\pi/3)i}$ 11. $f(z) = -2i\bar{z}$

4. $f(z) = z+i$ 8. $f(z) = ze^{240°i}$ 12. $f(z) = 0.5iz$

13. Let $z = a+bi$ and $w = c+di$ be two complex numbers, and let m be the midpoint of the segment joining z and w. If $f(z) = \bar{z}+2$, show that $f(m)$ is the midpoint of the segment joining $f(z)$ and $f(w)$.

14. A function f is defined by $f(z) = z+k$ for some complex constant k. Find k if $f(-2+i) = 2i$.

15. A function f is defined by $f(z) = kz$ for some complex constant k. Find k if $f(1+i) = -1+i$.

16. A function f is defined by $f(z) = k\bar{z}$ for some complex constant k. Fin k if $f(3+2i) = 10-11i$.

17. If $f(z) = z+k$ for some complex constant k, then f is called a *translation*. Show that *distance is invariant under translation*; that is, if z and w are two complex numbers, then the distance between $f(z)$ and $f(w)$ is the same as the distance between z and w. [Hint: Show that $|f(z) - f(w)| = |z-w|$.]

18. If $f(z) = ze^{\alpha i}$ for some real number α, then f is called a *rotation*. Show that *distance is invariant under rotation*.

19. If $f(z) = \bar{z}e^{\alpha i}$ for some real number α, then f is called a *reflection*. Show that *distance is invariant under reflection*.

20. If f is the translation $f(z) = z+k$, through what distance does f translate the plane?

21. If f is the rotation $f(z) = ze^{\alpha i}$, through what angle does f rotate the plane?

22. If f is the reflection $f(z) = \bar{z}e^{\alpha i}$, what is the line of reflection?

Chapter 6

JULIA AND MANDELBROT SETS

§1. What Is A Julia Set?

Or maybe you'd rather ask, "Who is Julia?" Julia turns out to be Gaston Julia (1893-1978), a man who published an article on the iteration of rational functions (when he was only 25!). The article made him briefly famous, but his work was largely forgotten until shortly before his death when it was revived by Benoit Mandelbrot.

A Julia Set is a set of points on the complex plane that is defined through a process of function iteration. The goal of this chapter is to give a careful definition of Julia Sets and to explore their properties by investigating their image on the calculator.

The Unit Circle

Our investigation of Julia Sets starts with the dynamical properties of the function $f(z) = z^2$ whose geometry we explored in Example 5 of the last section. In that example we saw that what happens to the orbit of a seed depends entirely on its absolute value. For the seed $z_0 = r_0 e^{\theta_0 i}$, there are three cases: $r_0 < 1$, $r_0 > 1$, or $r_0 = 1$; that is, z_0 is *inside*, *outside*, or *on* the unit circle. In each case, $f(z_0) = z_0^2 = r_0^2 e^{2\theta_0 i}$, so the modulus is squared and the argument is doubled. The geometric effect of squaring the modulus depends on its size.

Case I: If $r_0 < 1$, then $r_0^2 < r_0$ so that the modulus shrinks under repeated iteration:

$$r_0 > r_0^2 > r_0^4 > r_0^8 > \cdots > 0.$$

This is a geometric sequence with common ratio less than 1, so we know it approaches 0. Hence, the orbit of any seed with a modulus less than 1 is attracted to 0. Geometrically, we can say that the iteration of any seed *inside* the unit circle determines an orbit that *spirals in towards the origin*. Figure 6.1 shows the orbit of

Figure 6.1

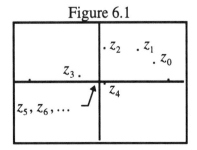

$z_0 = 0.8 + 0.3i$ under the squaring function $f(z) = z^2$.

Case II: If $r_0 > 1$, then $r_0^2 > r_0$ so that the modulus stretches out under repeated iteration. We have

$$r_0 < r_0^2 < r_0^4 < r_0^8 < \cdots$$

This is also a geometric sequence, but this time the common ratio is greater than 1, so the modulus squares itself out to infinity while the argument doubles. Thus any orbit that starts *outside* the unit circle *escapes from any finite boundary*. We can say that the orbit "is attracted to the point at infinity." Figure 6.2 shows a graph of the orbit of $z_0 = 1.1 + 0.1i$.

Figure 6.2

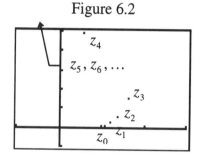

Case III: If $r_0 = 1$, then $r_0^2 = r_0 = 1$ so that the modulus remains unchanged under repeated iteration while the argument doubles. Thus any orbit that *starts* on the unit circle *stays* on the unit circle.

Prisoner Points and Escaping Points

In short, $f(z) = z^2$ distinguishes three kinds of seeds:

(1)   those whose orbits are attracted to 0 ("Prisoner Points"),
(2)   those whose orbits are attracted to infinity ("Escaping Points"), and
(3)   those whose orbits do neither ("Julia Points").

Figure 6.3

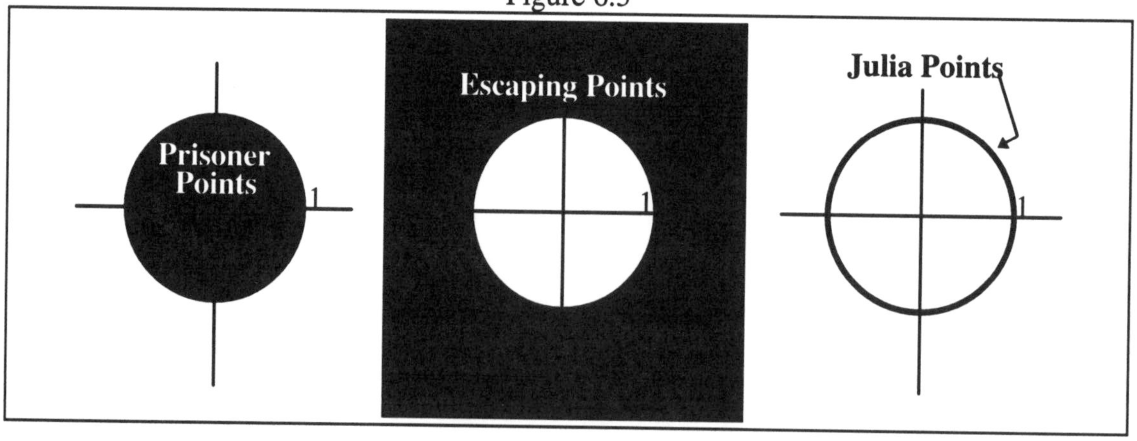

Example 1: Describe the orbit of $0.2 - 0.5i$ under iteration of the function $f(z) = z^2$.

Solution:

$$f(.2-.5i) = (.2-.5i)^2 = .04-.2i+.25i^2 = -.21-.2i$$
$$f(-.21-.2i) = (-.21-.2i)^2 = .0441+.084i+.04i^2 = .0041+.084i$$
$$f(.0041+.084i) = -.00703919+.0006888i$$

And so on. It appears that the seed $0.2 - 0.5i$ is headed towards the origin. If you check its absolute value, you'll see that $|.2-.5i| = \sqrt{.2^2+.5^2} = \sqrt{.29} = .5385...$ which is less than 1. Therefore the orbit is eventually attracted to 0.

In Example 1, you can see that the algebra of iterating complex numbers through a relatively simple function gets tedious rather quickly. The calculator can simplify the task. First make sure the 7th line of the **MODE** menu is set to a+bi. After you enter .2-.5i, press **2nd[ANS] x²** and then **ENTER** repeatedly to generate the orbit. Of course, this orbit eventually gets so close to the origin that the calculator cannot distinguish the orbit points from 0, and it tells you that the orbit lands on its attractor. *Wrong answer.* Once again you need to remember the limitations of the calculator: *The attractor is not a point of the orbit.*

Example 2: Describe the orbit of $0.6 + 0.8i$ under $f(z) = z^2$.

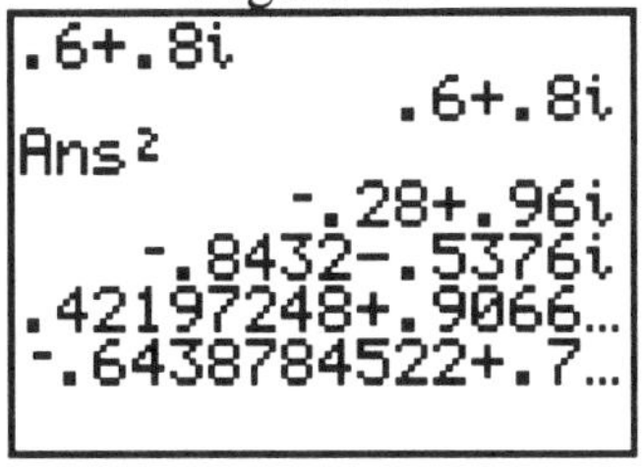

Solution: The first four iterations are shown in Figure 6.4. It's hard to tell what's going on, even if you use the right cursor arrow to get all the digits of the imaginary part that your calculator will give you. The answer is in the absolute values:

$$|.6+.8i| = \sqrt{.36+.64} = \sqrt{1} = 1.$$

Figure 6.4

```
.6+.8i
                .6+.8i
Ans²
            -.28+.96i
    -.8432-.5376i
.42197248+.9066...
-.6438784522+.7...
```

The seed is on the unit circle; therefore the entire orbit must stay on the unit circle. If you check the other three points, you'll discover that their absolute value is also 1. This point stays on the unit circle forever; it is neither a Prisoner nor an Escaping Point; it is a Julia Point.

If, in Example 2, you continue pressing **ENTER** long enough, your calculator will give you $-.9346740815-.3555057838i$ whose absolute value is 1.000000001. In a few more iterations, you'd begin to see numbers well outside the unit circle and you would conclude that $0.6 + 0.8i$ is an Escaping Point. Sensitivity has struck again, and your calculator gives another wrong answer. Calculators are very useful but not infallible. Sometimes you have to use the abstraction of algebra which you can trust.

Another way to see the orbit of Example 2 is to change the **MODE** menu from a+bi to re^θi. Then enter .6 +.8i and change to polar form (**MATH > > CPX 7: ▸Polar**). If you then press **2nd[ANS] x²** and then **ENTER** repeatedly, you would see the screen in Figure 6.5 showing the modulus remains 1 while the angle changes.

Figure 6.5

```
.6+.8i▸Polar
1e^(.927295218i)
Ans²
1e^(1.854590436...
1e^(-2.57400443...
1e^(1.135176437...
1e^(2.270352874...
```

Example 3: Describe the orbit of $\dfrac{1}{2} + \dfrac{\sqrt{3}}{2} i$.

Solution: The first four iterations are shown in Figure 6.6. The orbit lands on a 2-cycle $\left\{ -\dfrac{1}{2} + \dfrac{\sqrt{3}}{2} i, \ -\dfrac{1}{2} - \dfrac{\sqrt{3}}{2} i \right\}$; the seed is an eventually periodic point. Take a closer look at the seed in this example. If you recognize that $\cos 60° = \dfrac{1}{2}$ and $\sin 60° = \dfrac{\sqrt{3}}{2}$, then you see that the seed

Figure 6.6

```
1/2+√(3)/2i
 .5+.86602540838i
Ans²
-.5+.86602540838i
-.5-.86602540838i
-.5+.86602540838i
-.5-.86602540838i
```

is $\cos 60° + i \sin 60°$; that is, $e^{60°i}$. Thus the seed of this orbit is a point on the unit circle, and so the squaring function simply doubles its argument. Hence, another way to see the orbit is as follows:

$$ e^{60°i} \rightarrow e^{120°i} \rightarrow e^{240°i} = e^{-120°} \rightarrow e^{-240°i} = e^{120°i} \rightarrow e^{-120°i} \rightarrow e^{120°i} \rightarrow \cdots $$

The orbit continues hopping back and forth between $e^{120°i}$ and $e^{-120°i}$.

Based on the example of the squaring function whose Julia Set is the unit circle, we make the following generalized definitions:

Definition: Let f be a function with complex domain. If f has an attracting fixed point or cycle, then the points that approach the attractor as a limit are called *Prisoner Points*. The points whose orbits under f tend to infinity are called *Escaping Points*. The remaining points, whose orbits do not tend to an attracting fixed point or cycle and which do not tend to infinity, are called *Julia Points*.

Definition: The set of all Prisoner Points is called the *Prisoner Set*. The set of all Escaping Points is called the *Escaping Set*. The set of all Julia Points is called the *Julia Set*.

Prisoner Points and Julia Points have one thing in common: Their orbits stay on the finite plane. The difference is this: Prisoner Points have orbits that tend to an attractor; Julia Points do not. The orbits of Julia Points *do* stay on the plane, but they *do not* approach an attractor. Look what happens to $e^{30°i}$ in Example 3. It ends up in a cycle, and so its orbit stays on the finite plane. But the cycle is *not an attracting cycle*. The only way a seed ends up there is to hop onto one of the points $e^{120°i}$ or $e^{240°i}$. If an orbit just misses one of these points, no matter how close it comes, it will eventually move away because the cycle is repelling. The orbit of $e^{30°i}$ does not approach a limiting cycle, so $e^{30°i}$ is not a Prisoner Point. The only attractor for $f(z) = z^2$ is the point $z = 0$, the origin, and the orbit of $e^{30°i}$ is not attracted to it. But the orbit does stay on the finite plane, so $e^{30°i}$ is not an Escaping Point. It is a Julia Point.

To summarize, points in a Julia Set do not tend to an attractor but they do stay on the finite plane. Thus there are three possibilities for a Julia Point:

1) It may be a fixed or an eventually fixed point (*repelling*); or
2) it may be a periodic or an eventually periodic point (*repelling*); or
3) it may wander the Julia Set forever, landing on just about every point except the (*repelling*) fixed points or cycles.

Notice in the case of $f(z) = z^2$ that the Julia Set forms a boundary between the Prisoner Set and the Escaping Set. In this case, the boundary is the circumference of the unit circle, relatively easy to define and to see.

Calculating Orbits

To analyze the dynamics of $f(z) = z^2$, it is useful to trace orbits both numerically and graphically using a split screen on the calculator. The top half of the screen displays the graph, the bottom half the numbers. The heart of the program is a loop to do the iteration. Call the program SQUAREZ.

Program – SQUAREZ	Calculator Hints	Purpose
Horiz	**MODE** ∨ ∨ ∨ ∨ ∨ ∨ **> ENTER**	Splits screen horizontally
a+b*i*	**MODE** ∨ ∨ ∨ ∨ ∨ **> ENTER**	Complex mode
ClrHome	**PGM > I/O 8:ClrHome**	⎫
ClrDraw	**2nd[DRAW] 1:ClrDraw**	⎪
AxesOff	**2nd[FORMAT]** ∨ ∨ ∨ **ENTER**	⎬ Clears the screens
FnOff	**VARS > Y-VARS 4:On/Off 2:FnOff**	⎪
DispGraph	**PGM > I/O 4:DispGraph**	⎭

`⁻3.9→Xmin`		Sets the window
`3.9→Xmax`		
`1→Xscl`		
`⁻1.3→Ymin`		
`1.3→Ymax`		
`1→Yscl`		
`Prompt Z`		Input the seed
`Lbl 1`		Starts iteration loop
`real(Z)→U`	**MATH > > CPX 2:real(**	
`imag(Z)→V`	**MATH > > CPX 3:imag(**	
`Pt-On(U,V)`	**2nd[DRAW] > POINTS 1:Pt-On(**	Plots z
`Disp Z`		Displays z numerically
`Disp " "`		Empty line on display screen
`Pause`		Allows contemplation time
`Z²→Z`		Squares current z and stores the value as new input z
`Goto 1`		

A run of SQUAREZ produces displays such as in Figure 6.7. Illustrated are iterations 1, 2, 3, and 25 for the seed $z = 0.6 + 0.8i$.

Figure 6.7

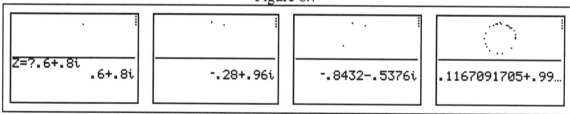

(Sharp programmers will notice that SQUAREZ is not particularly elegant: There is no way to end the loop. To stop it, you must press **ON**. You will see an error message with two choices, either quit and return to the home screen, or transfer to the editing screen and go to the step where the run was interrupted. Assuming you want to quit, select the option **1:Quit**. If you want to avoid this messiness, get out the manual for the TI-83 and improve on this program.)

§1. Exercises

1. Do Example 3 with your calculator using polar form and degree mode. Verify that the orbit eventually cycles between $e^{120°i}$ and $e^{-120°i}$.

2. Give the first five points in the orbit of the following seeds under iteration of the function $f(z) = z^2$:

a) -1 b) $-0.6 + 0.8i$ c) $0.2 - 0.5i$ d) $0.8 + 0.8i$

3. Describe the orbit of each of the following seeds under iteration of $f(z) = z^2$:

a) $0.05 - 0.12i$ b) $1.1i$ c) $-0.3 - 0.3i$ d) $0.61+0.79i$

e) $e^{10°i}$ f) $e^{(\pi\sqrt{2}/2)i}$ g) $2e^{2°i}$ h) $0.999e^{(\pi/3)i}$

4. Identify all the fixed points of $f(z) = z^2$.

a) Which fixed points are attracting, which are repelling and which are neutral?

b) Describe the set of all points that tend to the attracting fixed points in part (a).

5. Describe the orbit of the following seeds under iteration of the function $f(z) = z^2 - 1$:

a) i b) 1   c) $0.2 - 0.2i$ d) $-0.3 + i$

6. Apply the definition of Julia Set to the logistic function $f(x) = 2x(1-x)$, using a domain of all real numbers. Identify all Prisoner, Escaping, and Julia Points.

7. What is the Julia Set of the function $f(x) = x^2$ with a domain of all real numbers?

8. What is the Julia Set of the function $f(x) = x^2 - 1$ with a domain of all real numbers?

9. You know that the unit circle is the Julia Set for the complex function $f(z) = z^2$.
Theoretically, any point on the unit circle must stay on the unit circle when iterated.

a) Explain why that statement is true.

b) Explore the statement with your calculator as follows:

      i) Show that the following complex numbers lie on the unit circle:

$$z_1 = .6+.8i,\ z_2 = -i,\ z_3 = e^{(2\pi/3)i},\ z_4 = e^{13°i}$$

      ii) Use SQUAREZ to investigate the orbits of these points and describe the results.
(For z_4, make sure you stay with it for 25 iterations.)

      iii) How do you explain the results you got in (ii)?

c) Can you find a point on the unit circle that has a 3-cycle? A 4-cycle? A 5-cycle? An n-cycle?

10. Find the fixed points of the function $f(z) = z^2 - 1$. Does either of these points lie in the Julia Set of the function? Explain your answer.

§2. Filled Julia Sets

The unit circle, as explained in the last section, is the Julia Set for the function $f(z) = z^2$. This function is a special example of the quadratic family $f(z) = z^2 + c$ with $c = 0$. The purpose of this section is to generalize and look at examples of Julia Sets for values of the parameter c different from 0. For example, what happens when $c = -1$? Does it simply move the circle one unit to the left? (Before going any further, you might modify the program SQUAREZ to check it out. See Exercises 1 and 2.)

To see an image of the Julia Set for non-zero values of the parameter c, you first need to determine which points are Prisoners and which are Escaping. Throw them out, graph the rest, and you'll have a picture of the Julia Set.

The Escape Criterion

Easier said than done. As a first approach, we will lump the Julia Set in with the Prisoner Set and graph both, calling the result a *filled* Julia Set. The strategy is to identify Escaping Points, color them white, and color all the others black. So the first problem is to decide if a point is Escaping. How can you tell when z has gotten big enough to know it will continue on to infinity? The answer, it turns out, is whenever $|z|$ is bigger than 2 and at least as big as $|c|$. This is The Escape Criterion. It tells us that as soon as an orbit gets outside a circle of radius 2, then it is headed off towards infinity.

The Escape Criterion: Given the quadratic function
$f(z) = z^2 + c$, if $|z| \geq |c|$ and $|z| > 2$, then the orbit of z
escapes to infinity.

Proof: Assume that $|z| \geq |c|$ and $|z| > 2$. First, we need to show that the application of f results in an output point which is farther from the origin than the input point; that is, that $|f(z)| > |z|$. Then, a second application of f to $f(z)$ would move the orbit even further out. Finally, we need to show that repeated iteration moves the orbit beyond any finite boundary.

The first step makes clever use of one form of the triangle inequality from the last chapter:

$$\left| z^2 + c \right| = \left| z^2 - (-c) \right| \geq \left| z^2 \right| - \left| -c \right| = \left| z^2 \right| - |c|.$$

It follows that

$$\left| f(z) \right| = \left| z^2 + c \right| \geq \left| z^2 \right| - |c|$$

and therefore

$$
\begin{aligned}
|f(z)| \;&\geq \left|z^2\right| - |z| \quad \text{because } |c| \leq |z| \\
&= |z|^2 - |z| \quad \text{because } \left|z^2\right| = |z|^2 \\
&= |z|(|z| - 1) \qquad\qquad\qquad\qquad (*) \\
&> |z| \qquad\quad \text{because } |z| > 2 \rightarrow |z| - 1 > 1.
\end{aligned}
$$

So now we see that each iteration of f moves the orbit further from the origin. But do we know yet that it goes off to infinity? Not quite. It is conceivable that the distance from the origin increases but is bounded by an upper limit to which it gets infinitely close. One more trick shows this is not the case. In the step of the proof marked (*), we have $|z|(|z| - 1) > |z|$ because $|z| - 1 > 1$. Take this a step further. If $|z| - 1 > 1$, then $|z| - 1 = 1 + \varepsilon$ for some (presumably tiny) positive number ε. Therefore,

$$|f(z)| \geq |z|(1 + \varepsilon).$$

After a second iteration, we have:

$$
\begin{aligned}
\left|{}^2 f(z)\right| &= |f(f(z))| \\
&\geq |f(z)|(1 + \varepsilon) \\
&\geq |z|(1 + \varepsilon)(1 + \varepsilon) \\
&= |z|(1 + \varepsilon)^2
\end{aligned}
$$

And in general: $\qquad\qquad \left|{}^n f(z)\right| \geq |z|(1 + \varepsilon)^n.$

But this is a geometric sequence with common ratio $(1 + \varepsilon)$, a ratio greater than 1 since $\varepsilon > 0$. Therefore, the terms grow without bound, and we can conclude that $\left|{}^n f(z)\right| \rightarrow \infty$. This completes the proof of the Escape Criterion.

Suppose now that $|c| \geq 2$. Then as a seed, c satisfies both conditions of the Escape Criterion, and so it has an escaping orbit. Since $f(0) = c$, then the orbit of 0 also escapes. But 0 is the critical value of the quadratic family, the point that is guaranteed to find an attracting point or cycle of there is one. Since 0 is an Escaping Point when $|c| \geq 2$, we can conclude that there are no attracting points or cycles when $|c| \geq 2$. Therefore, there are no Prisoner Points when $|c| \geq 2$. On the other hand, if $|c| < 2$, then whenever $|z|$ is greater than 2, it is greater than both 2 and $|c|$, so the Criterion assures us that the orbit of z escapes. Thus, no matter what the value of c, we can conclude that there are no Prisoner Points outside a circle of radius 2 around the origin. It follows that, for every c, the Prisoner Set, and hence its boundary the Julia Set, is entirely contained within a circle of radius 2 around the origin. Therefore, the search for Julia Points can be limited and makes a computer or calculator program possible.

The Program

The goal is to plot a graph of filled Julia Sets for any choice of parameter. That means for every seed z with $|z| < 2$, we will iterate the function $f(z) = z^2 + c$ some reasonable number of times till we're sure we know the behavior of the orbit. If z turns out to be an Escaping Point, we color it white; otherwise, we color it black. We end up with a black filled Julia Set on a white background.

But what is a "reasonable number" of iterations? How many do we need to look at to be sure we know the orbit's behavior? There is some leeway for individual judgment here. In the following program the decision was made (somewhat arbitrarily but based on a number of trials) to use 50 iterations. If the point has not escaped in 50 iterations, it is called a Prisoner or Julia Point and it is colored black.

So here's the idea for the program. To encompass all seeds within 2 units of the origin, the real axis goes from −2 to 2 and the imaginary axis from −2i to 2i. (This means the seed −2 − 2i lives in the lower left corner and the seed 2 + 2i in the upper right corner.) Recall that the window of the TI-83 is a grid of pixels, 95 wide by 63 high. (See Figure 6.9.) Therefore, there are 95 steps for the real parts to take from −2 to 2, and 63 steps for the imaginary parts from −2 to 2. There are $95 \times 63 = 5985$ seeds to be tested, by running out their orbits for at most 50 iterations, and coloring the seed black if the orbit does not escape. There are two nested loops to pick the seeds; the outer loop fixes an x and the inner loop runs through all the y's vertically for

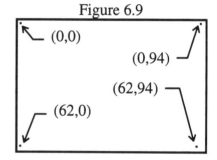

Figure 6.9

that x; then the outer loop goes to the next x; and so on. For each choice of x and y, there is an inner *inner* loop that iterates up to 50 times, checking each time to see if the orbit is outside the circle of radius 2. If the answer is yes, the program skips to the next seed; if the answer is no, it continues the iteration. If it actually reaches 50 iterations, then the orbit has not escaped, and the program puts a dot on the point representing that seed before going to the next seed.

This program also makes use of symmetry in Julia Sets to cut the computation time in half. Notice that the equations for x_{n+1} and y_{n+1} are unchanged when x_n and y_n are both replaced with their negatives. This implies that whatever is true about the seed $z = x + yi$ will also be true about its negative $-z = -x - yi$. In particular, if z is a Prisoner or Julia Point, then so is $-z$. Therefore, the program needs to look at the orbits of only half the seeds in the window, plotting $-z = -x - yi$ whenever it plots $z = x + yi$.

Two final notes: (1) When the TI-83 graphs a point, it may change the values of variables called X and Y, so we avoid them and use other letters, U and V, for the real and imaginary parts of the seed Z. (2) The innermost loop, the one that does the iteration, does not use the command For, because a deeply nested For-loop does not operate correctly with an If command buried inside it. Since that is required in this program, we construct the innermost loop with a loop-counter (J), a starting label (1), and a `Goto` command.

The program is called `JULIA1`.

Program – JULIA1	Purpose
`ClrHome`	
`ClrDraw`	
`FnOff`	
`AxesOff`	
`a+b`i	
`-2→Xmin`	
`2→Xmax`	
`0→Xscl`	
`-2→Ymin`	
`2→Ymax`	
`0→Yscl`	
`Input "PARAMETER? ",C`	
`ClrHome`	
`4/95→S`	Horizontal step size
`4/63→T`	Vertical step size
`For(U,-2,2,S)`	Begins outer loop choosing real part of seed
`For(V,0,2,T)`	Begins inner loop picking imaginary part, using only the upper half of screen
`U+V`i`→Z`	
`0→J`	⎫ Starts loop-counter J at 0; can't use a For-loop
`Lbl 1`	⎬Innermost loop to investigate orbit
`Z²+C→Z`	⎪ Iteration step: $f(z)$ becomes new z
`If abs(Z)>2:Goto 2`	⎪ If modulus > 2, stops iterating, gets new seed
`J+1→J`	⎪ Otherwise, adds 1 to loop counter
`If J<50:Goto 1`	⎭ If loop counter < 50, begins loop again
`Pt-On(U,V)`	Otherwise plots seed U+Vi
`Pt-On(-U,-V)`	Plots negative of U+Vi
`Lbl 2`	
`End`	Ends V-loop
`End`	Ends U-loop

If you run `JULIA1` with $C = -0.2 + 0.8i$, you get a filled Julia Set for the function $f(z) = z^2 - 0.2 + 0.8i$. (See Figure 6.10.) In Figure 6.11 are Julia Sets for the parameters $c = -1.25$, $c = -0.5 + 0.5i$, and $c = 0.251$.

The images that JULIA1 gives of filled Julia Sets are a bit clunky, because of the limited resolution of the TI-83. Moreover, the program runs very slowly. (You'll want to let your calculator run while you eat dinner or do the rest of your homework.) Our immediate goal is simply to *understand* these sets; shortly we will look at computer generated images that we allow more appreciation of their intricate beauty.

Figure 6.10

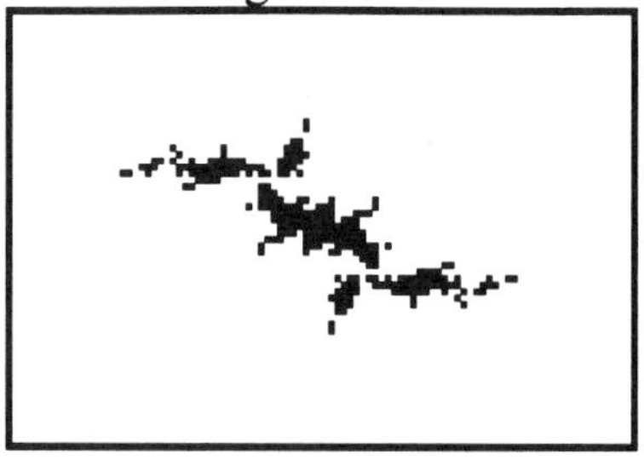

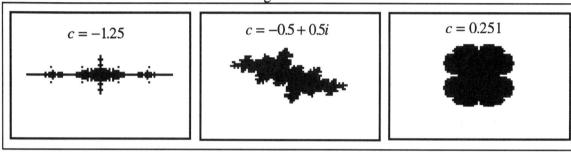

Figure 6.11

| $c = -1.25$ | $c = -0.5 + 0.5i$ | $c = 0.251$ |

The parameter $c = 0.251$ of Figure 6.11 was carefully chosen to be just a little bigger than 0.25, the upper bound for attracting points in the case of the real function $f(x) = x^2 + c$. All real seeds orbit off to infinity under $f(x) = x^2 + 0.251$; so all real seeds are Escaping Points. But in this picture of the complex case, it looks as if there are a lot of Prisoner Points. However, if you trace the orbit of just about any seed you can think of, your calculator will show you it's an Escaping Point. In fact the chance of your finding a seed that *doesn't* escape is so close to 0 that you might as well say it is impossible. So how come there's a nice big dark blob of a filled Julia Set in the picture? Because we were using 50 iterations as the upper limit, and lots of points stayed around that long only to disappear after a few more. For example, it takes 83 iterations for 0 to escape. (You should modify the program SQUAREZ to allow the input of a parameter so you can easily investigate orbits of different seeds with any parameter. See Exercise 1.)

To take a second look, you could modify JULIA1 to allow 100 iterations. If you did so, you would see the graph in Figure 6.12. Lots more white space now. That means the Julia Set no longer separates the plane between Escaping Points and Prisoner Points because *there are NO Prisoner Points!* There is only a dusting of scattered points in the Julia Set and everything else escapes. That's why the probability of your finding a Julia Point is 0. We will

Figure 6.12

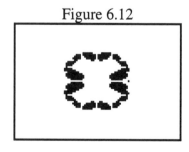

consider this type of Julia Set in more detail in the next section, and we will devise a program to draw a graph of an unfilled Julia Set.

§2. Exercises

1. Modify SQUAREZ to permit the specification of a parameter as well as a seed. Before the command :Prompt Z, include a Disp command to identify this input as the seed. Also write analogous commands to prompt the input of a parameter. Finally, modify the computation command :$Z^2 \to Z$ to account for the addition of c to z^2. Call this modification CPXORBIT.

2. You know that the Julia Set of $f(z) = z^2$ is the unit circle. It is reasonable to conjecture that the Julia Set of $f(z) = z^2 - 1$ is a translation of the unit circle. Check out that conjecture. [You can use JULIA1, CPXORBIT, or a method of your own.]

Use JULIA1 (or write your own program) to draw graphs of the filled Julia Sets for the quadratic function $f(z) = z^2 + c$ for the values of c given in Exercises 3-10. (Be prepared to let the programs run while you are doing something else. The program takes a long time, and it is not very enlightening to watch the slow progress. If you want to speed things up a bit, drop the number of orbital iterations from 50 to 30 or so.)3.

3. $c = -0.12 - 0.75i$ 4. $c = -1.76$ 5. $c = -1.15 + 0.26i$
6. $c = 0.27 + 0.59i$ 7. $c = 0.40 + 0.34i$ 8. $c = 0.40 - 0.34i$

9. If $c = 1.5$, verify that the orbit of 0 escapes.
  a) As a result, you can conclude that there are no Prisoner Points. Why?
  b) What happens when you run JULIA1 with $c = 1.5$? What does this mean?
  c) Find the fixed points of the function $f(z) = z^2 + 1.5$. Are they Julia Points?
  d) How do you reconcile the answers in (b) and (c)?

10. Find the points in the non-trivial 2-cycle of $f(z) = z^2 + 1.5$. Are they Julia Points?

11. Find the fixed points and 2-cycles of $f(z) = z^2 + 3$. Is any attracting? Are they Julia Points?

Exercises 12-15 develop a modification of JULIA1 to explore the Julia Sets of the logistic function.

12. Consider the application of the logistic function $f(z) = rz(1-z)$ to complex numbers. Let $z = x + yi$ and $r = a + bi$ (where x, y, a, and b are all real numbers). Verify that $f(z) = (-ax^2 + ay^2 + ax - by + 2bxy) + (-bx^2 + by^2 + bx + ay - 2axy)i$.

13. To modify $\mathtt{JULIA1}$ for the logistic function, it is helpful to know that its Julia Sets are symmetric about the point $\left(\dfrac{1}{2},0\right)$. [Recall that $\mathtt{JULIA1}$ used the fact that Julia Sets for the quadratic family were symmetric about the origin.] Show the logistic family's symmetry in the following two steps:

a) First show that $\left(\dfrac{1}{2},0\right)$ is the midpoint of the segment joining (p, q) to $(1 - p, -q)$.

b) Then use the results of Exercise 12 to show that $f(p+qi) = f(1- p - qi)$.

14. To modify $\mathtt{JULIA1}$ for the logistic function, you also have to decide on an escape criterion. Use the triangle inequality and the properties of absolute value to show that if $|z| > \dfrac{1}{|r|} + 1$, then $|f(z)| > |z|$. Then imitate the proof of the Escape Criterion in this section to conclude that the orbit of z is attracted to infinity when $|z| > \dfrac{1}{|r|} + 1$.

15. Use the results of Exercises 12-14 to modify $\mathtt{JULIA1}$ so that it works for the logistic function. Use the same window as for the quadratic family. Use 30-50 iterations and run your program for the following parameters:

a) $c = i$　　　　b) $c = 0.6 + 0.8i$　　　　c) $c = 2$　　　　d) $c = -0.9 + 0.3i$

§3. Unfilled Julia Sets

The program JULIA1 plots pictures of filled Julia Sets. We found the filled image misleading when $c = 0.251$, because there are no Prisoner Points for this value of the parameter. In this case it is important to see just the Julia Points without the Prisoner Points, but in general it is very hard to locate a point on the Julia Set. Recall that the orbit of any point in a Julia Set stays in the set, whether the point is fixed, periodic, or wandering. Furthermore, all Julia Points are *repelling*: nearby points orbit away from them. And repelling points are just about impossible to find.

In the special case where $c = 0$, the Julia Set is the unit circle, so we can easily draw its graph. No other parameter gives us this possibility. And in the case of the unfilled sets, at least, we have to improvise.

The idea is to use the fact that points on the Julia Set are repelling. If you pick a point the tiniest bit off of the set and make a film of its orbit, you would see it moving away, either towards an attractor or towards infinity. Now think about what you would see if you run the film backwards: points rushing in toward the Julia Set. It is an attractor under *backward iteration*.

Backward Iteration

To do backward iteration, you pick any point *off* the Julia Set (call it w) and find out what its *preimage* is under the function $f(z) = z^2 + c$. That means you have to find a complex number z which when put through the function f lands on w. In short, you have to solve for z in the equation

$$w = z^2 + c.$$

The solution is a new point, now closer to the Julia Set, so you repeat the process to find *its* preimage. And so on. You pick a point anywhere on the plane, then use the preimage to find the next preimage, and continue the process, iterating backwards, each time getting a point closer to the original Julia Set. Keep it up for, say, 5,000 points, and all but the first few will be very, very close to the points in the Julia Set. The calculator will do this work very easily and give us a good picture of the Julia Set in outline. To write the program, however, you have to be careful about some mathematical details when you look for preimages.

Suppose the seed is $w = x + yi$. The preimage is the solution to the equation $z^2 + c = w$. Solving for z, we have:

$$z^2 + c = w$$
$$z^2 = w - c$$
$$z = \pm\sqrt{w - c}$$

Remember, everything is a complex number here, and to take square roots you need to use deMoivre's Theorem in reverse. That means $w - c$ has to be expressed in polar form. Since $w = x + yi$ and $c = a + bi$, then (in rectangular form) $w - c = (x - a) + (y - b)i$. To convert to polar form, first find the modulus

$$r = \sqrt{(x-a)^2 + (y-b)^2}$$

and then the angle

$$\theta = \tan^{-1}\left(\frac{y-b}{x-a}\right).$$

Using these definitions of r and θ in terms of x, y, a, and b, the polar form of $w - c$ is simply $re^{\theta i}$. Therefore the solution of $z = \pm\sqrt{w - c}$ is found by solving:

$$z^2 = re^{\theta i}.$$

From deMoivre's Theorem, we conclude that:

$$z = \sqrt{r}e^{(\theta/2)i}, \quad \sqrt{r}e^{(\pi+\theta/2)i},$$

or, in rectangular form again:

$$z = \sqrt{r}\cos\frac{\theta}{2} + \sqrt{r}\sin\frac{\theta}{2}i \quad \text{or} \quad \sqrt{r}\cos\left(\frac{\theta}{2}+\pi\right) + \sqrt{r}\sin\left(\frac{\theta}{2}+\pi\right)i.$$

Programming the Calculator

This formula may not be as neat algebraically as you would like, but your calculator isn't too fussy. It handles trigonometric functions about as easily as polynomials. But here's a complication: you started with one seed $x + yi$ and end up with *two* new seeds for the next iteration. Which one do you use? It doesn't matter. To keep things unbiased, just let the calculator choose randomly between the two by using the random number function `rand` (**MATH > > PRB 1:rand**). The trick is to set the angle equal to $\frac{\theta}{2} + \text{int}(2*\text{rand})*\pi$. Since `rand` is a number between 0 and 1, then 2*`rand` is between 0 and 2, so `int(2*rand)` is either 0 or 1. (You find `int` at **MATH > NUM 5:int(**.) About half the time the value is 0, and half the time it's 1. So half the time you add nothing to $\frac{\theta}{2}$ and half the time you add π, the choice made randomly by the calculator.

The following program, `JULIA2`, does backward iteration using any seed you choose to enter. The seed is not important, and you could arbitrarily use the same one every time if you want. Although this program does 5000 backward iterations, it throws out the first 100 points so the early transient behavior of the backwards orbit is not recorded. The final image contains only points that are close to the Julia Set.

Program – JULIA2	Purpose
ClrHome	
ClrDraw	
FnOff	
Radian	
a+bi	
AxesOff	
-2→Xmin	
2→Xmax	
0→Xscl	
-2→Ymin	
2→Ymax	
0→Yscl	
Input "PARAMETER? ",C	
Input "SEED? ",Z	
ClrHome	
For(J,1,5000,1)	
abs(Z-C)→M	Modulus of (point minus parameter)
angle(Z-C)→A	Angle of (point minus parameter)
A/2+int(2*rand)*π→θ	Angle of one of the square roots, chosen at random
√(M)→R	Modulus of square root
Rcos(θ)→U	Real part of square root
Rsin(θ)→V	Imaginary part of square root
If J≤100	Ignores first 100 iterations
Goto 1	
Pt-On(U,V)	Plots points after 100th iteration
U+Vi→Z	Old square root becomes new z for next iteration
Lbl 1	
End	

Figure 6.13

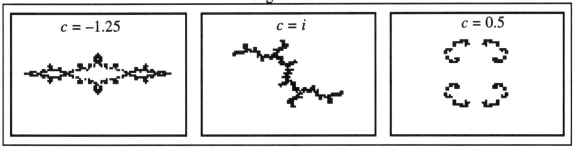

The results of JULIA2 for the parameters $c = -1.25$, $c = i$, and $c = 0.5$ are shown in Figure 6.13. Of course the boundary that we're looking for is a little fuzzy in these images, partly because of the limited resolution available on the TI-83, and partly because the points continually cluster close to the Julia Set, but they are not actually on it.

One final note on JULIA2: This program explicitly utilizes deMoivre's Theorem to solve the equation $z_{new}^2 = z_{old} - c$. The angles of the two square roots differ by π radians or 180°. That means that one square root is the negative of the other. (Not a big surprise.) The TI-83 is programmed to do the work of deMoivre's theorem when you use the square root function (**2nd[√]**) with complex numbers. It automatically selects the square root whose angle is between –90° and +90°. If you wish to, you could rewrite the computation in the iteration using the square root function, choosing randomly between the value returned by **2nd[√]** and its negative.

§3. Exercises

1. Explain why the Julia Set is a repeller.

2. Explain why a repeller becomes an attractor under backward iteration.

3. Find two preimages of w under the function $f(z) = z^2 + c$, given the indicated parameter. Express your answers in polar form:

a) $w = 2 + 3i,\ c = -1$ b) $w = 0,\ c = i$ c) $w = 1,\ c = -i\sqrt{3}$

4. The Julia Sets in Figure 6.13 ($c = -1.25$, $c = i$, and $c = 0.5$) have some similarities and some differences in their appearance.
a) How is the first one different from the other two?
b) How is the last one different from the first two?

Use JULIA2 to graph the Julia Sets for the quadratic function with the parameters given in Exercises 5-16. Save up to 10 of these images for use in Exercise 1 of the next section. (After a graph has been drawn, press **2nd[DRAW] > > STO 1:StorePic**, then **VARS 4.Picture... 1:Pic1** (for example), and finally **ENTER**.

5. $c = .2$	6. $c = -.4 + .8i$	7. $c = .48 + .48i$
8. $c = -i$	9. $c = .28 + .53i$	10. $c = 1.5i$
11. $c = -1.5 + .2i$	12. $c = -.11 + .86i$	13. $c = -.5 + .57i$
14. $c = -.1 + .75i$	15. $c = -1.32$	16. $c = -.4 + .4i$

Exercises 17-23 are a further exploration of those points that lie on the Julia Sets, specifically the repelling fixed points.

17. Write a program to solve the quadratic equation $z^2 - z + c = 0$ where c is complex and use it to find the fixed points of the function $f(z) = z^2 + c$ for the following parameters. Determine in each case whether the points are attracting or repelling:

a) $c = i$ b) $c = -0.4 + 0.4i$ c) $c = 0.2 - 0.8i$ d) $c = -0.2 - 0.6i$

18. The repelling points you discovered in Exercise 17 must lie on the Julia Set for that function. (Why?) If you trace their orbits with CPXORBIT, what happens? Explain.

19. A set is called *invariant* under a function f if for every number z in the set, $f(z)$ is also in the set. Show that the unit circle is invariant under the function $f(z) = z^2$.

20. Explain why every Julia Set is invariant under the generating function.

§4. Properties of Julia Sets

Look again at the three Julia Sets in Figure 6.13.

Figure 6.13

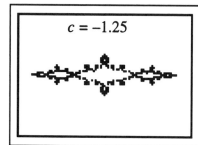 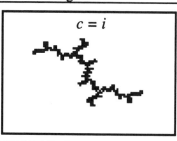 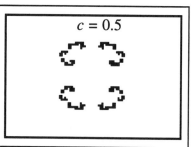

There are several aspects of these graphs worth noting:

- When $c = -1.25$, the Julia Set has an inside and an outside, just as did the unit circle. In this case also, there is a Prisoner Set inside and an Escaping Set outside. The Julia Set forms a continuous boundary between the two.

- When $c = i$, the Julia Set is a single continuous path, but the ends are not attached so there is no inside. In fact, there are no Prisoner Points in this case; there are Julia Points along the path and Escaping Points everywhere else.

- When $c = 0.5$, there are clearly four separate parts to the Julia Set. Again there is no inside, but this time the path itself has holes in it; it is not continuous.

To understand better what is going on in these Julia Sets, you could start by zooming in on one of the graphs, say $c = 0.5$. For example, magnify the upper right portion of the image by modifying JULIA2 as in Figure 6.14. You will see the image in figure 6.15.

Figure 6.14

```
:0→Xmin
:1.5→Xmax
:0→Ymin
:1.5→Ymax
```

There are two important things to note in this picture: 1) There is a strong hint of self-similarity, and 2) there are more holes than we saw before. We'll look at each of these ideas in a little more detail.

Figure 6.15

Self-similarity of Julia Sets

One way to pursue the hint of self similarity is to zoom in again on Figure 6.15. For example, change Xmin and Ymin to 0.6, Xmax and Ymax to 0.9, and the number of iterations to 8000, and you'll see the image in Figure 6.16.

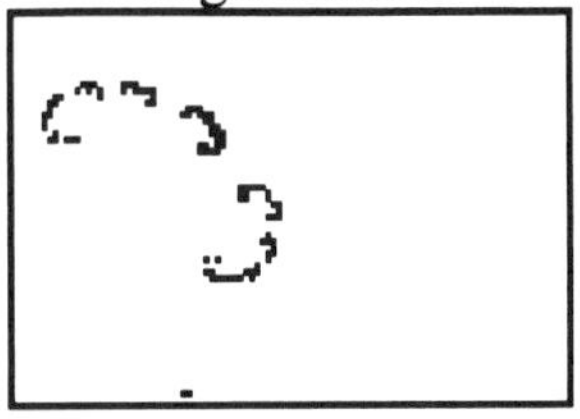

The self-similarity is even more clear. While it is not strictly self-similar, you can certainly see small reproductions of one of the four main sections as you zoom in deeper and deeper into this Julia Set. In the Exercises, you'll find ways to pursue this investigation a little further to convince yourself that Julia Sets are indeed self-similar.

Figure 6.16

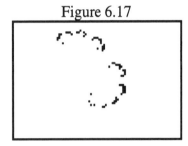

Peitgen (1992) describes the self-similarity of Julia Sets as follows:

> Take any small section of the Julia set, e.g., intersect a small disk with the Julia set and assume that this intersection is not empty. Then we apply the iteration $z \rightarrow z^2 + c$ to every point in this set. We obtain a new, typically larger, subset of the Julia set. Iterating this procedure a *finite* number of times will result in the complete Julia set! This says that the immensely complicated global structure of the Julia set is already contained in any arbitrarily small section of it.

Connected and Disconnected Sets

In addition to a deeper level of self-similarity, each of the magnifications of the Julia Set with parameter 0.5 revealed more holes. Figure 6.17 shows the picture for $c = 0.5$, with the window narrowed again (0.68-0.73 for the x's and 0.78-0.83 for the y's), and the number of iterations raised to 10,000. You can see that the holes are still there.

Figure 6.17

What is surprising about the Julia Set for $c = 0.5$ is the extent of disconnection. Each time we magnify, we see more holes. You can imagine that if this is kept up, we will never see a curve without holes. Do you see what that means? There is *NO connected arc* in the curve! The Julia Set for 0.5 is a set of disconnected points, no one of which is right up next to its neighbor. It is fractal dust, like the Cantor Set on the real line. It consists of isolated points, containing no intervals, no connected subsets.

This type of set is called *totally disconnected*. According to Peitgen (1993, pp. 803-804), "A set is called *connected* if it cannot be decomposed into two disjoint, non-empty subsets ... On the other hand, a set which is not connected can be decomposed into disjoint parts. In particular, a set is called *totally disconnected* provided its connected components ... are single points."

It turns out that there are two types of Julia Sets: connected ones and totally disconnected ones. *Nothing in between.* No partially connected sets. No Julia Sets with a lot of little connected pieces. It's either one connected curve or else it's fractal dust. This quality is called the *structural dichotomy of Julia Sets* in the complex plane.

How can you tell which you've got? One way is to conduct a calculator or computer experiment, plunging deep into the magnification of Julia Sets. These experiments will reveal a surprising fact: The behavior of the orbit of one seed, 0 for the quadratic function, tells what the Julia Set looks like:

- When the orbit of 0 escapes to infinity, the Julia Set of $f(z) = z^2 + c$ is totally disconnected.

- When the orbit of 0 does not escape, the Julia Set of $f(z) = z^2 + c$ is connected.

Example 1. Use the program CPXORBIT to trace the orbit of 0 under iteration by the quadratic function with $c = 0.2 - 0.8i$. Use JULIA2 to graph the Julia Set for $c = 0.2 - 0.8i$ and observe that it is not connected.

Solution: You should obtain the following orbit (if you round decimals to 4 places):

$$0 \to 0.2 - 0.8i \to -0.4 - 1.12i \to -0.8944 + 0.096i \to 0.9907 - 0.9717i \to 0.2373 - 2.7254i \to \cdots$$

At this point, the orbit is outside a circle of radius 2, so we know it is heading off to infinity. Check a few more points if you like, and you have:

Figure 6.18

$$\cdots \to -7.1717 - 2.0935i \to 47.2508 + 29.2285i \to 1378.5326 + 2761.3481i.$$

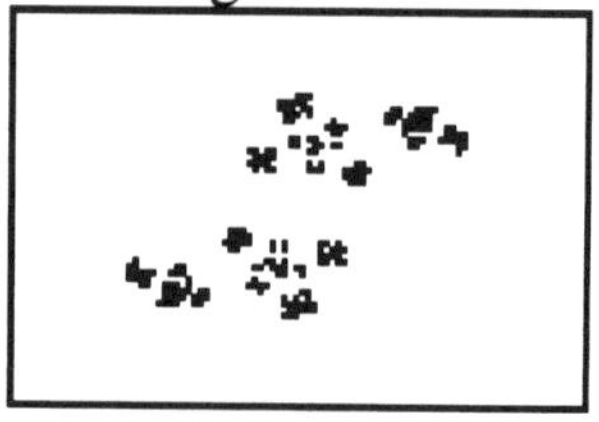

This orbit escapes. Figure 6.18 shows the graph drawn by JULIA2. While it is hard to see that this set is totally disconnected, it is clear that it is not connected; and we know from the structural dichotomy principle that it must be totally disconnected.

Computer Exploration of Julia Sets

We have pushed the TI-83 to its limits. It takes a lot of patience to wait for pixels to appear as we zoom in on a Julia Set. The pixels themselves are not fine enough and our patience probably not adequate to deepen this exploration. At this point we need the power of a computer. This text will assume a PC as equipment with Windows and WINFEED (Parris, 1997) as software.

For instance, using WINFEED for Example 1, we would open the program, select Example, and then select Julia set. The program uses a random parameter to automatically draw a Julia Set in color. Prisoner Points are colored black; Escaping Points are given other colors according to the length of time they remain inside the "infinite threshold" (the radius beyond which it is assumed that orbits are attracted to infinity, the default being 2). Thus the default image is of a filled Julia Set, the white background replaced by colors coded by escape time. The critical orbit of 0 is also displayed in white. To turn off the critical orbit, select Orbit and uncheck Overlay orbit. To draw the Julia Set with the parameter $c = 0.2 - 0.8i$, select Adjust and then Julia constant... In the dialog box, enter the new parameter by changing the real part to $a = 0.2$ and the imaginary part to $b = -0.8$. Then select Draw to plot a Julia Set with the new parameter. Figure 6.19 shows a black and white image of what you would see in color on the computer screen.

Figure 6.19

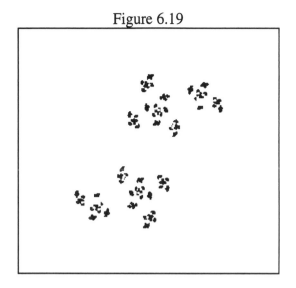

If the Overlay orbit option is left checked, you will also see a few white dots heading off the screen, indicating the escaping orbit of 0. A more graphic way to check an orbit is to specify a seed with the mouse or the keyboard, and then move the orbit forward by pressing the space bar. For this example, the most accurate way to specify the seed is by keyboard, so select Orbit and then Keyboard start... In the dialogue box, enter $x = 0$ and $y = 0$ as the real and imaginary parts of the seed. When you click OK, you see a little square indicating the seed at the origin. Press the space bar and you see the second point of the orbit with its coordinates displayed at the top of the frame. If you continue pressing the space bar, you can watch the orbit evolve until it leaves the infinite threshold. Then the point indicator disappears from the screen and no coordinates are displayed. To see the coordinates of the entire orbit, however,

Figure 6.20

0.	0.000000	0.000000
1.	0.200000	-0.800000
2.	-0.400000	-1.120000
3.	-0.894400	0.096000
4.	0.990735	-0.971724

you can select Orbit and then Display coords... You will see the real and imaginary parts of the points traced out by the orbit as long as it remains within the infinite threshold, points z_0 through z_4 for this parameter. (See Figure 6.20.)

Example 2. Use WINFEED to explore the Julia Set for $c = -0.32 + 0.62i$.

Solution: First adjust the Julia constant for the new parameter, $a = -0.32, b = 0.62$, and select Draw. You will see a colored image, the black part of which is shown in Figure 6.21. Notice this is a filled Julia Set with Prisoner Points. Therefore, there *is* an attractor, and the orbit of 0 will find it. Select Orbit and then Keyboard start...; in the dialogue box, specify $x = 0$ and $y = 0$, and click OK. Now when you press the space bar, you see an orbit that stays inside the black area, appearing to cycle through some relatively large number of points. If you select Orbit and then Display coords... after 30 iterations, you will see the orbit shown in Figure 6.22. Can you see a pattern? It isn't obvious, but you can program the mouse to display the period by selecting Click and then checking

<u>P</u>eriod. If you set the arrow on the origin and click the left button of the mouse, you see displayed the coordinates of the point and the period of the orbit. You can move the cursor around while holding down the left button till you get as close to the seed as possible. Seeds close to the origin for this parameter all show a period of 19. Looking again at Figure 6.22, you can see a 19-period already beginning to appear in the first 30 iterations.

Figure 6.21

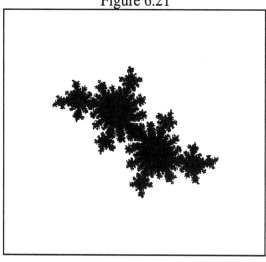

Figure 6.22

0.	0.0000000	0.0000000
1.	−0.3200000	0.6200000
2.	−0.6020000	0.2232000
3.	−0.0074142	0.3512672
4.	−0.4433336	0.6147912
5.	−0.5014235	0.0748846
6.	−0.0741821	0.5449021
7.	−0.6114153	0.5391559
8.	−0.2368604	−0.0392964
9.	−0.2654413	0.6386155
10.	−0.6573707	0.2809701
11.	0.0331920	0.2505970
12.	−0.3816971	0.6366356
13.	−0.5796122	0.1339959
14.	−0.0020045	0.4646685
15.	−0.5359128	0.6181370
16.	−0.4148908	−0.0425352
17.	−0.1496748	0.6552949
18.	−0.7270089	0.4238376
19.	0.0289036	0.0037324
20.	−0.3191785	0.6202157
21.	−0.6027926	0.2240809
22.	−0.0068532	0.3498513
23.	−0.4423489	0.6152047
24.	−0.5028042	0.0757295
25.	−0.0729228	0.5438456
26.	−0.6104503	0.5406824
27.	−0.2396878	−0.0401196
28.	−0.2641593	0.6392323
29.	−0.6588378	0.2822816
30.	0.0343844	0.2480443

WINFEED also does backwards iteration. Select <u>A</u>djust, then <u>D</u>isplay, and then <u>I</u>IM (for Inverse Images) to plot a Julia Set in color on a black background. For a black and white image, also select <u>W</u>hite background. Choosing this option and the parameters of Figure 6.13 results in the images in Figure 6.23.

Figure 6.23

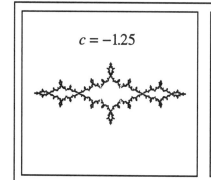

$c = -1.25$

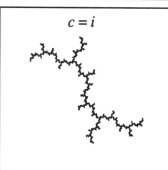

$c = i$

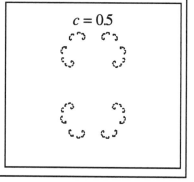

$c = 0.5$

To zoom in on portions of a Julia Set with WINFEED, use the mouse to place the arrow at some point of the image and click with the right button. A square centered at the arrow point, with sides one-tenth those in the original image, is then blown up to fill the frame. To reduce or increase the magnification factor, select <u>V</u>iew and then <u>F</u>actor, and change the default from 0.1 to your choice. Another way of zooming in is to select <u>V</u>iew and then <u>C</u>en/wid..., opening a dialog box where you can specify the center and width of the region you wish to see. In Figure 6.24 is a series of zooms in on the Julia Set for $c = 0.25 - 0.55i$, with the approximate square of magnification for the next frame indicated in each of the first three frames.

Figure 6.24

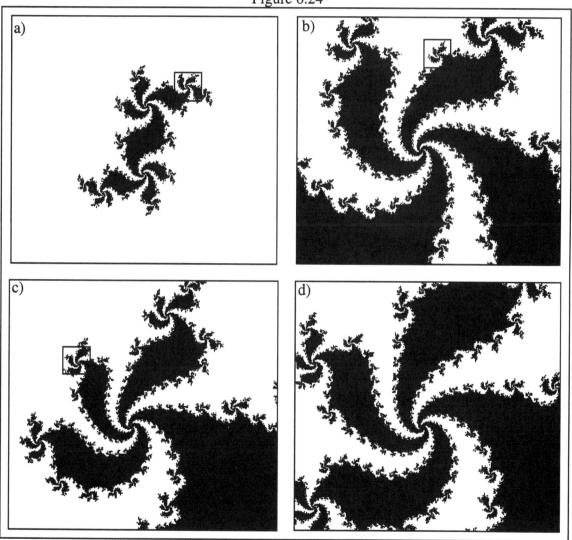

Fractal Properties of Julia Sets

Several fractal properties are evident in these calculator and computer images of Julia Sets. Recall the five properties of fractals presented in §2.1: 1) Fine structure is

evident in the magnifications of Julia Sets which show detail on arbitrarily small scales.
2) Since Julia Sets are defined by iterating $f(z) = z^2 + c$, they are the result of a
recursive process. 3) While something similar to spirals and circles are sometimes visible
in Julia Sets, they are in general too irregular to be described in traditional geometric
language. 4) Self-similarity is evident in Figures 6.15, 6.16 and 6.17, and you can see it
again in Figures 6.19 and 6.24. 5) As for their dimension, the infinitely complex patterns
of boundaries and disconnected points indicate that we are indeed dealing with fractal
dimension. Because they are not strictly self similar, however, we cannot apply the
formula $D = \dfrac{\log n}{\log r}$, and even boxcounting is difficult. Though WINFEED can help, it is
not always able to give correct answers (see Exercises 10-12). In truth, the dimension of
Julia Sets is not clearly understood. You might think that someone could have come up
with a formula in terms of the parameter, but it hasn't happened yet. (Remember, the
field is wide open. Maybe this is your Ph.D. topic!) From our knowledge of fractal
dimension, however, we can say that Julia Sets that are connected (such as $c = -1.25$ and
$c = i$) have a dimension somewhere between 1 and 2; those that are not (such as $c = 0.5$)
have a dimension between 0 and 1.

§4 Exercises

1. Use JULIA2 and CPXORBIT to graph Julia Sets and trace the orbit of 0 for the function $f(z) = z^2 + c$ using the given parameters. In each case, tell whether the orbit of 0 escapes or not, and note whether the Julia Set appears connected or disconnected.
a) $c = .2$ 　　　　b) $c = -i$ 　　　　c) $c = -.1 + .75i$ 　　　d) $c = -1.5 + .2i$

2. a) In JULIA2, change the window so that the horizontal axis runs from 0.708 to 0.716 and the vertical from 0.806 to 0.812. Raise the number of iterations to 12000 and run the program for $c = 0.5$.
　　b) Define a new window and number of iterations to zoom in on one of the four pieces of the picture in (a).

3. Determine whether the Julia Sets for the following parameters are connected or totally disconnected.
a) $c = -0.5 + 0.5i$ 　　b) $c = -0.75 + 0.35i$ 　　c) $c = -1.25$ 　　　d) $c = 1 + i$

4. Use WINFEED to explore Julia Sets for the following values of c. Plot the graph and trace the orbit of 0 in each case. Record the behavior of the orbit and the connectedness of the set.
a) $c = -.4 + .8i$ 　　b) $c = .28 + .53i$ 　　c) $c = -1.32$ 　　　d) $c = .48 + .48i$

5. Use WINFEED to explore Julia Sets for the following values of c. What is the graphical result of changing signs of the real and imaginary parts?
a) $c = .11 + .86i$ 　　b) $c = .11 - .86i$ 　　c) $c = -.11 + .86i$ 　　d) $c = -.11 - .86i$

6. Use WINFEED to graph Julia Sets for the following parameters by backwards iteration (Inverse Images). Determine which are connected by tracing the orbit of 0.
a) $c = 1.5i$ 　　　b) $c = -.4 + .4i$ 　　c) $c = -.5 + .57i$ 　　d) $c = -.1 + .9i$

7. Use WINFEED to graph Julia Sets for the parameters $c = -0.36 + 0.62i$, $c = -0.36 + 0.63i$, $c = -0.36 + 0.64i$, and $c = -0.36 + 0.65i$.
a) Does the Julia Set for $c = -0.36 + 0.64i$ appear to be connected or totally disconnected?
b) What happens to the orbit of 0 for $c = -0.36 + 0.64i$?
c) Do other seeds appear to be Prisoner Points? Is this possible?
d) Increase the maximum number off iterations (Adjust, Max reps...) from 100 to 300, and redraw the Julia Set for $c = -0.36 + 0.64i$. What differences do you observe?
e) Draw the Julia Set for $c = -0.36 + 0.64i$ using Inverse Images, and compare the image with the default graph for this parameter. Which do you think is more accurate in this case? Why?

8. Demonstrate the self-similarity of Julia Sets by a series of well-chosen zooms for the following parameters:
$c = i$ 　　　　　$c = 0.3 - 0.2i$ 　　　　$c = 0.2 - 0.55i$ 　　　　$c = -1 + 0.3i$

9. Is the self-similarity of Julia Sets strict or not? Explain.

Exercises 10-12 explore the dimension of Julia Sets using the boxcounting program of WINFEED. Start by opening WINFEED, selecting Example and then Julia set. Erase the orbit of 0 by selecting Orbit and then Overlay orbit. Change to backwards iteration by selecting Display and then IIM. The image must be black on white to be counted correctly, so select Display again and then White background. Now select Draw and stop the iteration at any time by pressing a key on the keyboard. You now have an image that can be analyzed by the boxcounting program. First save it to the clipboard as a bitmap by selecting File and then Bitmap to clipboard. Now open the boxcounting program by selecting from the main window Example and then Box-counting. From the boxcounting window select File, Old, and then Clipboard. (Be sure you select Clipboard from the Old submenu. This imports the image from the clipboard. There is also a Clipboard option in the File menu, but that is for saving images from the boxcounting window to the clipboard.) Now you should have the Julia Set outlined by backward iteration, waiting in the boxcounting window for analysis. Select Boxes and then Calculate. You will see a table with grid size running from $r = 1$ to $r = 128$ in powers of 2, and in the last column ("Hits") the number of boxes, n, containing a portion of the Julia Set. Put these data in the **STAT** lists of your calculator and follow the procedure in §2.3 to compute the boxcount dimension.

10. Use the procedure outlined above with WINFEED and the TI-83 to calculate the boxcount dimension of the Julia Sets with the following parameters:
a) $c = -1.25$ b) $c = 0.5$ c) $c = 0.3 - 0.4i$ d) $c = -0.25 + 0.65i$

11. Do you have doubts about the accuracy of the results of Exercise 10? Explain.

12. Pick a parameter for which you know the Julia Set is totally disconnected.
a) What can you say about its dimension?
b) Use WINFEED and the calculator to do a boxcount dimension on your Julia Set.
c) Are the results of (b) consistent with your answer to (a)? Explain.
d) Try redrawing your Julia Set and stop the iteration quickly. Recompute the boxcount dimension. Any difference from the result in (b)?
e) Zoom in on a portion of your Julia Set and compute its boxcount dimension. Any difference from the results in (b) and (d)?
f) In a few sentences, briefly write up the moral of this story.

§5. The Mandelbrot Set

Probably the most visible icon of Chaos Theory is the Mandelbrot Set. A figure of deep complexity and beauty, it has even made its way into popular culture by way of calendars, tee-shirts and psychedelic posters. Like all great objects of artistic veneration, the Mandelbrot Set combines striking simplicity with intricate detail in an image that is at once life-like and mysterious.

Yet, as we shall see, the Mandelbrot Set is simply a visual catalog. The image contains detailed information about the set of all Julia Sets. That is its function. That such a mundane task should be performed by such a beautiful image is one of the wonders of Chaos Theory.

Definition

Each point c of the Mandelbrot Set is a value of the parameter in the quadratic function $f(z) = z^2 + c$ which yields a connected Julia Set. That's it. That's the complete definition of the Mandelbrot Set. You check each complex number c to see whether the corresponding Julia Set is connected. If so, c is in the Mandelbrot Set; if not, it's not. In the last section you learned that a Julia Set is connected if the orbit of 0 does not escape, and in this section you will use that fact to determine whether a parameter value is in the Mandelbrot Set or not.

Recall that Julia Sets are graphs of *seeds*. If a complex number z is used as a seed in the function $f(z) = z^2 + c$, and the orbit stays on the plane without being attracted to a fixed point or cycle, then z is in the Julia Set, and we colored it black in our programs. In contrast, the Mandelbrot Set is a graph of *parameters*. If the parameter c corresponds to a connected Julia Set, then it is in the Mandelbrot Set and we color it black in the program of this section.

The output of the program will once again be an image in the complex plane, but this time all numbers on the plane represent parameters. We could call it the c-plane. The program will examine every c on (a portion of) the plane and check to see whether the orbit of 0 under $f(z) = z^2 + c$ stays on the plane. If so, the program colors c black; if not, it leaves it white.

As with Julia Sets, the search has to be narrowed down, because there's no way to look at every point on the plane, or even every point on a very big portion of it. It turns out that all parameters in the Mandelbrot Set lie inside the same circle of radius 2 as did the seeds for the Julia Sets, and therefore we can choose a viewing window running from -2 to 2 for the graph. To be convinced of that fact, you need to know that any function $f(z) = z^2 + c$, with a parameter $|c| > 2$, will send the orbit of 0 off to infinity. Here's why: Suppose $|c| > 2$, and start with the seed $z_0 = 0$. After one iteration, the orbit is at

$z_1 = f(0) = c$. Now z_1 satisfies both conditions of the Escape Criterion (§6.2), so we know that the orbit of z_1 escapes. Therefore the orbit of 0 escapes, and consequently the Julia Set corresponding to this parameter is fractal dust. It follows that we need look only at parameters with $|c| \leq 2$.

The Program

By now you can probably write your own program for the Mandelbrot Set, and it will probably look like MANDEL1.

Program – MANDEL1	Purpose
ClrHome	
ClrDraw	
FnOff	
PlotsOff	
a+bi	
-2.3→Xmin	
0.7→Xmax	
0→Xscl	
-1→Ymin	
1→Ymax	
0→Yscl	
AxesOff	
(Xmax-Xmin)/95→S	
(Ymax-Ymin)/63→T	
For(A,Xmin,Xmax,S)	
For(B,0,Ymax,T)	
A+Bi→C	
0→Z	Sets the seed to 0
1→N	Counter for iterations
Lbl 1	
Z²+C→Z	
abs(Z)→R	
If R>2:Goto 2	Iteration loop
IS>(N,30)	
Goto 1	
Pt-On(A,B)	
Pt-On(A,-B)	
Lbl 2	
End	
End	

The window settings in MANDEL1 were chosen to be large enough to contain the entire Mandelbrot Set but as small as possible to preserve detail. The vertical range is two-thirds the horizontal range to compensate for the aspect ratio of the TI-83's screen.

Notice that there's a 2-for-1 deal in this program as there was in the Julia Set programs. After computing the orbit of 0 for $c = a + bi$, both c and its conjugate $\bar{c} = a - bi$ are plotted. This shortcut works because 0 suffers the same fate under both $f(z) = z^2 + c$ and $g(z) = z^2 + \bar{c}$. Here's why: First notice that $g(\bar{z})$ is the conjugate of $f(z)$ because $g(\bar{z}) = \bar{z}^2 + \bar{c} = \overline{z^2} + \bar{c} = \overline{z^2 + c} = \overline{f(z)}$. Therefore:

$$g(0) = \bar{c} = \overline{f(0)}$$
$$^2g(0) = g(\bar{c}) = \overline{f(c)} = \overline{^2f(0)}$$

and in general,

$$^ng(0) = \overline{^nf(0)}.$$

Hence, if 0 escapes under f, then it also escapes under g; and therefore $\bar{c}$ is in the Mandelbrot Set whenever c is.

If you run MANDEL1 on your own calculator, you will see an image like the one in Figure 6.25.

Figure 6.25

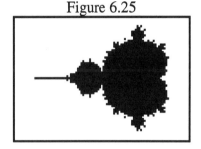

In order to explore this image later, save it by pressing **2nd[DRAW] > > STO 1:StorePic VARS 4:Picture...1:Pic1** (or one of the other picture storage options). At the same time, save the window settings by doing the same procedure, but choosing **3. GDB** (Graph DataBase) from the **VARS** key.

Figure 6.26

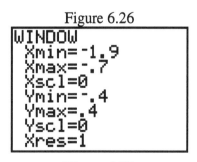

Even though the resolution on the screen of the TI-83 permits only a rough approximation of the Mandelbrot Set, you can still get a sense of some of its intricacy. It is clear that there is a main section that is roughly heart-shaped with various decorations around its circumference. To the left there is a "head" with a long "nose" pointing off the screen. You can zoom in on the head by changing the window as in Figure 6.26, and you would see the image in Figure 6.27. (You should modify your program, run it and save the image and its window settings.)

Figure 6.27

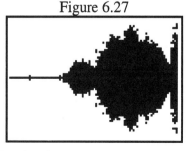

Some self-similarity emerges through magnification. The "head" also has a "head" and is decorated with bulbs around its perimeter. You can also see some dots around the exterior which hint at even deeper intricacies than we have yet seen. Once again, we are pushing the limits of the TI-83 and turn to the computer.

Figure 6.28

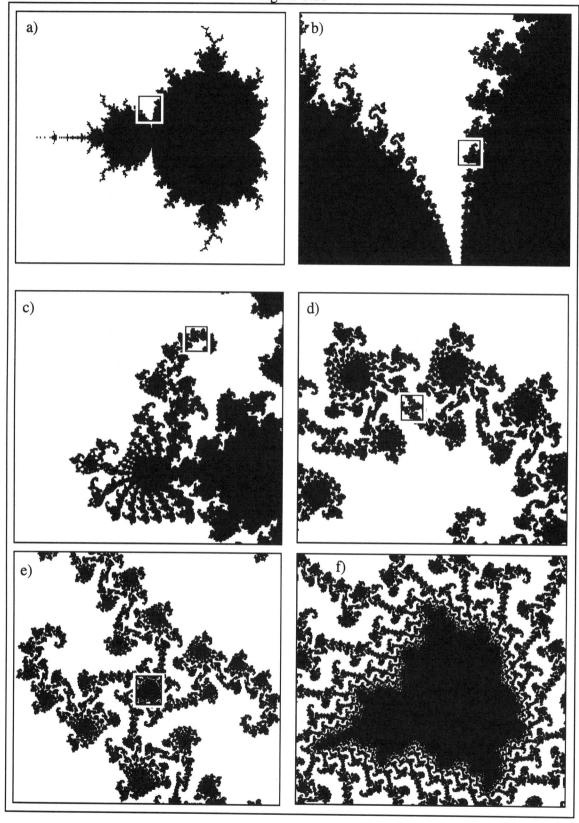

Figure 6.28 was made with WINFEED by opening the program, selecting
Example, and then Mandelbrot set. The program automatically draws in color the image
of Figure 6.28(a). Once again, the colors represent escape times for the orbit of 0, and
black represents those parameters for which the orbit of 0 does not escape. Figures
6.28(b)-(f) are successive zooms, made, as in the Julia Sets, by clicking the right mouse
button with the arrow at the center of the square to be magnified.

Mandelbrot and Feigenbaum

It may have occurred to you that the Mandelbrot Set is similar to the Feigenbaum
plot, because both explore the effect of changing parameters in an iterated function. For
the quadratic function, the Feigenbaum plot graphs the (real) parameter c horizontally,
with the eventual outcome of the orbit of 0 vertically. The Mandelbrot Set consists of
parameters only, because it deals with *complex* parameters and therefore requires both
horizontal and vertical coordinates for each c. The Feigenbaum plot contains information
about the eventual behavior of the orbit of 0 in the real case, whereas the Mandelbrot Set
only indicates whether the orbit of 0 is bounded. In the Mandelbrot Set, the real c's are on
the horizontal axis, running from −2 at the tip of the nose on the left to 0.25 in the cusp
on the right. Recall that this interval corresponds to the horizontal axis for the
Feigenbaum plot of the real quadratic function.

Figure 6.29

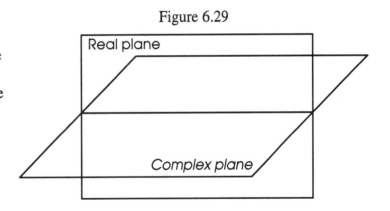

You can think of the
complex plane lying
horizontally and the real plane
intersecting it at right angles
along the real axis as in Figure
6.29. Now think of the
Mandelbrot Set lying flat in
the complex plane and the
Feigenbaum plot drawn
vertically in the real plane.
For the quadratic, the
Feigenbaum plot has a domain of [−2, 0.25] and a range of [−2,2]. So the Feigenbaum
plot would rise up out of (and sink below) the center of Mandelbrot set. Figure 6.30
shows how the two graphs fit together.

Notice in Figure 6.30 that the periodic behavior indicated in the Feigenbaum plot
corresponds exactly to the bulbs of the Mandelbrot Set as you go along the axis from the
"body" through the "head" and "nose." Moving from right to left along the real axis, you
have c running from 0.25 to −0.75, where the Feigenbaum plot shows a single fixed point
for the orbit of 0. The juncture of head and body in the Mandelbrot Set is at −0.75 where
the Feigenbaum Plot bifurcates, indicating the orbit of 0 is attracted to a 2-cycle. That
situation obtains until $c = -1.25$, where the head joins the nose and the Feigenbaum Plot
bifurcates a second time. The region of chaos begins at the needle coming out of the

Mandelbrot nose, and the windows of order are reflected in the decorations on the needle. In particular, note where the 3-cycle window appears and what shows up at the same point in the Mandelbrot Set. You will have an opportunity to explore this connection in more depth in the Exercises.

Figure 6.30

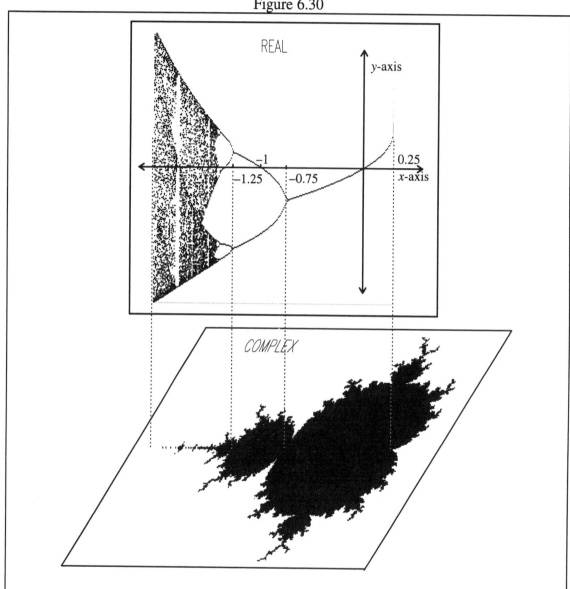

§5. Exercises

1. The following points are all chosen from the heart-shaped body of the Mandelbrot Set. Use CPXORBIT to verify that the orbit of 0 with these parameters does not escape.
a) $c = -0.1 + 0.6i$ b) $c = -0.5 - 0.4i$ c) $c = -0.6 - 0.3i$ d) $c = 0.1 + 0.2i$

2. Describe the eventual behavior of the orbits in Exercise 1. What do they appear to have in common?

3. The following points are all chosen from the circular head of the Mandelbrot Set. Use CPXORBIT to verify that the orbit of 0 with these parameters do not escape.
a) $c = -1 + 0.2i$ b) $c = -0.9 - 0.15i$ c) $c = -1.2 - 0.05i$ d) $c = -1.1 + 0.2i$

4. Describe the eventual behavior of the orbits in Exercise 3. What do they have in common?

5. Pick three points in the main decoration at the north end of the Mandelbrot Set (the "arm"). Describe the eventual behavior of the orbit of 0 under these parameters.

6. In Figure 6.27, there is a "pimple" about two-thirds of the way out the nose of the Mandelbrot Set that corresponds to the 3-cycle window of the Feigenbaum plot. Magnify this area by setting the window's horizontal range to run from –1.795 to –1.720 and the vertical range to run from –0.025 to 0.025. What image do you see? In what further way does it correspond to the Feigenbaum plot in this window? Save this image and its window settings.

7. In the graph of Exercise 6, there is a dot that appears free-floating at the top center of the screen. Your cursor will give its coordinates as $x = -1.261702$, $y = .38709677$. Modify MANDEL1 to zoom in on this dot as follows:
a) Set the horizontal range to [–1.262, –1.250] and the vertical range to [0.377, 0.385]. Notice that this screen is no longer symmetric about the real axis, so you can't plot both c and $\bar{c}$ to cut down the running time. You have to look at every point $c = a + bi$, with $0.377 \leq b \leq 0.385$, and plot one point at a time. At this level of magnification, parameters where 0 escapes are very close to those where 0 is a prisoner. In order to make finer boundaries, modify the program again by raising the number of iterations from 30 to at least 60. Run MANDEL1 with these modifications. [Warning: This program will take several hours to run; let it run overnight.]
b) Place your cursor in the center of the image you get in (a) and note the coordinates of the parameter. Use this parameter in CPXORBIT with a seed of 0 to determine what type of attracting cycle occurs here.

8. Describe the self-similarity you see in Figure 6.28.

9. Use WINFEED to do a series of zooms into the Mandelbrot Set. Referring to the five fractal properties given in §2.1, would you say that the Mandelbrot Set is a fractal? Explain, using evidence from your zooms.

10. WINFEED gives a dynamic feeling to a series of zooms using a kind of slide show. To do the zoom of Figure 6.28, for instance, select Example, then Mandelbrot set. Because Figure 6.28 goes so deep into the Mandelbrot Set, the results are rough unless a large number of iterations are investigated before deciding whether or not an orbit stays on the plane. In the Mandelbrot menu, select Adjust and then Max reps... to bring up a dialog box where you can specify, say, 1200 iterations. Then select Misc and then Mandelbrot zoom... to bring up another dialog box where you can specify the center, the magnification factor, and the number of slides of your zoom series. For Figure 6.28, the center is $x = -0.73495$ and $y = 0.19705$, and the zoom factor is 0.5 with 16 as the number of slides.

a) Using the information as given, create a slide show for Figure 6.28.
b) Create a slide show to zoom in on the "pimple" on the Mandelbrot nose.
c) Create a slide show to zoom in on one of the decorations around the body of the Mandelbrot Set. For example, use as a center $x = -0.64386$ and $y = 0.450948$.

§6. Properties of the Mandelbrot Set

You know that the Mandelbrot Set is a record of the parameters c which insure that the orbit of 0 is bounded. This is equivalent to saying the Mandelbrot Set consists of those parameters which have a connected Julia Set. Simple. Yet the Mandelbrot Set is extraordinarily complex, a veritable treasure of information, of which we will glimpse a few gems.

You have observed that there are clearly distinguishable parts of the Mandelbrot Set (as well as others not so clearly distinguishable). For instance, there's the main body, looking like a rounded heart on its side, a *cardiod*. Then there's a circular head to the left of the main body, and another circular nose to the left of the head. Decorating the circumference of all of these parts are bulbs of various shapes, all embellished with decorations of their own. Figure 6.28 showed the extraordinary complexity of these decorations under magnification, with mini-Mandelbrots hidden deep inside the fillagree. It turns out that each of these bulbs contains more special information about the orbit of 0 and the associated Julia Set.

Exploring the Bulbs with the TI-83

If you did Exercises 1-5 of the last section, you have already used the calculator to uncover some of the information contained in the separate parts of the Mandelbrot Set. In this section, you will deepen your exploration using WINFEED as well as the calculator. The plan is to pick parameters from the Mandelbrot Set, and for each one to investigate both the orbit of 0 and the shape of the Julia Set. If the parameter comes from inside the Mandelbrot Set, we already know that the orbit of 0 is bounded and that the Julia Set is connected. The question is, what other information does the particular location of the point in the Mandelbrot Set tell us about the orbit of 0 and about the shape of the Julia Set?

The calculator exploration requires three programs, one to pick a parameter, a second to trace the orbit of 0 with that parameter, and a third to draw the Julia Set for that parameter. The first program, MANPARAM, uses the Mandelbrot images that you have already stored, along with their associated window settings. It will permit you to place your cursor in any part of the Mandelbrot Set to specify a parameter. The second program, MANORBIT, will trace the orbit of 0 using the parameter under your cursor. The third program, MANJULIA, will draw the Julia Set corresponding to this parameter. First run MANPARAM to bring a Mandelbrot image to your screen. Then use the cursor arrows to pick the parameter you wish to investigate. You will see a flashing pixel and the coordinates of the point. Then press **2nd[QUIT]** to return to the home screen, and run MANORBIT. (This program is a modification of CPXORBIT, designed to stop after 100 iterations. If you want to interrupt the program and not complete all 100 iterations, press **ON** as you did to terminate CPXORBIT.) Finally, run MANJULIA to see an image of the Julia Set for this parameter plotted by backwards iteration.

MANPARAM	MANORBIT	MANJULIA
Full ClrDraw FnOff PlotsOff RecallGDB GDB1 RecallPic Pic1	a+bi X+Yi→C PlotsOff FnOff ClrHome ClrDraw Horiz -3.9→Xmin 3.9→Xmax 1→Xscl -1.3→Ymin 1.3→Ymax 1→Yscl 0→Z AxesOn For(J,1,100,1) real(Z)→U imag(Z)→V Pt-On(U,V) Disp Z Disp " " Pause Z²+C→Z If abs(Z)>4 Then Disp "INFINITY" 101→J End End	a+bi 0→Z ClrHome ClrDraw FnOff Full Radian AxesOff -2→Xmin 2→Xmax 0→Xscl -2→Ymin 2→Ymax 0→Yscl ClrHome For(J,1,1000,1) abs(Z-C)→R angle(Z-C)→θ θ/2+int(2*rand)*π→θ √(R)→R Rcos(θ)→U Rsin(θ)→V If J≤50 Goto 1 Pt-On(U,V) U+Vi→Z Lbl 1 End

A run of these three programs, with a parameter chosen from the main body of the Mandelbrot Set, resulted in the screens shown in Figure 6.31. (Because the 100th point of the orbit had too many digits to fit on the screen, there are two screens from the run of MANORBIT to show both the real and imaginary parts.) The orbit of 0 is attracted to a fixed point, and the Julia Set appears to be a simple connected closed curve.

Figure 6.31

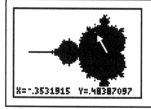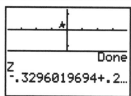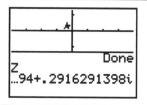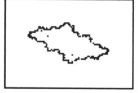

In Figure 6.32, the results of another run of the three programs is shown, this time with a parameter chosen from the head of the Mandelbrot Set. The orbit of 0 appears to be attracted to a two cycle, and the Julia Set seems pinched together in several spots, with two regions radiating out from each pinch.

Figure 6.32

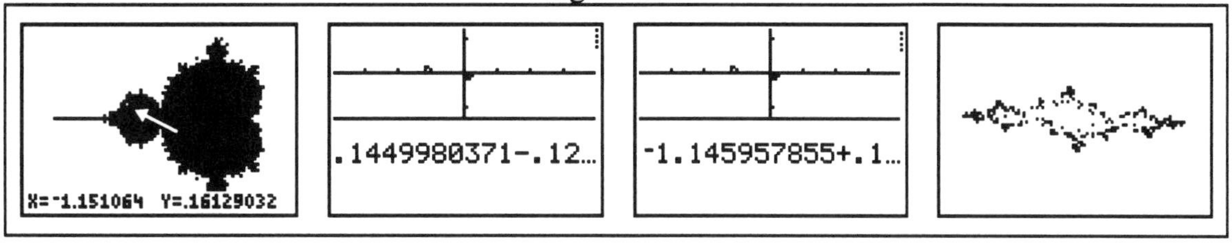

If you run these programs with other points in the main body, you will discover that all the orbits of 0 are attracted to a fixed point, and the Julia Sets resemble the one in Figure 6.31. With any point from the head, the orbits of 0 are attracted to a 2-cycle, and the Julia Sets resemble that in Figure 6.32. The limitations of the calculator make it difficult to deepen this investigation, however, so we turn once again to WINFEED and the computer.

Exploring the Bulbs with WINFEED

When you open WINFEED, select Example and then Mandelbrot set. The Mandelbrot Set is automatically drawn in color. A black pixel represents a parameter for which the orbit of 0 does not escape; a colored pixel represents a parameter for which the orbit of 0 *does* escape, and the different colors stand for the different number of iterations before the orbit crosses the threshold to infinity.

As a first step in your investigation, place the arrow cursor somewhere within the Mandelbrot Set, and click and hold the left button. Alongside the Mandelbrot Set, you see another image, the Julia Set corresponding to the parameter you have clicked on. The Julia Set is formed by backwards iteration, and the image includes the orbit of 0 (in white dots), the parameter (a blue dot), and the fixed points for this parameter (the red dots). If you clicked on a parameter in the main body of the Mandelbrot Set, you'd see a Julia Set with the white orbit of 0 attracted to one of the red fixed points.

The Julia image stays on the screen as long as you hold down the left button. If you continue to hold the left button and move the mouse to drag the cursor around the Mandelbrot Set, you see the Julia Set changing with the different parameters which are indicated at the top of the Julia screen. The exercises suggest routes of exploration using this kind of tour of the Mandelbrot Set.

Another way to explore the properties of the Mandelbrot Set is by reprogramming the mouse so that a left click on a point of the set produces a colored Julia Set for this parameter and also indicates the period of the attractor. You can do this by selecting Click and then Julia child. Now when you click on a point in the Mandelbrot Set, the corresponding filled Julia Set is drawn in color, and the period of the attractor is indicated at the top of the screen.

Example 1. Use WINFEED to pick a parameter from the large bulb on north end of the Mandelbrot Set, to draw the corresponding Julia Set and to compute the period of the attractor.

Solution: Figure 6.33 shows a black-and-white version of what you would see when you click and hold the left button at (approximately) $c = -0.14 + 0.76i$, shown by the little white square in the Mandelbrot Set.

Figure 6.33

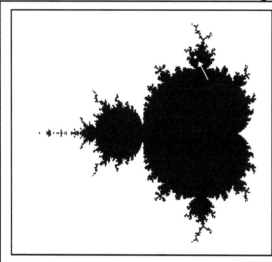 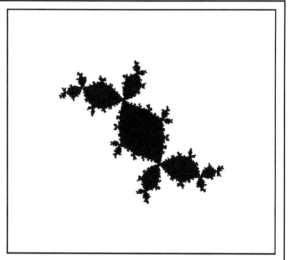

The Julia frame in Example 1 carries a message indicating that the period of the attractor for this parameter is 3. Notice that the number 3 is also reflected in the shape of the Julia Set: 3 black regions come together at all the junction points. The next example explores these properties in another bulb of the Mandelbrot Set.

Example 2. Pick a parameter from the next largest bulb to the right of the top bulb, draw its Julia Set and note the period of the attractor.

Solution: Figure 6.34 (next page) shows the point selected ($c \approx 0.27 + .55i$) and the resulting Julia Set. The period of the attractor is 4 and the Julia Set shows 4 regions joined at the juncture point.

While two examples do not a theory make, you may wonder if there are some patterns developing here. There are, and the exercises suggest ways to explore them. The exploration requires a computer with WINFEED. Otherwise you can see the exploration done on a video called *Professor Devaney Explains The Fractal Geometry of the Mandelbrot Set* (Devaney, 1996). In either case, you will find numerical patterns of a simplicity, complexity and mystery to match the visual patterns in the remarkable Mandelbrot Set.

Figure 6.34

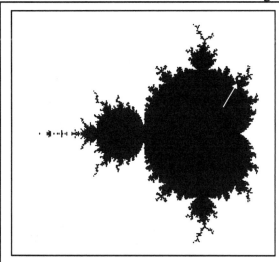

§6. Exercises

1. Use your image of the main Mandelbrot Set in MANPARAM and run MANORBIT to verify the following results:
a) When the parameter is chosen from the head, the orbit of 0 is attracted to a 2-cycle.
b) When the parameter is chosen from the arm at the north, the orbit of 0 is attracted to a 3-cycle.
c) When the parameter is chosen from the arm at the south, the orbit of 0 is attracted to a 3-cycle.

2. Use your magnification of the head to verify that:
a) When the parameter is chosen from the head, the orbit of 0 is attracted to a 2-cycle.
b) When the parameter is chosen from the nose, the orbit of 0 is attracted to a 4-cycle.

3. Use your magnification of the "pimple" in Exercise 6 of the last section to verify that:
a) For parameters chosen from the body of this mini-Mandelbrot, the attractor is a 3-cycle.
b) For parameters chosen from the head of this mini-Mandelbrot, the attractor is a 6-cycle.

4. Explore the mini-Mandelbrot you discovered in Exercise 7 of the last section. What is the behavior of the orbit of 0 with a parameter chosen form the main body? From the head?

The remaining exercises use WINFEED to investigate the Mandelbrot Set. With WINFEED running, select Example and then Mandelbrot set. In Exercises 5-8, use the method of Examples 1 and 2 to draw Julia Sets corresponding to selected parameters from the Mandelbrot Set. Select Click and then Julia child to program the left button of the mouse.

5. Select three more parameters from the north bulb (Figure 6.33). In each case, note the period of the attractor and the shape of the Julia Set shown in the Julia frame. Do the results agree with Example 1?

6. Select three more parameters from the next largest bulb to the right of the top bulb (Figure 6.34). In each case, note the period of the attractor and the shape of the Julia Set shown in the Julia frame. Do the results agree with Example 2?

7. From the 3-bulb at the north, continue in a clockwise direction around the exterior of the Mandelbrot Set, each time picking a parameter in the next largest bulb. [It helps to blow up the northeast quadrant of the Mandelbrot set for this investigation. Select View and then Cen/Wid... In the dialog box you can define a new viewing screen by specifying its center and width. A good first choice is to place the center at $0.2 + 0.3i$ (by setting

hor = 0.2 and *ver* = 0.3), and use a width of 0.8 (by setting *wid* = 0.8)]. Write a sentence or two to report what you discover.

8. In a similar manner, investigate the periods of five bulbs going in a counterclockwise direction from the period-3 bulb at the north, each time selecting the next largest bulb to the left. What pattern do you find?

Exercises 9-11 explore the periods of the decorations around the period-7 bulb from Exercise 7. Select Click and then Period.

9. To magnify the period-7 bulb and its antennae, select View and then Cen/wid... to redefine the viewing window. Use *hor* = 0.385, *ver* = 0.145, and *wid* = 0.04. From the Adjust menu, set Max reps to 500.
a) Verify that the period in the main body of this bulb is indeed 7.
b) There is a bulb attached to the period 7 bulb in the southeast quadrant, resembling the head attached to the main body of the Mandelbrot Set. Make a conjecture about its period and verify your conjecture.
c) There is a nose on the head. Guess its period and confirm.
d) There is a needle pointing southeast out of the nose, and a black pimple about half way to the antennae juncture. Guess the period in the pimple and confirm.
e) Notice the number of antennae joined at the junctures.

10. Starting from the head at the southeast of the period-7 bulb, and moving in a counterclockwise direction, locate the next largest bulb around the outside of the main body of the period-7 bulb.
a) Guess the period in the main body of this bulb and verify.
b) Guess the period in the head of this bulb and verify. (Magnify the bulb and increase Max reps to 800.)

11. Starting from the bulb of Exercise 10, continue moving in a counterclockwise direction around the outside of the period-7 bulb. Explore three more bulbs, selecting the next largest at each step. In each case guess and verify the period of the main body of these decorator bulbs.

Exercises 12-19 are an exploration of the Mandelbrot Set using the "tour," the default setting for the left mouse button. Select Click and then Tour. Place your cursor on a point in the Mandelbrot Set and click the left button. In a side window, you will see the Julia Set corresponding to the parameter under your cursor, plotted by backwards iteration. Recall that the parameter is also shown as a blue dot, the fixed points as red dots, and the trace of the orbit of 0 as white dots. As you hold down the left button and move the cursor around, the tour window changes to reflect the new parameter chosen.

12. Put your cursor inside the main body of the Mandelbrot Set. As you drag your cursor around the main body, the shape of the Julia Set changes, but the blue dot always has a white dot in it. Why?

13. Whenever your cursor is in the main body of the Mandelbrot Set, the white dots seem to cluster around and even cover one of the red dots. Sometimes the white dots spiral in on the red dot and sometimes the red dot is completely obliterated by a region of white dots. Why?

14. Put your cursor at 0. Note where the fixed points and parameter are. Now drag your cursor along the x-axis till it exits the Mandelbrot Set at the right (at $c = 0.25$). Watch the Julia Set "explode." Explain what is going on.

15. Start at 0 and drag your cursor to the left along the x-axis. When the cursor reaches the head, note the shape of the Julia Set, the position of the two fixed points, and the eventual fate of the orbit of 0. What is the period of the orbit of 0 here and how is that reflected in the image you see?

16. Continue on into the nose. What is the period of the orbit of 0 here and how is that reflected in the image you see?

17. Start in the main body of the Mandelbrot Set and drag your cursor north into the 3-bulb. Move around and then in and out of the 3-bulb, and observe the changes in the behavior of the orbit of 0. Note how the rabbit shape of the Julia Set reflects the 3-cycle of the orbit of 0 when the cursor is in the 3-bulb.

18. Repeat the exploration of Exercise 17 in the 4-bulb to the right of the 3-bulb.

19. When your cursor is in one of the decorative bulbs of the main body, the red dot does not contain a white dot. Why not?

Chapter 7

THE MATHEMATICS OF CHAOS

§1. Differentiation

The attraction properties of fixed points depend on the slope of the tangent to $y = f(x)$ at its intersection with $y = x$. You know that the slope of the tangent to the function f at the point x is called the derivative of f at x and is denoted $f'(x)$. But so far, unless you have had a course in the calculus, your only means of finding this slope was numerically, using your calculator. The purpose of this section is to develop techniques of deriving a formula for $f'(x)$ from the formula for $f(x)$. This will allow you to make more general statements about the attraction properties of some of the functions we have considered in this course.

The Derivative Function

In calculus, you learn the definition of derivative, and you learn techniques to find the derivative of many different functions. While the development of a general definition is beyond the scope of this course, it is not hard to learn the techniques that work with simple polynomials such as the logistic function and the quadratic function.

The process of transforming the formula for $f(x)$ into the formula for $f'(x)$ is called *differentiation*. To differentiate polynomials, you need to know four rules. And here they are:

For any real number $n \neq 0$ and any constant k:

1. If $f(x) = x^n$, then $f'(x) = nx^{n-1}$.
2. If $f(x) = k \cdot g(x)$, then $f'(x) = k \cdot g'(x)$.
3. If $f(x) = g(x) + h(x)$, then $f'(x) = g'(x) + h'(x)$.
4. If $f(x) = k$ then $f'(x) = 0$.

The following examples show how to use these rules both individually and collectively.

Example 1. Find the derivative of $f(x) = 3x^5$.

Solution: Apply rules 1 and 2. Think of $3x^5$ as $3 \cdot x^5$. First Rule 2 says the derivative of $3 \cdot x^5$ is 3 times the derivative of x^5, and Rule 1 says the derivative of x^5 is $5x^4$. Putting all this together, we have

$$\begin{aligned} f(x) &= 3x^5 \\ &= 3 \cdot x^5 \end{aligned}$$

Therefore,

$$\begin{aligned} f'(x) &= 3 \cdot 5x^4 \\ &= 15x^4 \end{aligned}$$

Example 2. If $f(x) = 3x^5 + 4x^2$ find $f'(x)$.

Solution: Think of f as the sum of two functions, $3x^5$ and $4x^2$. According to Rule 3, you find the derivatives of each and add them.

$$f(x) = 3x^5 + 4x^2 \quad \longrightarrow \quad f'(x) = 15x^4 + 8x.$$

Example 3. If $f(x) = x^2 - 5x + 3$, find $f'(x)$.

Solution: Apply Rule 1 to x^2 and $-5x$, Rule 4 to the constant 3, and then add up all the derivatives using Rule 3.

$$f(x) = x^2 - 5x + 3 \quad \longrightarrow \quad f'(x) = 2x - 5.$$

Note in this example that $x = x^1$, so the derivative of x is $1 \cdot x^0$ or 1. Thus the derivative of $-5x$ is -5.

Example 4. Find the slope of the tangent to $f(x) = x^2 - 5x + 3$ at the point $x = 3.5$.

Figure 7.1

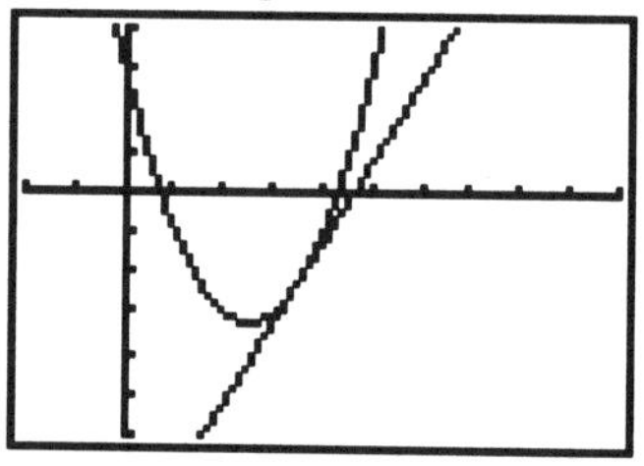

Solution: The slope of the tangent at 3.5 is the value of the derivative of f at 3.5. First find the derivative and then substitute 3.5 for x in $f'(x)$.

$f(x) = x^2 - 5x + 3$
$f'(x) = 2x - 5$
$f'(3.5) = 2 \cdot 3.5 - 5 = 7 - 5 = 2$

Therefore slope of the tangent at $x = 3.5$ is 2. The graph is in Figure 7.1.

Example 5. Find the attracting fixed point of the logistic function $f(x) = 2.5x(1-x)$.

Solution: First find the fixed points by solving $f(x) = x$:

$$\begin{aligned}
2.5x(1-x) &= x \\
2.5x - 2.5x^2 &= x \\
1.5x - 2.5x^2 &= 0 \\
.5x(3 - 5x) &= 0
\end{aligned}$$

Therefore, $x = 0 \text{ or } x = 0.6.$

So the fixed points are $x = 0$ and $x = 0.6$. Now find f' and check both $f'(0)$ and $f'(0.6)$.

$$\begin{aligned}
f(x) &= 2.5x(1-x) \\
f(x) &= 2.5x - 2.5x^2 \\
\therefore \ f'(x) &= 2.5 - 5x
\end{aligned}$$

So $f'(0) = 2.5 \text{ and } f'(0.6) = -0.5$

The slope of the tangent where $x = 0$ is greater than 1; hence 0 is a repelling point. The slope of the tangent where $x = 0.6$ is less than 1 in absolute value; hence 0.6 is an attracting point.

Example 6. Find the 2-cycles of $f(x) = x^2 - 1$ and determine if any is attracting.

Solution: If $f(x) = x^2 - 1$ then $^2f(x) = (x^2 - 1)^2 - 1 = x^4 - 2x^2$. We look for the fixed points of ^2f.

$$\begin{aligned}
x^4 - 2x^2 &= x \\
x^4 - 2x^2 - x &= 0
\end{aligned}$$

The fixed points of f are the trivial 2-cycles, so we need to divide out their factor which is $x^2 - x - 1$:

$$x^2 - x - 1 \overline{\smash{\big)}\ x^4 - 2x^2 - x} \qquad \overset{\textstyle x^2 + x}{}$$

Hence the non-trivial 2-cycles satisfy:

$$x^2 + x = 0$$

whose solutions are

$$x = 0 \ \text{ and } \ x = -1.$$

You can check that $f(0) = -1$ and $f(-1) = 0$. To determine if this cycle is attracting, check the slope of the tangent to ^2f at these points to see if it is less than 1 in absolute value. (It is sufficient to check just one of the points because if *its* 2-cycle is attracting then so is the other's since they lie in the same cycle.) We need the derivative $^2f'$.

$$^2f(x) = x^4 - 2x^2 \quad \longrightarrow \quad ^2f'(x) = 4x^3 - 4x.$$

Hence, $$^2f'(0) = {^2f'}(-1) = 0.$$

Therefore, the 2-cycle $\{0, -1\}$ is attracting because the slope of the tangents to these points on ^2f is less than 1 in absolute value.

§1. Exercises

1. Find the derivative $f'(x)$ given the following polynomial functions:

a) $f(x) = 3x - 3x^3$

b) $f(x) = 5x^2 - 3x + 2$

c) $f(x) = x^4 - 81$

d) $f(x) = x^4 - 2x^3 + 4x^2 - 1$

e) $f(x) = (2x - 1)(3x + 4)$

f) $f(x) = 3x^2(1 - x)$

2. Given the following functions, find the slope of the tangent to the graph of $y = f(x)$ at the given point x:

a) $f(x) = x^3 - x, \quad x = 0$

b) $f(x) = x^4 - 16, \quad x = 1.5$

c) $f(x) = 2x^3 + 3x^2 - 5x - 3, \quad x = 0.5$

d) $f(x) = 8x^5 + 5x^2 - 1, \quad x = 0.1$

e) $f(x) = 3x(1 - x), \quad x = \dfrac{2}{3}$

f) $f(x) = \dfrac{2x - 1}{10}, \quad x = -4$

3. Find the equation of the tangent to the graph of $y = f(x)$ at the given point x:

a) $f(x) = x(x - 1), \quad x = 1$

b) $f(x) = 4x(1 - x), \quad x = \frac{3}{4}$

c) $f(x) = x^3 - 8x, \quad x = 2$

d) $f(x) = x^4 + 4x^3 - 5x - 1, \quad x = -\frac{1}{2}$

4. Find all the fixed points of the following quadratic functions over the domain $[-2, 2]$. Use the derivative to classify each as attracting, repelling or neutral.

a) $f(x) = x^2 + \frac{1}{4}$

b) $f(x) = x^2$

c) $f(x) = x^2 - \frac{1}{4}$

d) $f(x) = x^2 - 1\frac{1}{4}$

5. Find all the fixed points of the following logistic functions over the domain $[0, 1]$. Use the derivative to classify each as attracting, repelling or neutral.

a) $f(x) = 0.5x(1 - x)$

b) $f(x) = x(1 - x)$

c) $f(x) = 2.5x(1 - x)$

d) $f(x) = 3.2x(1 - x)$

6. Find all the fixed points of the following functions and use the derivative to classify each as attracting, repelling or neutral.

a) $f(x) = x^3 - 3x^2 + 3x$

b) $f(x) = x^4 - 2x^2 + x$

c) $f(x) = \dfrac{x^3 - 2x^2 - x + 2}{3}$

d) $f(x) = 9x(1 - 4x + 6x^2 - 3x^3)$

7. Find the 2-cycles of the following functions and use the derivative of ^2f to determine which are attracting.

a) $f(x) = 3.2x(1 - x)$

b) $f(x) = 3.5x(1 - x)$

c) $f(x) = x^2 - 1.2$

d) $f(x) = x^2 - 1.5$

e) $f(x) = -x^3$

f) $f(x) = x - x^3$

§2. The Quadratic Route to Chaos

In this section you will use the derivative of the logistic and quadratic functions to focus in on the bifurcation points of these functions as they begin their route to chaos. In the last section, we found derivatives of particular members of these families; in this section we will find derivatives in terms of the parameter and thus have a general formula for the slope of any logistic or any quadratic function. First, the logistic function.

The Logistic Function

To find the slope of a tangent to the logistic function for any value of r, you differentiate $f(x) = rx(1-x)$. First multiply out the expression in parentheses to express $f(x)$ as a quadratic:

$$f(x) = rx(1-x)$$
$$= rx - rx^2.$$

Now apply the famous rules for differentiation, specifically Rule 1 and Rule 2. Don't forget that the parameter r is a constant, and you are differentiating with respect to the variable x.

$$f'(x) = r - 2rx.$$

The derivative at x tells you the slope of the tangent at x. The fixed points are $x = 0$ and $x = 1 - \frac{1}{r}$. Substituting these values for x in the derivative, you have

$$f'(0) = r - 2r \cdot 0 = r$$

and
$$f'\left(1 - \frac{1}{r}\right) = r - 2r\left(1 - \frac{1}{r}\right) = r - 2r + 2 = 2 - r.$$

Therefore the slope of the tangent at 0 is r, and the slope of the tangent at $1 - \frac{1}{r}$ is $2 - r$.

Now you can use this information to confirm the attraction properties of the logistic function that we arrived at experimentally in chapter 4. The point 0 is attracting provided $|f'(0)| < 1$. Since $f'(0) = r$, we conclude that 0 is attracting whenever $|r| < 1$ or $-1 < r < 1$. Since r is restricted to the range 0 to 4, we can say finally that 0 is an attracting point when $0 \le r < 1$.

In a similar way, we can deduce the attraction properties for $1 - \frac{1}{r}$:

$$f'\left(1 - \frac{1}{r}\right) < 1 \quad \rightarrow \quad |2 - r| < 1 \quad \rightarrow \quad 1 < r < 3.$$

This confirms that $1 - \dfrac{1}{r}$ is an attracting fixed point when r is between 1 and 3. with a little more algebraic effort, you can show that $1 - \dfrac{1}{r}$ is neutral at the endpoints, that is when $r = 1$ and $r = 3$. In summary:

Fixed Point	$0 \leq r < 1$	$1 < r < 3$	$3 < r \leq 4$
0	attracting	repelling	repelling
$1 - 1/r$	outside the interval	attracting	repelling

Attracting 2-cycles

In Chapter 4, we discovered that the non-trivial 2-cycles of the logistic function were the solutions to the quadratic equation

$$r^2 x^2 - r(r+1)x + (r+1) = 0,$$

which are

$$x = \frac{(r+1) \pm \sqrt{r^2 - 2r - 3}}{2r}.$$

Therefore, the non-trivial 2-cycle consists of the points

$$\frac{(r+1) + \sqrt{r^2 - 2r - 3}}{2r} \quad \text{and} \quad \frac{(r+1) - \sqrt{r^2 - 2r - 3}}{2r}.$$

Because these points exist and are different only when the expression under the radical sign is positive, we solved $r^2 - 2r - 3 > 0$ to conclude that 2-cycles occur when $r > 3$. To check their attraction properties, we have to take the derivative of $^2 f$ and evaluate it at either of the two points in the cycle. After expanding $f(f(x))$, we have:

$$^2 f(x) = r^2 x - r^2(r+1)x^2 + 2r^3 x^3 - r^3 x^4.$$

so that

$$^2 f'(x) = r^2 - 2r^2(r+1)x + 6r^3 x^2 - 4r^3 x^3.$$

To find the derivative at the fixed points $\dfrac{(r+1) + \sqrt{r^2 - 2r - 3}}{2r}$ and $\dfrac{(r+1) - \sqrt{r^2 - 2r - 3}}{2r}$ you have to substitute these expressions for x in the formula for the derivative. The algebra gets a bit nasty here, and there's ample opportunity for error. But, as the saying goes, no pain, no gain; so give it your best effort and see if you get this answer:

$$^2 f'\left(\frac{r+1 \pm \sqrt{r^2 - 2r - 3}}{2r} \right) = -r^2 + 2r + 4.$$

Isn't that nice? All the square roots disappear, and the derivative turns out to be the same for both points, a relatively simple quadratic.

To determine where this 2-cycle is attracting, we need to know which values of r make the absolute value of the derivative less than 1. That is, we need to solve:

$$\left|-r^2 + 2r + 4\right| < 1,$$

or

$$-1 < -r^2 + 2r + 4 < 1.$$

With your graphing calculator, you can easily find the points where the graph of $y = -r^2 + 2r + 4$ lies between the lines $y = -1$ and $y = 1$.

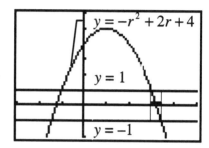

Remember we are only interested in the domain where $0 < r < 4$, and in this domain the points of intersection turn out to be 3 and 3.4494897.... Therefore, 2-cycles are attracting when r is between 3 and 3.4494897.... If you are curious about the last number, you will have to solve these inequalities algebraically using the quadratic formula:

$$-1 < -r^2 + 2r + 4 < 1$$

is equivalent to:

$-1 < -r^2 + 2r + 4$	and	$-r^2 + 2r + 4 < 1$
$r^2 - 2r - 4 < 1$	and	$r^2 - 2r - 4 > -1$
$r^2 - 2r - 5 < 0$	and	$r^2 - 2r - 3 > 0$
$\left[1 - \sqrt{6} < r < 1 + \sqrt{6}\right]$	and	$\left[r < -1 \text{ or } r > 3\right]$

Putting together all the conditions in the last row, we finally conclude that

$$3 < r < 1 + \sqrt{6} \; (= 3.4494897...).$$

Thus when r is in this range, the corresponding logistic function will have its orbits attracted to a 2-cycle. When r moves through and beyond $1 + \sqrt{6}$, the 2-cycle becomes repelling.

The Quadratic Family

Using your differentiation skills on the function $f(x) = x^2 + c$ (and recalling that c is a constant), you can do a similar analysis for the quadratic function. First, find (or recall) the fixed points:

$$f(x) = x \rightarrow x^2 + c = x \rightarrow x^2 - x + c = 0 \rightarrow x = \frac{1 \pm \sqrt{1 - 4c}}{2}.$$

Recall also that there are two distinct fixed points when the expression under the radical sign is positive; that is, when $c < \frac{1}{4}$. Next, differentiate f:

$$f(x) = x^2 + c \rightarrow f'(x) = 2x.$$

Finally evaluate the derivative at the fixed points:

$$f'\left(\frac{1 \pm \sqrt{1 - 4c}}{2}\right) = 2\left(\frac{1 \pm \sqrt{1 - 4c}}{2}\right) = 1 \pm \sqrt{1 - 4c}.$$

Using the notation of Chapter 4, we have:

$$f'(p_{right}) = 1 + \sqrt{1 - 4c} \text{ and } f'(p_{left}) = 1 - \sqrt{1 - 4c}.$$

Note that when $c = \frac{1}{4}$, $f'(p_{right}) = f'(p_{left}) = 1$ so that both are neutral. However, when $c < \frac{1}{4}$, the expression under the radical sign is positive, so that $f'(p_{right}) > 1$ and $f'(p_{left}) < 1$ for all values of the parameter in the domain of interest, $[-2, \frac{1}{4})$. Thus, p_{right} is always repelling. In contrast, p_{left} has an interval of attraction that can be found by solving $\left| f'(p_{left}) \right| < 1$.

$$\left| 1 - \sqrt{1 - 4c} \right| < 1$$
$$-1 < 1 - \sqrt{1 - 4c} < 1$$
$$-2 < -\sqrt{1 - 4c} < 0$$
$$2 > \sqrt{1 - 4c} > 0$$
$$4 > 1 - 4c > 0$$
$$3 > -4c > -1$$
$$-\tfrac{3}{4} < c < \tfrac{1}{4}$$

This confirms algebraically that p_{left} is an attracting fixed point when $-\tfrac{3}{4} < c < \tfrac{1}{4}$.

What about 2-cycles for the quadratic family? The procedure is similar to that for the logistic function though the answers, of course, are different, and the algebra, happily, is easier. Here is an outline of the procedure, along with the answers; the algebra, however, is left to you as an exercise:

1. Express $^2f(x)$ as a polynomial: $^2f(x) = x^4 + 2cx^2 + c^2 + c$.

2. Find the non-trivial fixed points of ^2f by dividing $x^4 + 2cx^2 - x + c^2 + c$ by $x^2 - x + c$ and solving the resulting quadratic: $x = \dfrac{-1 \pm \sqrt{-3 - 4c}}{2}$.

3. Differentiate ^2f: $^2f'(x) = 4x^3 + 4cx = 4x(x^2 + c)$.

4. Substitute the fixed points of ^2f into the derivative formula to find their slope. (Simplify your work by noting that if x is one of the fixed points of ^2f, then $x^2 + c$ is the other. Do you see why?) $^2f'\left(\dfrac{-1 \pm \sqrt{-3 - 4c}}{2}\right) = 4(1 + c)$.

5. By solving $\left| {^2f'}\left(\dfrac{-1 \pm \sqrt{-3 - 4c}}{2}\right) \right| < 1$, find the values of c that yield attracting 2-cycles: $-\frac{5}{4} < c < -\frac{3}{4}$.

6. Conclude that attracting 2-cycles are born as c decreases through $-\frac{3}{4}$ and remain attracting until c decreases through $-\frac{5}{4}$ when they become repelling.

§2. Exercises

Exercises 1-5 refer to the logistic function $f(x) = rx(1-x)$.

1. Show that $^2f(x) = r^2x - r^2(r+1)x^2 + 2r^3x^3 - r^3x^4$.

2. The fixed points of f are solutions of $f(x) - x = 0$. The 2-cycles of f are solutions of $^2f(x) - x = 0$. Therefore, the *non-trivial* 2-cycles are solutions of $\dfrac{^2f(x) - x}{f(x) - x} = 0$. Do the division to verify that the non-trivial 2-cycles are solutions of the equation $r^2x^2 - r(r+1)x + (r+1) = 0$. Verify that the solutions are $x = \dfrac{(r+1) \pm \sqrt{r^2 - 2r - 3}}{2r}$.

3. Show algebraically that $f\left(\dfrac{(r+1) + \sqrt{r^2 - 2r - 3}}{2r}\right) = \dfrac{(r+1) - \sqrt{r^2 - 2r - 3}}{2r}$.

4. Use the differentiation rules to verify that $^2f'(x) = r^2 - 2r^2(r+1)x + 6r^3x^2 - 4r^3x^3$.

5. Verify that $^2f'\left(\dfrac{r+1 \pm \sqrt{r^2 - 2r - 3}}{2r}\right) = -r^2 + 2r + 4$ by substituting each in the formula for the derivative and simplifying algebraically.

Exercises 6-10 refer to the quadratic function $f(x) = x^2 + c$.

6. Express $^2f(x)$ as a polynomial.

7. Find the non-trivial fixed points of ^2f by dividing $x^4 + 2cx^2 - x + c^2 + c$ by $x^2 - x + c$ and solving the resulting quadratic.

8. Differentiate ^2f.

9. Substitute one of the fixed points of ^2f into the derivative formula to find its slope.

10. What values of c yield attracting 2-cycles?

§3. The Mandelbrot Structure

In Chapter 6, you used the technology of calculator and computer to explore the structure of the Mandelbrot Set and discovered that each bulb, antenna and mini-Mandelbrot has a distinctive shape that gives information about the orbit of 0 and the shape of the corresponding Julia Set. In this section we will apply some of the tools of algebra and calculus to verify deductively the results of your earlier experimentation.

Fixed Points

The main body of the Mandelbrot Set appeared to be the home of all parameters c that define a quadratic function $f(z) = z^2 + c$ under which the orbit of 0 is attracted to a fixed point. When you toured around the interior of the main body using WINFEED, you saw the Julia Set with the parameter in blue, the fixed points in red, and one of the red points as the focus of the orbit of 0 in white. That fixed point was attracting. To investigate attracting fixed points algebraically, we need to apply the definition of *attracting* and the definition of *fixed point*. Recall that

- If f has a <u>fixed point</u> z, then z is a solution of the equation $z^2 + c = z$.

- Furthermore, if it is <u>attracting</u>, then $|f'(z)| < 1$.

But what is a derivative of a complex function? Without developing the whole theory, suffice it to say that in the case of a function as simple as this quadratic, the complex derivative is the same as in the case for real numbers; that is, $f'(z) = 2z$. Thus any attracting fixed point z must satisfy these two equations:

(1) $z^2 + c = z$
(2) $|2z| < 1$

What do these equations tell us about c? We can answer that question by looking first at equation (2): If $|2z| < 1$, then $|z| < \dfrac{1}{2}$. Thus z lies in the interior of the circle with radius 0.5 whose polar equation is $z = \frac{1}{2} e^{\theta i}$. Therefore the *boundary* points satisfy:

(1) $z^2 + c = z$
(3) $z = \frac{1}{2} e^{\theta i}$

Substituting (3) into (1) and solving for c, we have:

$$c = z - z^2$$
$$= (\tfrac{1}{2} e^{\theta i}) - (\tfrac{1}{2} e^{\theta i})^2$$
$$= \tfrac{1}{2} e^{\theta i} - \tfrac{1}{4} e^{2\theta i}$$

And therefore,

$$c = \left(\tfrac{1}{2}\cos\theta - \tfrac{1}{4}\cos 2\theta\right) + i\left(\tfrac{1}{2}\sin\theta - \tfrac{1}{4}\sin 2\theta\right). \qquad (4)$$

This boundary curve can be graphed using parametric equations on the TI-83. Press **MODE** and choose Radian in the third line, Par in the fourth line, Real in the seventh and Full in the eighth. Press **2nd[FORMAT]** and choose AxesOn in the fourth line. Finally, in the Y= menu set

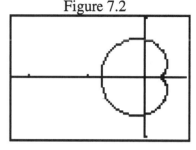

Figure 7.2

$$X_{1T} = .5\cos T - .25\cos 2T$$

and

$$Y_{1T} = .5\sin T - .25\sin 2T.$$

In the **WINDOW** menu, set T to run from 0 to 2π in suitably small steps and use the X and Y settings from the Mandelbrot Set. The graph is shown in Figure 7.2.

This curve is called a *cardioid* and is in fact the heart of the main region of the Mandelbrot Set. It is the boundary of the set of parameters with attracting fixed points, as you found by experimentation in Chapter 6.

Complex 2-cycles

The cardioid intersects the real axis where $\theta = 0$ and $\theta = \pi$. Substitution of these values into the equation (4) gives $c = 0.25$ and $c = -0.75$. Recall that these were precisely the bifurcation points for the quadratic function in the real case, and that in the interval between these points the real function had an attracting fixed point. At $c = -0.75$ the attracting point switched to repelling, and an attracting 2-cycle sprang to life. This situation lasted till the next bifurcation point at $c = -1.25$. Using the real case as a base of conjecture, you might guess that the head of the Mandelbrot Set, where you found 2-cycles, fits between -0.75 and -1.25. A little algebra proves that to be the case. (If you worked through the algebra for the *real* quadratic in the last section, you'll find the *complex* case offers no surprises.)

If z is on a 2-cycle of $f(z) = z^2 + c$, then it is a fixed point of ${}^2f(z)$ and solves the equation ${}^2f(z) = z$. But ${}^2f(z) = (z^2 + c)^2 + c = z^4 + 2cz^2 + c^2 + c$, so z satisfies the equation:

$$z^4 + 2cz^2 + c^2 + c = z.$$

or

$$z^4 + 2cz^2 - z + c^2 + c = 0$$

Two of the solutions of this equation are the trivial 2-cycles, that is, the fixed points of f. Using the tricks you are used to by now, you note that the fixed points both satisfy

$$z^2 + c = z \qquad \text{or} \qquad z^2 - z + c = 0.$$

It follows that $z^2 - z + c$ is a factor of $z^4 + 2cz^2 - z + c^2 + c$. We can divide out the factor using long division, and find the other factor: $z^2 + z + 1 + c$. Thus we have:

$$(z^2 - z + c)(z^2 + z + 1 + c) = 0.$$

We conclude that the *non-trivial* 2-cycles satisfy:

$$z^2 + z + 1 + c = 0$$

whose solutions are:

$$z = \frac{-1 \pm \sqrt{-3 - 4c}}{2}.$$

But *attracting* 2-cycles must have a derivative with absolute value less than 1. Again the derivative follows the same rules as for real functions. Since

$$^2f(z) = z^4 + 2cz^2 + c^2 + c,$$

then

$$^2f'(z) = 4z^3 + 4cz.$$

Therefore, *attracting* non-trivial 2-cycles must satisfy:

$$\left|4z^3 + 4cz\right| < 1.$$

Notice that

$$4z^3 + 4cz = 4z(z^2 + c) = 4z \cdot f(z).$$

And if z is one point of a 2-cycle, then $f(z)$ must be the other. So z and $f(z)$ are the two points we just found, and their product is:

$$\begin{aligned}
z \cdot f(z) &= \frac{-1 + \sqrt{-3 - 4c}}{2} \cdot \frac{-1 - \sqrt{-3 - 4c}}{2} \\
&= \frac{1 - (-3 - 4c)}{4} \\
&= \frac{4 + 4c}{4} \\
&= 1 + c
\end{aligned}$$

Going back to the condition for attraction then, we have:

$$\begin{aligned}
\left|4z^3 + 4cz\right| &< 1 \\
\left|4z \cdot f(z)\right| &< 1 \\
4|1 + c| &< 1 \\
|1 + c| &< \frac{1}{4}
\end{aligned}$$

This tells us that c lies in the interior of the circle centered at -1 with radius $\frac{1}{4}$. This is precisely the region to the left of the main cardioid, the "head" of the Mandelbrot Set, intersecting the real axis at $c = -1.25$ and $c = -0.75$. If we add the circle to the picture of the cardioid we have the image in Figure 7.3.

Look familiar?

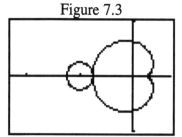

Figure 7.3

So far our algebraic approach has confirmed that 0 is attracted to a fixed point for parameters in the main body of the Mandelbrot Set, and to 2-cycles for parameters in the head. We have shown algebraically that the main body is a cardiod and the head is a circle. So far so good. Now how about those 3-bulbs, 4-bulbs, and so on?

Once again we have reached the limit of what we can do in this course, and you'll have to take those questions with you as you continue your journey into chaos. The intricate structure of this remarkable set is still not fully understood. New patterns emerge as more questions are asked and more researchers look deeper into the set. The best we can do now is hint at some of that structure in the exercises.

§3 Exercises

1. Use the parametric mode on your calculator to plot $c = z - z^2$ for $z = k\,e^{\theta i}$ using the following values of k:
   a) 0.2   b) 0.4   c) 0.6   d) 0.8   e) 1

2. Some of the cardiods in Exercise 1 have an inner loop. Experiment with different values of k and different window settings to discover at which value of k the loop appears.

3. Prove algebraically that the value of k you discovered in Exercise 2 is correct. [Hint: If initial values of θ insure that $k \sin\theta - k^2 \sin 2\theta < 0$, then you have an inner loop. What does this condition imply about k?]

In Exercises 4-6, use WINFEED to discover more numerical structure in the bulbs decorating the Mandelbrot Set.

4. Select the biggest bulb between the 2-bulb (the head) and the northern 3-bulb, and note that it is a 5-bulb. Repeat the process, starting from the 5-bulb and heading again toward the 3-bulb, selecting the largest intermediate bulb and recording its period. Repeat the process again, and write a sentence or two to state what pattern you are seeing.

5. Between the northern 3-bulb and the 4-bulb to its right, there are several smaller bulbs. Select the largest of these intermediate bulbs and note its period. Continue the process in a clockwise direction, selecting the largest intermediate bulb between your present position and the 4-bulb, noting the period of three more bulbs. Write a sentence or two to state what pattern you are seeing.

6. Investigate the periods of the largest intermediate bulbs between the sequence of bulbs with periods 3 through 12 that you encounter moving clockwise from the north to the east and south around the Mandelbrot Set. It will help to magnify the areas under investigation using the Cen/Wid... dialog box. As you magnify, you may need to raise the maximum number of iterations to define the Mandelbrot points more clearly. Here are suggestions for four zooms:

Period of bulbs in	Center		Width	Max reps...
zoom region:	*hor =*	*ver =*	*wid =*	
3-5	0.15	0.55	0.6	100
5-7	0.3	0.25	0.4	300
7-9	0.37	0.11	0.1	600
9-12	0.33	0.053	0.055	1000

Select the largest intermediate bulb between each pair of bulbs in the sequence (3, 4, 5, ... 12), note its period, and write a few sentences to describe the pattern you discover.

7. *For students with calculus.* The complex derivative is defined by

$$f'(z_0) = \lim_{h \to 0} \frac{f(z_0 + h) - f(z_0)}{h}$$

where z_0 and h are complex numbers. (Note that h can approach 0 from any direction on the plane, not just from the left or right as on the real axis.) Use this definition to show that the derivative of the complex quadratic $f(z) = z^2 + c$ is $f'(z) = 2z$.

8. *For students with calculus.* Use the definition in exercise 8 to show that the complex conjugate function $f(z) = \bar{z}$ has no derivative. [Hint: Show that the limit as h approaches 0 along the real axis is different from the limit as h approaches 0 along the imaginary axis.]

§4. The Doubling Function

A more mathematical exploration of chaos requires a more rigorous definition, permitting us to move beyond experimentation to proof. In Chapter 4, we stated the three properties of a *chaotic* function:

1. *It is sensitive to initial conditions*: Arbitrarily close to every seed is another whose orbit moves far away

2. *It mixes the domain*: If you specify any two subintervals of the domain, you can always find a seed in the first interval whose orbit gets into the second.

3. *Periodic points are dense in its domain*: Any point of the domain is arbitrarily close to a periodic point

To make this definition useful to a mathematician, we need to make it more precise (What does "arbitrarily close" mean?), and rephrase it in the language of mathematics. Here is a more formal version of the definition that can be used in a mathematical proof:

A function f is *chaotic* on the domain $[a, b]$ if

1. There is a positive number ε (the "threshold") such that for any given seed x_0 in $[a, b]$, any (small) positive number δ, there exists another seed w_0 and a positive integer n such that $|x_0 - w_0| < \delta$ and $|{}^n f(x_0) - {}^n f(w_0)| \geq \varepsilon$.

2. Given any two subintervals of $[a, b]$, say $[a_1, b_1]$ and $[a_2, b_2]$, there exists a seed x_0 in $[a_1, b_1]$ and a positive integer n such that ${}^n f(x_0)$ is in $[a_2, b_2]$.

3. Given any point w in $[a, b]$ and any (small) positive number ε, there exists a periodic seed x_0 such that $|x_0 - w| < \varepsilon$.

In Chapter 4, we first looked at the chaotic properties of the logistic function $f(x) = 4x(1 - x)$. It would be nice now to use our new definition to prove that this function is chaotic. That turns out to be too big an order at the moment, but we can prove that one of its cousins is chaotic.

Stretch-and-Fold → Stretch-and-Layer

Recall that the logistic function's chaotic properties come from the way it stretches and folds the domain: It stretches [0, ½] out over the whole unit interval [0, 1], and then it stretches [½, 1] over the unit interval again but in reverse order. (See Figure 7.4.)

Figure 7.4 $f(x) = 4x(1-x)$

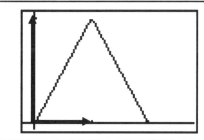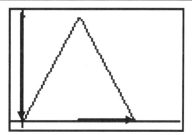

Figure 7.5 shows another function that also stretches and folds but in a linear fashion.

Figure 7.5 $f(x) = \begin{cases} 2x & \text{if } 0 \leq x \leq 0.5 \\ 2 - 2x & \text{if } 0.5 < x \leq 1 \end{cases}$

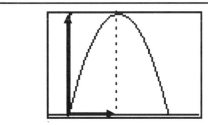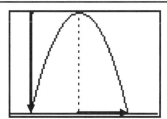

Related to the linear stretch-and-fold function is the *doubling function*: It stretches but simply layers instead of folding. The doubling function is denoted by the letter D, and its graph is given in Figure 7.6.

Figure 7.6 $D(x) = \begin{cases} 2x & \text{if } 0 \leq x \leq 0.5 \\ 2x - 1 & \text{if } 0.5 < x \leq 1 \end{cases}$

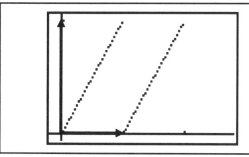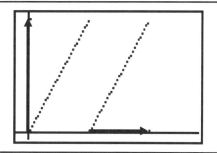

Orbits under the Doubling Function

The doubling function D is the cousin of the logistic function that we will prove chaotic. First, let's get familiar with the function by looking at some orbits.

Example 1. Analyze the orbits of 0.1, 0.36, and $\frac{1}{3}$ under the doubling function D.

Solution: You can probably do 0.1 in your head: $.1 \rightarrow .2 \rightarrow .4 \rightarrow .8 \rightarrow .6 \rightarrow .2 \rightarrow \cdots$. The orbit is periodic with a prime period of 4.

You may want to use the calculator for 0.36. The function fPart ("the fractional part of") will do the trick. fPart essentially eliminates anything to the left of the decimal point; so, for example, fPart(0.259) = 0.259 and fPart(1.647) = 0.647. The doubling function can be written as fPart(2X). Press **MATH > NUM 4:fPart(2 X)**. Using 0.36 as a seed, you will generate the sequence:

$$.36 \rightarrow .72 \rightarrow .44 \rightarrow .88 \rightarrow .76 \rightarrow \cdots \rightarrow .36 \rightarrow \cdots.$$

After 20 iterations, the orbit lands on 0.36 again. Therefore it is also periodic, but with prime period 20.

Using $\frac{1}{3}$ as a seed, and doing the arithmetic by hand instead of using the calculator, you will see the orbit $\frac{1}{3} \rightarrow \frac{2}{3} \rightarrow \frac{1}{3} \rightarrow \cdots$, so you know that $\frac{1}{3}$ is in a 2-cycle. (If you use your calculator, however, you will see an orbit that eventually wanders away from this cycle and continues moving chaotically around the unit interval. By now you should not be surprised that the difference between the fraction $\frac{1}{3}$ and the calculator's decimal approximation is sufficient to throw everything off. This result is a graphic illustration of this function's sensitivity.)

Example 2. Determine the fixed and eventually fixed points of the doubling function.

Solution: A glance at the graph in Figure 7.7 shows that the only two fixed points are 0 and 1. Eventually fixed points can be determined by working backward from the fixed points; that is, by solving $D(x) = 0$ and $D(x) = 1$.

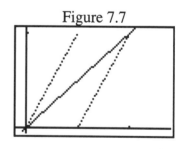

Figure 7.7

The only solution of $D(x) = 0$ is $x = 0$, so that leads nowhere. Figure 7.8 shows that $D(x) = 1$ has two solutions, $x = 1$ and $x = \frac{1}{2}$. Therefore, $\frac{1}{2}$ is an eventually fixed point.

So now we have to solve $D(x) = \frac{1}{2}$, and we have the two solutions $x = \frac{1}{4}$ and $x = \frac{3}{4}$

shown in Figure 7.9.

Solving $D(x) = \dfrac{1}{4}$ and $D(x) = \dfrac{3}{4}$ we have the

four solutions $\dfrac{1}{8}, \dfrac{3}{8}, \dfrac{5}{8}, \dfrac{7}{8}$. Continuing in this way, it

should be clear that eventually fixed points can be

characterized as fractions of the form $\dfrac{p}{2^n}$ where p is an

odd integer between 0 and 2^n.

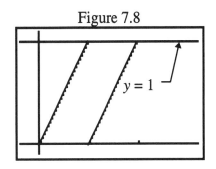

Figure 7.8

The Exercises contain more explorations of the
doubling function. Now we are almost ready to prove
that it is chaotic. The proof will be easier if you know
something about binary numbers, so that is the starting
point.

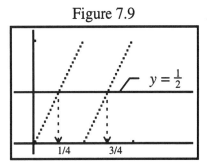

Figure 7.9

Binary Arithmetic

We are used to seeing numbers expressed in the decimal system, using the
numerals 0, 1, 2, ..., 9, and representing powers of 10 by appropriate placement of a digit
in relation to the decimal point. Thus, for example, we know that

$$238.97 = 2 \times 10^2 + 3 \times 10^1 + 8 \times 10^0 + 9 \times 10^{-1} + 7 \times 10^{-2}.$$

In the binary number system, we use only the numerals 0 and 1, and we represent
numbers in powers of 2 using a similar placement in relation to the decimal (or binary)
point. (If necessary to make things clear, some material that follows will use the
subscript *dec* for numbers represented in the decimal system and the subscript *bin* for
numbers represented in the binary system.) So a binary number would look like this, for
example:

$$10010.011_{bin}.$$

The decimal equivalent would be:

$$\begin{aligned}
10010.011_{bin} &= 1 \times 2^4 + 0 \times 2^3 + 0 \times 2^2 + 1 \times 2^1 + 0 \times 2^0 + 0 \times 2^{-1} + 1 \times 2^{-2} + 1 \times 2^{-3} \\
&= 16 + 2 + \tfrac{1}{4} + \tfrac{1}{8} \\
&= 18.375_{dec}
\end{aligned}$$

All the numbers we are interested in lie in the unit interval. Every number in the
unit interval can be represented by a string of 0's and 1's following the binary point:
$0.a_1 a_2 a_3 a_4 a_5 \ldots$ where $a_i = 0$ or 1 for every i.

Example 3. Express the binary numbers 0.1101 and 0.101010101... in decimal form.

Solution:
$$0.1101_{bin} = \frac{1}{2} + \frac{1}{4} + 0 + \frac{1}{16} = \frac{13}{16}_{dec}$$

$$0.10101010..._{bin} = \frac{1}{2} + \frac{1}{2^3} + \frac{1}{2^5} + \frac{1}{2^7} + \cdots_{dec}$$

Therefore, $0.101010101..._{bin}$ is an infinite geometric series with an initial term of $\frac{1}{2}$ and a common ratio of $\frac{1}{4}$. The sum is $\frac{\frac{1}{2}}{1 - \frac{1}{4}} = \frac{\frac{2}{4}}{\frac{3}{4}} = \frac{2}{3}$, and hence

$$0.10101010..._{bin} = \frac{2}{3}_{dec}.$$

Example 4. Show that 0 and 1 can be expressed in the form $0.a_1a_2a_3a_4a_5...$ in binary.

Solution: Clearly $0_{10} = 0.00000..._{bin}$. The number 1 is a little trickier but works because it can be expressed as an infinite geometric series:

$$0.11111..._{bin} = \frac{1}{2} + \frac{1}{4} + \frac{1}{8} + \frac{1}{16} + ... = \frac{\frac{1}{2}}{1 - \frac{1}{2}} = 1_{dec}.$$

The purpose of this foray into binary numbers is to make it easier to analyze the doubling function. What does it mean to double a number in binary form? The same as when you multiply a decimal number by 10: Shift all the digits one place to the left. Here's why. Suppose we have a number in the unit interval whose binary representation is $0.a_1a_2a_3a_4a_5...$ where $a_i = 0$ or 1 for every i. Then

$$0.a_1a_2a_3a_4a_5..._{bin} = \frac{a_1}{2} + \frac{a_2}{2^2} + \frac{a_3}{2^3} + \frac{a_4}{2^4} + \cdots_{dec}.$$

Doubling $0.a_1a_2a_3a_4a_5...$ gives

$$2\left(\frac{a_1}{2} + \frac{a_2}{2^2} + \frac{a_3}{2^3} + \frac{a_4}{2^4} + \cdots\right) = a_1 + \frac{a_2}{2} + \frac{a_3}{2^2} + \frac{a_4}{2^3} + \frac{a_5}{2^4} \cdots_{dec}$$

which in binary form is

$$a_1.a_2a_3a_4a_5..._{bin}.$$

All the digits have been shifted one place to the left.

To use the doubling function, we have to know whether the input comes from the first or the second half of the unit interval. In binary, that is easy. Take the number $x = 0.a_1a_2a_3a_4a_5\ldots_{bin}$. If $a_1 = 0$ then $0 \le x \le \dfrac{1}{2}$; if $a_1 = 1$ then $\dfrac{1}{2} \le x \le 1$. Therefore, if

$$x = 0.0a_2a_3a_4a_5\ldots$$

then x comes from the first half of the interval and

$$D(x) = 0.a_2a_3a_4a_5\ldots.$$

On the other hand, if

$$x = 0.1a_2a_3a_4a_5\ldots,$$

then x comes from the second half of the interval so that

$$D(x) = 1.a_2a_3a_4a_5\ldots - 1 = 0.a_2a_3a_4a_5\ldots$$

In either case, the doubling function simply shifts every digit one place to the left and drops off anything that falls to the left of the point. Repeated iteration of D simply continues to shift everything to the left, dropping any digit that reaches the binary point:

$$^nD(0.a_1a_2a_3a_4a_5\ldots) = 0.a_{n+1}a_{n+2}a_{n+3}a_{n+4}\ldots$$

(If you look closely, you'll see there's a small problem when $x = \dfrac{1}{2}$: it has two representations in binary form, 0.10000... and 0.011111.... When we defined the doubling function, we included $\dfrac{1}{2}$ in the first half of the interval and not the second, so to be consistent we should permit only the binary representation with an initial digit 0. From now on, think of $0.011111\ldots_{bin}$ as the only permissible binary form of $\dfrac{1}{2}$.

This completes the preliminaries. We are now ready to prove that D is chaotic on the unit interval [0, 1].

The Doubling Function is Sensitive

For the doubling function we choose a threshold of $\dfrac{1}{2}$. We are going to require that orbits start as close as you like but end up as far apart as $\dfrac{1}{2}$. Let x_0 be any seed in

[0, 1] and let δ be any positive number. We need to find another seed w_0 that is within δ of x_0 but whose orbit separates from the orbit of x_0 by a distance of at least $\frac{1}{2}$. First, suppose the binary expansion of x_0 is $0.a_1a_2a_3a_4a_5...$ (where all the a's are either 0 or 1). Since $\delta > 0$, we can always find some power, say N, such that $0 < \frac{1}{2^N} < \delta$. Now let w_0 have the same binary expansion as x_0 except we change the digit a_{N+1}. If x_0 has a 0 in the $N+$ 1st place, then w_0 will have a 1 there, and vice versa. So if

$$x_0 = 0.a_1a_2...a_N 0a_{N+2}a_{N+3}...$$

then

$$w_0 = 0.a_1a_2...a_N 1a_{N+2}a_{N+3}...$$

Because x_0 and w_0 have the same digits in the first N places, they differ by less than $\frac{1}{2^N}$ and hence by less than δ. Therefore $|x_0 - w_0| < \delta$ as required. Now iterate both seeds N times and you get:

$$^ND(x_0) = 0.0a_{N+2}a_{N+3}...$$

and

$$^ND(w_0) = 0.1a_{N+2}a_{N+3}...$$

Thus $^ND(w_0) = \frac{1}{2} + {}^ND(x_0)$ so that $\left| {}^ND(x_0) - {}^nD(w_0) \right| = \frac{1}{2}$ and the threshold is reached. If on the other hand x_0 has a 1 in the $N+$ 1st place, then w_0 will have a 0 there, and the Nth iterates will still differ by the threshold number. Therefore, D is sensitive to initial conditions.

The Doubling Function Mixes the Domain

If A and B are any two subintervals of the domain [0, 1], we want to show that there is some seed in A that ends up in B after enough iterations. Suppose the midpoint of A is $a = 0.a_1a_2a_3a_4...$ and the midpoint of B is $b = 0.b_1b_2b_3b_4....$ Suppose further that the radius of A is at most $\frac{1}{2^N}$. If we pick a point x whose binary expansion agrees with the first N digits of a, then $|x - a| < \frac{1}{2^N}$ so we know that x is in the interval A. Now let

$$x = 0.a_1a_2a_3a_4...a_Nb_1b_2b_3b_4....$$

Then

$$^ND(x) = 0.b_1b_2b_3b_4...,$$

and therefore the Nth iterate of x falls right on b at the center of B. Thus we have found a point in A whose orbit under D ends up in B: The doubling function mixes its domain.

Periodic Points are Dense in the Domain of D

Suppose w is any point in [0, 1] with a binary expansion $w = 0.a_1a_2a_3a_4\ldots$.

Suppose ε is some small positive number and N is an integer such that $\dfrac{1}{2^N} < \varepsilon$. To insure that x_0 is within ε of w, we just have to make the binary expansion of x_0 agree with the expansion of w for the first N digits. We then add on any repeating pattern of digits, and we have created a periodic point. For example, let

$$x_0 = 0.a_1a_2a_3\ldots a_N a_1a_2a_3\ldots a_N\ldots.$$

Then

$$^N D(x_0) = x_0$$

and is therefore periodic with a period of N. Thus we have a periodic point x_0 with $|x_0 - w| < \varepsilon$, proving that periodic points are dense in the domain [0, 1].

Conclusion

This completes a relatively rigorous proof that D is a chaotic function. You might want to see these same methods applied to the logistic function $f(x) = 4x(1 - x)$ or the quadratic function $f(x) = x^2 - 2$, to prove that they are also chaotic. They are indeed chaotic, but the proof involves an intermediate function relating D to both logistic and quadratic functions in a way that shows they have the same properties as D. The proof is beyond the scope of this course, so you'll either have to trust me that it can be done, or else take more courses in dynamical systems and do it yourself.

When you take the next course, you might also prove that the three properties actually *over-define* the concept of chaotic. If you have mixing and periodicity, you have to have sensitivity. So a slimmed down definition would only require the mixing and periodicity properties, and then you would prove sensitivity as a theorem. But we can't be quite that elegant in our first look at chaos. Moreover, since sensitivity is the intuitive hallmark of chaos, it is appropriate that it be included right up front in the definition.

§4 Exercises

1. Without your calculator, compute the orbit of $\frac{1}{7}$ under the doubling function D, and verify that it is periodic. Now have the calculator do the orbit and iterate 50 times. What do you discover? How do you explain the difference of the two results?

2. a) Show that $\frac{1}{3}, \frac{1}{7}$, and $\frac{1}{15}$ are periodic points under the doubling function D, and record the length of their prime period.
b) There is a pattern beginning to emerge in the results of (a). What would be the next seed and its prime period? Verify the accuracy of your conjecture.
c) Generalize your conjecture.

3. a) Show that $\frac{1}{3}, \frac{1}{5}, \frac{1}{9}$, and $\frac{1}{17}$ are periodic points under the doubling function D, and record the length of their prime period.
b) There is a pattern in the results of (a). What would be the next seed and its prime period? Verify the accuracy of your conjecture.
c) Generalize your conjecture.

4. As seeds for the doubling function D, try several fractions $\frac{p}{q}$ (p and q both integers) first with q odd, then with q even. What do you discover? Make a conjecture about the fate of the orbit of any rational number.

5. Make a conjecture about the fate of the orbit of any irrational number under D.

6. Can you find a periodic point with a 7-cycle? A 10-cycle? An n-cycle?

7. Find the decimal representation of the following binary numbers:
a) 0.100100100100...   b) 0.110110110110...   c) 0.00010101010...

8. Finding the binary representation of a decimal number is not as straightforward as finding the decimal representation of a binary number. For instance, what sequence of powers of 2 would add up to $\frac{1}{5}$? Here's a surprising method to figure it out: Compute the orbit of $\frac{1}{5}$ under the doubling function D. Write down a 0 whenever the orbit is between 0 and 0.5; and write a 1 whenever the orbit is between 0.5 and 1. (If it lands right on 0.5, write 1.) The orbit is: $\frac{1}{5} \to \frac{2}{5} \to \frac{4}{5} \to \frac{3}{5} \to \frac{1}{5} \to \frac{2}{5} \to \frac{4}{5} \to \frac{3}{5} \to \frac{1}{5} \to \cdots$ so we would write

001100110.... If you put a decimal point at the beginning and continue the pattern, you have $0.001\overline{10011}$. Verify that this is the binary representation of $\frac{1}{5}$.

9. Use the results of Exercise 8 to find the binary representation of the following numbers:

a) $\frac{4}{7}$ b) $\frac{15}{16}$ c) $\frac{3}{10}$ d) $\frac{3}{8}$ e) $\frac{7}{20}$ f) $\frac{11}{30}$

10. Think about the orbit of the number whose binary representation consists of all possible permutations of 0's and 1's strung together:

$$0.\underline{0}\,\underline{1}\,\underline{00}\,\underline{01}\,\underline{10}\,\underline{11}\,\underline{000}\,\underline{001}\,\underline{010}\,\underline{011}\,\underline{100}\,\underline{101}\,\underline{110}\,\underline{111}\ldots.$$

What can you say about the itinerary of its orbit?

11. Closely related to the mixing property of a chaotic function is the *ergodic* property: Arbitrarily close to any point x of the domain is a seed x_0 whose orbit gets arbitrarily close to any other point w of the domain. Prove this property for the doubling function D on $[0, 1]$.

Chapter 8

THE MEANING OF CHAOS

§1. Chaos and the Sciences

Chaotic dynamics and fractal geometry can be seen throughout the natural world. Natural processes are often iterative, forming complex structures out of simple initial structures by the repeated application of a growth rule. To model this process, the iterative mathematics of chaos and fractals can be more useful than classical and Euclidean approaches. As we have already seen, many natural objects in the real world appear fractal-like to the naked eye because they are self-similar at many scales – cauliflower, ferns, trees, shorelines, mountains, and clouds, for example. According to Avnir (1994, p. 231), real objects can be described by the following "scaling law:"

number of features ~ resolution of measurement^D.

where D is a familiar measure of *dimension*. This formula is virtually identical to the theoretical definition of boxcount dimension given in Chapter 2:

$$n = kr^D.$$

What may have appeared a graphical game in Chapter 2 turns out to have analytical applications in the real world. Avnir confirms that fact when he writes:

> Fractal geometry emerges, therefore, as a natural descriptive tool of complex structures, which takes the very complexity as a starting point and not as a deviation. It should be noted that the descriptive applicability of fractal geometry crosses virtually all domains of the natural sciences, from molecular assemblies through geological features and up to galaxies (p. 231).

Chaotic dynamics appear in every domain from the microscopic to the macroscopic. Photons emerging from some lasers go through a period doubling route to chaos (Baker, 1996, p. 167). At the human scale, the rhythm of a normal heartbeat turns out to be chaotic; indeed a periodic rhythm may signal the onset of a heart attack (Goldberger, 1990, p. 44). At the galactic scale, it appears that stellar orbits may actually be three dimensional strange attractors instead of the simple ellipses of a Newtonian model (Gleick, 1988, p. 146).

So now science is beginning to find chaos and fractals all around us in the real world. The real world hasn't changed, of course, but science has. Working from new theoretical models, scientists actually *see* the world differently. Do you find this surprising? Most people assume that the real world sits out there waiting for dispassionate scientists in white lab coats to look, measure and test. With unbiased data in hand, so we have thought, scientists make up a theory to explain what they have found. But this isn't the way it really works. Scientists already have a sense of what they are going to find because they are guided by a theory when they look, measure and test. They have a tendency to see the world through theoretical lenses that filter out data inconsistent with their theory. So chaos and fractals escaped our attention when we had no theory to guide us. But human beings have the remarkable capacity to step outside the program, the paradigm and the theory, to see the world anew. Now we are beginning to see the chaotic dimension of our universe, and the rest of this section will present a few examples of the scientific application of chaos and fractals.

Chaos and Biology

The combination of structure and unpredictability seen in strange attractors is the result of the feedback process in iteration. Feedback is also responsible for the growth process of natural objects: The present structure determines what the next stage will be. Consider our own bodies, for example. According to Briggs (1992), "The branching of our lungs, nerves and circulatory systems is evidence that our bodies are a product of feedback" (p. 120). The hallmark of feedback is, of course, self-similarity.

According to Buldyrev (1994), "fractals are ubiquitous in biology" because they "have a very large *surface* area... In fact, they are composed almost entirely of 'surface'..." (p. 50, italics in the original). He goes on to examine the human lung whose "surface area ... is as large as a tennis court."

> The mammalian lung is made up of self-similar branches with many length scales, which is the defining attribute of a fractal surface. The efficiency of the lung is enhanced by this fractal property, since with each breath oxygen and carbon dioxide have to be exchanged at the lung surface. The structure of the bronchial tree has been quantitatively analyzed using fractal concepts (p. 50).

And he concludes that the fractal model predicts the actual lung structure better than the classical model.

Surprisingly, fractals and chaos show up in other ways in the pulmonary and vascular systems of the human body. In the lungs, for example, the intake of air causes "avalanches" of airway openings similar to those created by dropping grains of sand on a sandpile. And the size and sequence of these avalanches follow a fractal model (Buldyrev 1994, p. 50). In the heart, the pauses between heartbeats are not uniform but "fluctuate in a complex, apparently erratic manner in healthy subjects at rest" (Buldyrev 1994, p. 76). When the lengths of these pauses are plotted as a time series, the graph is self similar and reveals a chaotic rather than a purely random or classically periodic structure (Buldyrev 1994, p. 76-78). It is the diseased hearts whose graphs are periodic. Contrary to our expectations, it turns out that chaos is one of the normative features of life; "irregularity and unpredictability ... are important features of health" (Goldberger 1990, p. 42).

While these examples illustrate the use of fractals and chaos in biology at the human scale, the ideas have been applied by Stuart Kauffman (1995) to questions at all biological scales, from the origin of life to the broad sweep of evolution itself. In his book *At Home in the Universe*, Kauffman tells a new creation story, using chaos as one of the building blocks for his *theory of emergence*: the emergence of complexity from simplicity, the emergence of order from disorder, the emergence of something out of nothing. It may seem paradoxical to devise a theory to explain a subject as unpredictable as life itself. But just as you gained some understanding of a certain unpredictable system by knowing it was produced by the logistic function, so too Kauffman looks for patterns underlying the organization of life to help us understand its unknowable origins and unpredictable evolution.

"Life," writes Kauffman, "is an emergent phenomenon" (1995, p. 24). By *emergent* he means that it arises spontaneously; it emerges out of a chemical soup by itself. He goes on to explain that

> sufficiently complex mixes of chemicals can spontaneously crystallize into systems with the ability to collectively catalyze the network of chemical reactions by which the molecules themselves are formed. Such collectively autocatalytic sets sustain themselves and reproduce. This is no less than what we call a living metabolism, the tangle of chemical reactions that power every one of our cells. Life in this view, is an emergent phenomenon arising as the molecular diversity of a prebiotic chemical system increases beyond a threshold of complexity. ... Although life as an emergent phenomenon may be profound, its fundamental holism and emergence are not at all mysterious. A set of molecules either does or does not have the property that it is able to catalyze its own formation and reproduction from some simple food molecules. No vital force or extra substance is present in the emergent, self-reproducing whole. But the collective system does possess a stunning property not possessed by any of its parts. It is able to reproduce itself and to evolve. The collective system is alive. Its parts are just chemicals (p. 24).

In our universe, the molecular diversity is sufficiently complex and the number of chemical bonds sufficiently simple, according to Kauffman, that life emerges and remains poised precisely "at the edge of chaos" (p. 26). Just as water exists in three forms as ice, liquid and gas, so do many systems – of cells, of ecosystems, of economies – exist in three forms: frozen into a rigidly ordered state, floating in a chaotic gaseous state, or balanced in between order and chaos in a lovely liquid state with both structure and flow. "Networks in the regime near the edge of chaos – this compromise between order and surprise – appear best able to coordinate complex activities and best able to evolve as well" (p. 26).

The sensitivity of systems on the edge of chaos turns out to be key in the hypothesis that Kauffman develops. In his model, life is like a strange attractor where structure and limits are apparent, but spontaneity and unpredictability are defining qualities. The system remains stable enough to withstand shocks and return to its attracting path, but its route along that path is full of surprises. Like a good tennis player waiting to receive a serve, life bounces chaotically on the baseline, ready to respond in any direction, with enough order to have a solid grip on the racquet and enough flexibility to slam a forehand or slice a backhand.

The phase-transition, edge-of-chaos theme appears to be a general law that applies at many levels of biology, from the microscopic to the macroscopic. Evolutionary biologists frequently think in terms of "fitness landscapes, where the peaks represent high fitness, and populations wander under the drives of mutation, selection, and random drift across the landscape seeking peaks, but perhaps never achieving them" (Kauffman, 1995, p.26). Here is how the edge-of-chaos theme is revealed at the evolutionary scale:

> In scaling the top of the fitness peaks, adapting populations that are too methodical and timid in their explorations are likely to get stuck in the foothills, thinking they have reached as high as they can go; but a search that is too wide ranging is also likely to fail. The best exploration of an evolutionary space occurs at a kind of phase transition between order and disorder, when populations begin to melt off the local peaks they have become fixated on and flow along ridges toward distant regions of higher fitness (p. 27).

Kauffman goes on to describe the application of the edge-of-chaos law to coevolution; that is, the notion that "as we evolve, so do our competitors; to remain fit, we must adapt to their adaptations" (p. 27).

> In coevolving systems, each partner clambers up its fitness landscape toward fitness peaks, even as the landscape is constantly deformed by the adaptive moves of its coevolutionary partners. Strikingly, such coevolving systems also behave in an ordered regime, a chaotic regime, and a transition regime. It is almost spooky that such systems seem to coevolve to the regime at the edge of chaos. As if by an invisible hand, each adapting species acts according to its own selfish advantage, yet the entire system appears magically to evolve to a poised state where, on average, each does as best as can be expected (p. 27).

Chaos and Physics

Physicists are also using chaos and fractals to understand physical reactions in the real world. According to Baker (1996),

> [t]he foundations of physics are being significantly affected by recent insights into nonlinear dynamics. The impact of chaos on physics may be summarized by the statement that unpredictability enters physics in three major ways: (a) through nonlinearity; (b) through the uncertainty principle; (c) through the statistical behavior of large numbers of particles (p. 188).

He goes on to say that statistical unpredictability may turn out to be a consequence of nonlinearity. In other words, in chaos theory physicists have a new tool to study unpredictability, a new model that gives them the confidence to investigate phenomena such as turbulence, earthquake, or change-of-phase behavior for which previous models were inadequate. One important area opened up by chaos and fractals has been the study of *turbulence*.

Turbulence is not only interesting to study, it is also fascinating to behold. We search out waterfalls and follow the tumbling flow with excitement, fear and awe. We stare mesmerized into the flames of a campfire and see life-like images in the flickering dance. We are amazed when turbulence organizes itself into a stable pattern, like the "Red Eye" of Jupiter, created out of the energetic balance between the planet's rotation and its atmospheric friction. We see a stable vortex in the midst of swirling turmoil, like a tornado in our own atmosphere, or a tidal wave in our ocean.

The practical problems associated with turbulence have drawn the attention of engineers and scientists. If you are transporting oil through a long pipe, you want as little turbulence as possible where the oil touches the pipe, so that friction is reduced and the flow is smooth. On the other hand, each time you breathe out, you want a lot of turbulence efficiently mixing your exhalation with the surrounding air, so that your next inhalation will contain only a small part of the carbon dioxide you just exhaled. Paul Dimotakis (1996) describes the mixed blessings of turbulence in a jet engine:

> Our ability to fly at high speeds is limited, in part, by our ability to mix fuel and air quickly and efficiently at flow speeds that are high compared to the speed of sound, i.e., at high Mach numbers. The inherent unsteadiness that leads to and sustains turbulence tends to diminish as the Mach number increases. Flows that would be strongly turbulent at low Mach numbers often aren't at high Mach numbers, and less mixing results. But at the same time that we're trying to maximize mixing within the engine, we need to minimize mixing (and thus heat transfer) in the flow along the engine's interior surfaces, so they don't melt (p. 23).

This problem is one of the main reasons (along with economics) that "we've been flying at the same speed for the last 30 years or so," and a reduction in flight times will depend "on learning how to both promote and limit turbulent mixing" (p. 23).

In the 20th century, turbulence fell out of favor as a subject of research as quantum mechanics captivated the attention of modern physicists. In recent decades, however, chaos theory has brought renewed academic interest to the field. One example of recent research has been the study of Rayleigh-Bénard convection. In this experiment,

> a fluid is placed between two horizontal thermally conducting plates with the lower one warmer than the upper one [see the following figure]. When the temperature difference ΔT exceeds a critical value ΔT_C, convection occurs as a series of 'rolls' resembling rotating parallel cylinders. Hot fluid rises, cools, and falls in a spatially periodic pattern. The rolls begin to oscillate transversely in

complex ways as ΔT is increased beyond a second threshold ..., and chaotic behavior occurs for even higher values of ΔT (Baker, 1996, p. 171).

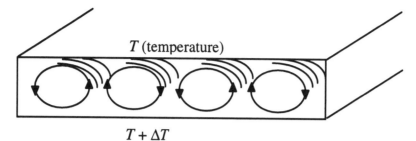

(Diagram adapted from Baker (1996) p. 171.)

When the local velocity of the fluid is repeatedly measured at a point in the box, a time series results that shows "the varieties of behavior typically associated with nonlinear systems ..., including period-doubling cascades, phase locking between distinct oscillatory modes, and sensitive dependence on initial conditions" (Baker, p. 171). If the shape of the container is varied as well as the temperature, the fluid may exhibit spatial as well as temporal chaos. If the width is much larger than the depth, the "rolls" become deformed in unpredictable ways, resulting in spiral patterns that follow another route to chaos as ΔT increases (Baker, p. 173-5). In one well-documented experiment on Rayleigh-Bénard convection in the late 1970s, Albert Libchaber, a French physicist, produced results that gave experimental verification to the computer-generated bifurcation theory of Mitchell Feigenbaum. "According to [Feigenbaum's] new theory, the bifurcations should have produced a geometry with precise scaling, and that was just what Libchaber saw, the universal Feigenbaum constants turning in that instant from mathematical ideal to physical reality, measurable and reproducible" (Gleick, 1988, p. 211).

At the California Institute of Technology, researchers have been developing ways to quantify turbulence, using lasers to produce photographic images whose fractal dimension can be determined with a boxcounting technique. Recently they have discovered that the boxcount dimension is sometimes more complicated than what we saw in Chapter 2. You should recall that we developed the notion of a boxcount dimension by covering an image with an r by r grid and counting the number n of boxes that contained a portion of the curve. By varying r from 1 to as large as we could, we obtained a set of ordered pairs (r, n) that we plotted. We found that n was roughly proportional to a power of r. Then, by fitting a power curve to the scatter plot, we obtained the constants k and D in the formula

$$n = kr^D.$$

The exponent D is the boxcount dimension.

Another way to explore this type of relationship is to transform the data so it falls along a straight line rather than a curve. This can be done by taking the logarithm of both variables and plotting log r against log n (called the "log-log graph"). Taking the log of both sides of the boxcount formula (and remembering the rules of logarithms), we have:

$$\log n = D \log r + \log k .$$

Note that this is a linear equation of the form $Y = mX + b$ where $Y = \log n$, $X = \log r$, $b = \log k$, and the dimension D is the slope m. The Cal Tech discovery was that the log-log graph did not quite straighten out. The part of the graph where r was small (bigger boxes) had a slope near 2, where r was large (tiny boxes) a slope closer to 1, and in the middle an interesting slope somewhere between 1 and 2. At first the solution was to ignore the extremes and call the intermediate slope the dimension D. But further research in the mid- to late-80s revealed that for most images of real-life turbulence, D never paused at an intermediate slope, that D was, in fact, "continuously dependent" on the box size r (Dimotakis, 1996, p. 29). These results were disappointing and controversial, but continuing experiments would only confirm them. As a result, Dimotakis draws a distinction between two types of fractals: one type with a nearly straight log-log graph has a constant value of D, called the "power-law" fractal dimension; and a second type with a curved log-log graph has a varying value of D, called the "scale-dependent" fractal dimension (p. 31). Dimotakis and his colleagues at Cal Tech have developed ways to apply their analysis to Cantor sets with dimension between 0 and 1 as well as to space-filling sets with dimension between 2 and 3. Their results even promise a solution to some of the jet engine problems described earlier. Dimotakis describes the research process this way:

> As with much of science, progress often awaits the development of a new technology, which allows a better view of nature, which improves our understanding, which begets new questions, which in turn await a new technology, which ... So it is with our quest for a better description of turbulence. In this round, first there was the excitement of fractals, because they promised a description of complex geometry. Then came the disappointment when we realized that we couldn't test the idea because we couldn't record and analyze adequate data to check it. Then the technology arose to do so, followed by the disappointment when we found that turbulence wasn't a power-law fractal. And now there's the excitement of realizing that the mathematics of fractals can be extended to accommodate the behavior that our experiments have revealed. Fractal language gives us the proper tools to talk about turbulence, if you're not bent on fitting lines to things that are curved. The new scale-dependent fractal dimension contains a lot more information and is better able to describe turbulent mixing and combustion. But valuable as that is, it isn't enough (p. 34).

He goes on to describe some of the new questions that have been raised and now await new measurement technology for the next round. While excited about the results he and his team have achieved, Dimotakis has no illusions about having solved the problem once and for all. "Victory over turbulence has been declared on a semiregular basis," he says, "every time based on different means. And every time, turbulence has risen, undefeated, to mock us." Recalling perhaps the origin of the word *chaos* in early Greek poetry (Abraham, 1994, p.2), he concludes philosophically with the thought that "[t]he ancient Greek gods may well have left this piece of the classical world as their legacy to remind us of the perils and pitfalls of hubris" (p. 34).

§1. Exercises

1. Show all the algebraic steps in the log-log transformation of $n = kr^D$ to $\log n = D \log r + \log k$.

2. The Cal Tech analysis of the boxcount dimension of turbulence showed a log-log graph with a slope near 1 where the boxes are small, and a slope near 2 where the boxes are large. How do you explain that result?

3. To illustrate the boxcounting problems that the Cal Tech team discovered, consider the Hilbert curve. The first four stages are as follows:

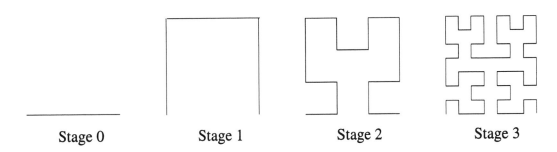

Stage 0   Stage 1   Stage 2   Stage 3

a) Fill in the following table with the reduction factor r and the replacement number n for stages 2 and 3:

Stage	0	1	2	3
r	–	1		
n	–	3		

b) Find formulas for r and n in terms of the stage number S.

c) Confirm your conjecture on a stage 4 Hilbert curve shown in the diagram at the right.

d) Use your formulas for r and n to find the self-similar dimension of the Hilbert curve as $S \to \infty$.

e) The boxcount data for a stage 4 Hilbert curve is as follows:

r	1	2	4	8	16	32	64	128
n	1	4	16	64	256	528	1058	2124

Compute the boxcount dimension of this data. Use your calculator to make a log-log transformation of the data, and draw a graph of the scatter plot.

f) In the **Y=** menu, set $Y_1 = 2X$ and $Y_1 = X + 1.2$. Observe the scatter plot with these lines added. Explain how this graph confirms the Cal Tech results.

g) Why are these results different from the dimension you arrived at in part (d)?

h) Use WINFEED software to explore more stages of the Hilbert curve. Click Example, then Fractal curve. Select File, and from the Library select Fillers, then Hilbert. Click Next to draw successive stages. For any stage, click Boxes and then Calculate to get boxcount data, or click a grid size to see a superimposed grid. Compute the boxcount dimension and draw the log-log graph for a stage 7 Hilbert curve. (Be patient; it takes some time to calculate the data at this stage.)

§2. Chaos and the Humanities

In the course of the past seven chapters, we have taken a detailed look at the mathematical models of dynamical systems that display the aperiodic and unpredictable behavior called "chaotic." You have recognized, of course, that this is a very special use of the word "chaos." To underscore the limited mathematical reference, we sometimes call it "deterministic chaos" (which may seem like an oxymoron). The point is that we developed a *mathematical* theory to deal with a *mathematical* model of certain dynamical systems. Period. There is no reference to random disorder, to confusion and incomprehensibility, or to the terrifying darkness of the Abyss.

But it would be disingenuous to suggest that the word "chaos" did not evoke associations like these no matter how often we hear "deterministic" or "mathematical." What happens if we follow these associations beyond the narrow confines of dynamical systems? For one thing, we make ourselves vulnerable to a charge of unprofessionalism from some in the scientific community. They argue that you cannot apply the insights of chaos theory beyond the discipline for which they were developed, that is, mathematical models of complex and unpredictable dynamical systems.

Others argue, however, that to ignore the mythic and cultural meanings of the word "chaos" is mathematical blindness. They believe that mathematical and scientific insights are *human* insights and thus may tell us something about the broader *human* experience. Personally, I prefer the charge of unprofessionalism to blindness, and in this section I examine some of the ways in which chaos theory and fractal geometry have been used in the humanities.

Order and Disorder

One of the great themes of individual human experience, of our social and religious organizations, and of our creative output in both arts and sciences has been the tension between order and disorder. Some of us fear disorder and do everything in our power to control our own lives as well as the environment we encounter. Others fear the confinement and rigidity of order and do everything we can to keep ourselves and others in a state of creative disorder. Most of us find ourselves somewhere between these extremes, but habitually leaning more one way than the other. For our ancestors, control meant comfort while disorder often meant death, so most of us are still genetically predisposed to have a positive reaction to order and a negative reaction to disorder.

According to Katherine Hayles (1991), order and disorder have "[t]raditionally ... been regarded as opposites. Order was that which could be classified, analyzed, encompassed within rational discourse; disorder was allied with chaos and by definition could not be expressed except through statistical generalization" (p. 1). But chaos theory introduced us to the surprising "discovery that hidden within the unpredictablility of chaotic systems are deep structures of order. 'Chaos,' in this usage, denotes not true randomness but the orderly disorder characteristic of these systems" (p. 1).

So chaos theory, like it or not, addresses the great human theme of order/disorder. Its insight is that a controlled, simple, orderly process produces complex, unpredictable, disordered behavior, and conversely, that windows of order can arise spontaneously out of disorder. Chaos theory calls into question the gulf that separates order from disorder and suggests an intimate connection between the two concepts. It challenges the traditional fear of chaos by suggesting that there are levels of order that make the chaotic comprehensible, even in what appears to be uncontrolled randomness. It reminds us that order and disorder coexist in natural processes, and together they create the life we know, life on the edge of chaos. Its fractal images present us with infinite complexity in highly structured patterns, helping us to understand the non-Euclidean order and symmetry of the natural world.

Chaos and Literature

Because literature is such a linear medium, it is hard to imagine what connection it might have with chaos and fractals. To convey meaning, a sentence needs to be organized according to strict grammatical rules, one word following in a line after the next. How would you make a fractal poem? Is a novel a dynamical system?

Yet chaos has made its way both into the content and into the form of literature in recent decades. Michael Crichton's *Jurassic Park*, for example, builds a story on the notion of the sensitivity of natural processes, ending with the moral that human beings cannot predict and control these processes with their science and technology. The natural – chaotic – process ultimately overwhelms human hubris (but human ingenuity and heroism *do* seem to win in the end, hmmmm). There are even a few lectures on chaos theory in the book (Crichton did his research!), virtually all cut from the movie, with the only survivor transformed into a seduction ploy. That adds a new dimension...

Tom Stoppard explores chaos theory in both the form and content of his play *Acadia*. In *The Visiting Professor*, Robert Littell's protagonist is a chaologist who ends up solving a crime by using his knowledge of chaos theory. Jorge Luis Borges explores bifurcation theory in *The Garden of Forking Paths*. And so on.

While these examples differ in their literary merit and the extent to which they are influenced by and reflect back the ideas of chaos and fractals, there are a number of scholars who are exploring the deeper connections between chaos, fractals and literature. William Paulson (1991), for example, says that "one major reason why students of literature and society need to study cybernetics, emergence, order from fluctuation and self-organization from noise is the potential pertinence of new kinds or concepts of causality..." (p. 51). By its focus on sensitivity, chaos theory raises questions about the linear cause-and-effect thinking that has characterized much of western culture for the last

300 years. After enough iterations, perhaps the flap of the butterfly's wing in Brazil *does* result in a tornado in Texas. Or was it a butterfly in Bermuda? Or an ant in Arizona? Paulson goes on to say, "We need the forms of rationality opened up by the ... sciences of information and disorder in order to understand the texts and criticism of postmodernism in the only context that really matters: our material, organic, and social world" (p. 51).

David Porush (1991) analyzes William Marshall's *Roadshow*, and sees sensitivity, bifurcation points, and the spontaneous appearance of order out of disorder (pp. 70-73). At a deeper level, he sees the relationship between chaos and literature reflected in the notion of a strange attractor. Think of the Lorenz butterfly attractor, for example. What you see is an infinite path, so complex that it weaves its way through a limited space, up, down and around, without ever intersecting itself. Though the system is chaotic, complex and unpredictable, yet there is a recognizable pattern that somehow "makes sense." Similarly, "a novel can be viewed as this sort of human product: a highly complex, designed system ... produced by a constant exchange between the mind and hand of the author... free invention within a structure of constraints" (p. 75). Perhaps the same could be said for any artistic creation: it is the result of an interplay between "free invention" and "a structure of constraints," between spontaneity and design, in short between chaos and order.

Chaos and the Visual Arts

The digital computer and high resolution color monitors and printers have poured out fascinating fractal images of chaos that evoke something like the wonder and awe we feel before natural beauty or a great work of art. Think of watching a sunset over the ocean or walking through a redwood forest. Think of seeing the *Mona Lisa* smile or sitting quietly in the Cathedral of Chartres. Now think of plunging deep into the Mandelbrot set, discovering the infinite variety hidden in its elaborate, Gothic decorations. In those magic moments, time stops and we feel an understanding of something bigger than ourselves, as if all of what *is* somehow fills us, and we become the whole.

But is the Mandelbrot set art? To answer this question would require a definition of *art*, a task that is difficult enough for artists and art scholars, and well beyond a layman's capabilities. But the question can be changed to an easier one that still moves us in the same direction: What qualities of the worlds of nature and art are captured by fractal images?

John Briggs (1992) responds that "one rather unexpected answer is 'holism'" (p.21). He goes on to define holism as,

> a harmony in which everything is understood to affect everything else. In
> mathematical fractals and also natural fractals, the holism appears as self-similarity,
> evidence of a holistic feedback process. In art, self-similarity—which can come in
> infinite variety—is not created by a slavish permutation of some form at different

scales. Rather it is closer to the self-similarity seen when we compare a human hand to a hummingbird's wing to a shark's fin, and to a branch of a tree. It is the artist's task to find and express this significant relation between forms and qualities that are simultaneously self-similar and self-different so as to create an artwork that allows us to glimpse the holistic nature of our universe and our being in it.

In a sense, the scientist studying a chaotic system and the painter responding to a natural scene are performing the same task: They are both looking for meaningful patterns. They seek to make order out of apparent disorder. In fact, the natural scene in front of the artist *is a dynamical system*, and it is perhaps no exaggeration to say that artists were the first chaologists. As Briggs says, "Artists have always exploited and valued what might be called 'the order that lies in uncertainty.'... Artists have perennially discovered in the doubt, uncertainty, and haphazard of life a harmony that goes straight to the essence of being" (p. 27-28). What is the aesthetic presented to an artist by the natural world? It is a fractal aesthetic characterized by self-similarity, asymmetric symmetries, interdependence, abundance and variety. The artist helps us see the similarities, symmetries and differences, the connections and disjunctions, the logic of pattern and the luxury of detail.

We respond to a painting the way the painter responds to nature: one fractal relating to another. When we look at a tree, we see a fractal cousin and we recognize something of ourselves. When a great artist gives us that same tree, he or she has added his or her own fractal being into the picture, and we find ourselves in relationship to a fractal community, a microcosm of the whole. But how do we respond when we see a series of utility towers carrying wires through a cut made in a mountain forest? Aesthetically we feel the straight lines and smooth curves a violation of the natural beauty of the landscape. The Euclidean geometry of engineering is extremely useful, but does not live as harmoniously in our fractal soul. As Michael McGuire (1991) puts it, "fractal geometry comprehends the irregular yet patterned aspects of nature in a way that conventional geometry could never do" (p. 112).

The great photographer Ansel Adams was conscious of the importance of conveying the fractal qualities of nature. For example, when he writes about photographing a rocky landscape he says,

> Beyond a certain distance, a great field of granite boulders will appear as perfectly smooth stones, the natural textures being beyond the resolving power of the lens and/or the emulsion. In order to suggest the substance of these stones it is necessary to include in the very near foreground a boulder in which the texture is adequately revealed. You can then say that the photograph "reads well." While you cannot see the texture in the distant boulders, you can see it in the near boulder, and you assume that all the boulders are the same material. It is this *awareness of substance* that is of vital importance in interpretative photography (quoted in McGuire 1991, p.112, italics in the original).

To "read well" is to convey similarity at multiple scales. This gives us the feel of a natural object, our fractal cousin.

Chaos and Music

The ideas of chaos theory have also moved contemporary musicians to explore the implications of fractal images in sound. Of course, some of these ideas have been explored for centuries without the vocabulary of chaos to describe them. Think of the self-similarity, for example, that one hears in *The Art of Fugue* by J. S. Bach. In this work, Bach fashions 13 fugues and 4 canons from a single simple theme. In the first fugue, the theme appears in a straightforward and unadorned version. In subsequent fugues we hear it upside down, backwards, stretched out in time and compressed. Parts of the theme are extracted, modified and amplified into additional themes which may appear by themselves or as an accompaniment to a version of the original. The whole is much more than the sum of its parts, more than an investigation of recursion and transformation. Bach manages to move us through many emotional states at the same time as he instructs us in the musical craft. Our mind is delighted while our heart is opened.

The transformation of musical themes has been explored in a more frankly fractal way by Nicholas Mucherino who explores the "uses of recursion, iteration and complex mathematics as an extension of traditional music-compositional practice" (p. 1). Just as a fractal shape can be constructed from an initiator and a recursion rule, so can a musical composition be created from a musical motif and a recursion rule. Suppose for example we borrow the opening of Bach's theme for *The Art of Fugue* and use it as our musical motif:

Suppose further that we take as a recursion rule: Shrink by half and append an inverted version of the reduction. The first two iterations would look like this:

Okay, this is not up to *The Art of Fugue* – or even *Three Blind Mice* – but it is a beginning of an interesting exploration. Maybe you want to add other transformations.

Say you want to imitate the Koch curve with a generating rule something like: Shrink by a factor of three; replace with four reduced copies, the first as is, the second transformed vertically by doubling intervals, the third doubled vertically and inverted, the fourth not transformed vertically but played backwards. You can see that things get complex rather quickly.

Another of Mucherino's ideas for "fractalizing" a musical theme starts from a representation of each note as a complex number $p + di$, where $p = pitch$, a number representing frequency, and $d = duration$, a number denoting the length of time *pitch* is to be held. A non-linear function could then be used as an iteration rule and applied to the original theme to produce a fractal melody.

Zach Davids (1995) has followed another path from chaos to music. Using the research on heartbeats done by Goldberger (1990) (who happens to be his father), he started with a recording of actual heartbeats and measured the length of intervals between beats. The inter-beat intervals were converted to integers and the integers converted to notes. As Goldberger's research showed, the sequence of inter-beat intervals formed a chaotic sequence, and the melodies they generated could be thought of as fractal music. To make his CD from these melodies, Zach Davids then chose his own duration for each note and composed a harmonic structure to underlie the fractal melodies. Davids himself says, "I cannot claim to have 'composed' these heartsongs. A more accurate description would be to say that I *completed them*."

Some of the groundbreaking research on this sort of fractal music was done by Richard Voss (1978). He distinguished among three kinds of chaotic sound: 1) purely random sound in which the frequency of one note is completely uncorrelated with the frequency of nearby notes ("white noise"), 2) highly correlated note sequences generated by random movements up or done from a previous note ("brown noise"), and 3) an intermediate kind of sound sequence characterized by a degree of correlation between nearby notes and a degree of randomness in the movement ("$1/f$ noise").

White noise is like the hiss that comes from an audio speaker or the roar of traffic from a highway. It consists of random sounds at all frequencies with no discernible pattern of repetition and no preference for any particular pitch. White sound could be simulated by using a random number generator to assign pitch and duration to successive notes.

Brown noise is not commonly heard in the real world but it is analogous to the Brownian motion of molecules (hence the name), and can be simulated by a process known as a "random walk." Starting from the first note of the melody, successive notes are generated by a coin flip: If the coin falls heads, the next note is a whole step up; if it falls tails, the next note is a whole step down. (Instead of a coin, you could use a spinner to allow more interval choices, and you could add a second spinner to modify the duration – you get the idea.) The sequence is randomly generated but with strong ties of dependence between notes. The resulting melodies are not very interesting.

Perhaps because $1/f$ sounds occur from a fractal source, there is no simple simulation game to produce them. (See Exercise 14 for one example.) The name "$1/f$" derives from the graph that results from standard analytical techniques applied to a time series. The techniques themselves (Fourier transforms and power spectra) are beyond the scope of this course, but have been applied to a wide variety of physical, biological and economic data, as well as to sounds. Fractal sounds produce a graph that is roughly hyperbolic; when frequency f is plotted on the horizontal axis, the power spectrum falls along the curve $y = 1/f$ (if an appropriate scale is chosen for y). It is interesting to note that the uncorrelated sounds of white noise produce a graph that is flat ($1/f^0$), and the highly correlated sounds of brown noise produce a graph that resembles $1/f^2$. Right in the middle we find $1/f$ noise.

Voss (1978) applied the standard techniques of analysis to the frequency distribution of broadcasts from four different kinds of radio stations: classical music, jazz and blues, rock, news and talk. The classical music graph was the most nearly hyperbolic, and the talk show radio graph was the least. The other two fell somewhere in between, basically hyperbolic but deformed at the ends toward the shape of the talk radio graph. (The cause, Voss speculates, may be that the jazz and rock stations have programmed more conversation and commercials than the classical station.)

Stock market movements also have a $1/f$ distribution, and so do earthquakes, floods of the Nile, and heartbeats. All these phenomena, along with $1/f$ music, have a time-series graph that is self-similar at many scales. Look at a minute-by-minute graph of the stock market alongside a daily, weekly or monthly chart, and you will see a similar form of peaks and valleys, all having roughly the same dimension. A graph of the heartbeat intervals displays the same self-similarity as do other $1/f$ phenomena, and the resulting "heartsongs" have fractal melodies.

If you create a fractal melody out of heartbeats or even the stock market, it sounds musical to our ears. Although produced by a mathematical process, it does not sound mechanical. Nor does it sound chaotic like white noise nor boring like brown noise. It sounds like a tune composed by a thinking, feeling, human being. Why should that be true? Referring to a "daring conjecture" by Voss, Martin Gardner (1978), suggests an answer:

> [t]he changing landscape of the world (or to put it another way the changing content of our total experience) seems to cluster around $1/f$ noise. It is certainly not entirely uncorrelated, like white noise, nor is it as strongly correlated as brown noise. From the cradle to the grave our brain is processing the fluctuating data that come to it from its sensors. If we measure this noise at the peripheries of the nervous system (under the skin of the fingers), it tends, Mandelbrot says, to be white. The closer one gets to the brain, however, the closer the electrical fluctuations approach $1/f$. The nervous system seems to act like a complex filtering device, screening out irrelevant

elements and processing only the patterns of change that are useful for intelligent behavior (pp. 23-4).

Our fractal nature opens up to receive the fractal sights and sounds of the universe; and when we create our own art and music we are guided by fractal rules. In making aesthetic choices, according to the American mathematician George David Birkhoff (1884-1944), we seek a $1/f$ balance between consistency and novelty: "[F]or a work of art to be pleasing and interesting, it should not be too regular and predictable nor pack too many surprises" (Schroeder, 1991, p. 109). That is, it should not be as highly correlated as brown noise nor as weakly correlated as white noise. The fractal nature of $1/f$ music has the right amount of predictability and surprise, enough order to comfort us, enough novelty to excite us, the perfect balance on the edge of chaos.

§2. Exercises

1. Describe your own relationship to the theme of order/disorder. If total chaos is 0 and total order is 10, at what level do you find yourself most comfortable? Is this the best level for you or would you rather move to another?

2. In what ways do you find order useful to you? In what ways do you find disorder useful to you?

3. a) Describe a process for creating a fractal poem.
    b) Write a fractal poem.

4. Robert Frost speaks of *freedom* as "going easy in the harness." Compare this definition to David Porush's description of a novel as "free invention within a structure of constraints."

5. Discuss the role of chaos and order in the process of creating something.

6. a) Define *holism*.
    b) Choose a painting that interests you and describe the ways in which it is holistic.

7. "An artist is one who can simultaneously reveal large abstract pattern and small idiosyncratic detail." Discuss this statement in the light of chaos theory.

8. Discuss the self similarity of *Three Blind Mice*.

9. Choose a tune that you like, and analyze it in terms of the frequency of its interval changes: Record the size of the intervals between successive notes (no change is 1, a half-step is 2, a whole step is 3, etc.) and keep a tally of the number of times each length of interval occurs. Draw a scatter plot of the results with interval length plotted horizontally and number of occurrences vertically. Does the number of occurrences appear to be roughly proportional to the inverse of the interval length?

10. Show that the log-log transformation of $N(f) = \dfrac{k}{f}$ is a line with a slope of -1.

11. Think of a way to fractalize a melody (use Bach's theme from *The Art of Fugue* if you wish) and write the first two iterations. What are your thoughts about your process?

12. Martin Gardner (1978, p. 25) suggests the following procedure to simulate $1/f$ noise: Using three dice, say red, blue and green, roll them all on your first throw, and note the sum. For the second throw, roll only the red and note the sum (of all three). For the third throw, roll red and green and note the sum (of all three). For the fourth throw, roll only the red again and note the sum (of all three). Then you repeat this sequence of four rolls; that is, for roll five, toss all three dice, for roll six only the red die, for roll seven the red

and green dice, for roll eight only the red. (The red gets tossed every time, the green every other time and the blue every fourth time.) You obtain a sequence of numbers from 3 to 18. If you label sixteen piano keys from 3 to 18, you can play the tune resulting from your particular sequence. How does it sound?

13. The procedure in Exercise 12 comes from Martin Gardner's article on fractal music in the *Scientific American* of April 1978. In the article, he also suggests simulation techniques for white and brown music. Look up the article and use all three simulation techniques to compose white, brown and 1/*f* music. Which do you find most pleasing? (If you can, make a tape of your music and play it for your friends and ask them the same question.)

14. Existential psychologists consider that the fundamental dilemma faced by every person is the resolution of one's relationship with freedom: coming to terms with one's desire for freedom and simultaneously one's fear of freedom, one's desire for and fear of limits.
a) What is the role of freedom and limits in the creative process?
b) How do you see the opportunities and challenges of freedom in your life?

§3. Chaos and Philosophy

The ideas of chaos theory have roots that extend back over 100 years, deep into the nineteenth century. As early as 1845, a Belgian biologist, Pierre François Verhulst, investigated the dynamics of the logistic equation as a model of population growth (Peitgen 1992, p. 42). In 1890, the great French mathematician, Henri Poincaré, wrote an important article on the stability of the solar system, in which questions about chaotic dynamics were raised if not answered (Peitgen 1992, p.507). Exploration of fractal geometry appears in the work of Georg Cantor in 1872, Giuseppe Peano in 1890, and Gaston Julia in 1918 (Peitgen 1992 p. 63). The mathematics was being discussed; the physical examples of turbulence were waiting to be explored; the biological questions about patterns of evolution were being raised. What happened to chaos theory? Why did it virtually disappear from mainstream mathematics and science for nearly five decades?

One answer is technological: Chaos theory required the digital computer, developed in the 1940s in response to the demands of World War II. While it is certainly true that the availability and power of the digital computer is inextricably bound up with the development of chaos theory, its *dependence* on digital computers is less clear. Indeed much of the early work, even in the 1960s, was done on *analog* computers which had been generally available in the 1930s, a generation before chaos was pursued in earnest. The technological answer seems too simple. The high speed computer was a necessary but not sufficient condition for chaos theory.

More fundamental perhaps was a major shift in *attitude* that opened society to the possibility of chaos theory in the latter part of the twentieth century. The attitude inherited from Descartes and Newton had prevented us from seeing chaotic phenomena, but several currents in recent social and intellectual culture gradually opened our eyes to see rich, non-linear patterns in our world.

Modernism

What is our Cartesian inheritance? It is what Walter Truett Anderson (1995) calls the "Enlightenment project" of the Modern era, "which lasted from the latter part of the eighteenth century until well into the twentieth (pp. 3-4)." Referring to David Harvey's book *The Condition of Postmodernity* he explains that the Enlightenment project

> was the project aimed at getting all the world's diverse peoples to see things the same way – the rational way. The thinkers of the Enlightenment, Harvey said, "took it as axiomatic that there was only one possible answer to any question. From this it followed that the world could be controlled and rationally ordered if we could only picture and represent it rightly. But this presumed that there existed a single correct mode of representation which, if we could uncover it (and this was what scientific and mathematical endeavors were all about), would provide the means to Enlightenment ends." The Enlightenment – and the twentieth century scientific rationalism that grew

out of it – was not only a philosophical effort, then, but an ideology of progress: a belief in "linear progress, absolute truths, and rational planning of ideal social orders" (p. 4).

The linearity of the Enlightenment project was manifest not only in a belief in "linear progress," but even more fundamentally in a belief that there is a straight line between cause and effect. Understanding a puzzling phenomenon meant finding a simpler, often hidden, phenomenon whose presence resulted in the puzzle. Germs *cause* disease. Gravity *causes* movement.

A major scientific project during the last three centuries has been to understand motion, and the primary investigative instrument has been systems of differential equations. Unfortunately, the only systems that yielded solutions were linear, and therefore linear systems were used to model *any* physical situation, linear or not. Non-linear, turbulent systems had to be approximated or ignored. For the scientific establishment, the world became essentially linear, not because it really *was* linear, but because the most useful *models* were linear.

Closely related to linear thinking is dualistic thinking, characterized by either/or, right/wrong, and true/false (or in the moral world by good/bad). Dualism has roots in the Law of the Excluded Middle, part of the Greek inheritance revived in the Renaissance, according to which any statement must be either True or False and not both. The simplicity and clarity of a dualistic approach was appealing, even if it concealed the complexity of life, leaving out, for example, the human tendency to hold two conflicting feelings or opinions at the same moment. In the dualistic world of the Modern era, Truth was a unique, transcendent and external value for which the human being searched. There was only one Truth: If I had it and you disagreed with me, then you didn't have it. We couldn't both know Truth if we didn't agree.

Supporting the Enlightenment project at its base was a belief that the universe is organized by a rational intelligence. You didn't have to believe in a divinity or supernatural being to agree that the universe was basically rational. Many called themselves atheists and still worshipped Reason. For those who found a home in traditional religions, the great organizing intelligence was called God. By whatever name, the Western culture generally subscribed to the principle that the universe was knowable by rational means. The rational approach to use was the only one we knew: the linear dualism we learned from the Greeks, from the Medieval Church and from the Enlightenment.

Cultural shifts of the 1960s

While scientific faith dominated the Western world during the Modern era, doubts were held and expressed primarily in the artistic community where they were safely contained and marginalized. But by the middle of the twentieth century, doubts began to spread in the intellectual community, and in the 1960s a turbulent wave rolled through the cultural waters of the Western world, throwing off a spray of new ideas, attitudes and beliefs. There was a loosening of respect for external authority. The institutions that had been the holders of Truth were challenged by a generation who put more faith in felt experience than in received wisdom. Young people generally were challenging the instructions of their elders, and in the scientific world a few young researchers were unwilling to ignore the non-linear parts of the world that their elders could not see.

A challenge to authority was also a challenge to order, not only to established political and social order, but even to the concept of order underlying scientific rationalism. During the Modern era, the goal of science appeared to be human control of the natural world. By dominating nature, the human was supposed to eliminate unpredictability and usher in the Golden Age of Order. While life had indeed been made more secure and comfortable by medical successes, by safer transportation and housing, and by more widely available nutrition, more than a few scientific advances had also had unforeseen negative consequences – insecticides that eliminated some pests but opened the door to others, atomic power that won a war but then put the world under a cloud of fear. There arose a new respect for the beauty and richness that the natural process brought forth in its own unpredictable way without help or interference from the human being. The chaos of the natural world could evoke wonder and excitement as well as fear.

Postmodernism

The cultural unrest of the 1960s was one manifestation of a broad philosophical shift that began to call into question the tenets of Modernism. This shift, most notably articulated by the French philosophers Michel Foucault, Jacques Derrida and Jean Baudrillard, came to be known as Postmodernism. Their writings reached this country in the 1970s and 1980s, just as chaos theory was emerging. The Postmodern movement became the intellectual context of chaos theory. Although a full treatment of Postmodernism is well beyond the scope of this book, the main trends can be sketched so you can see how the shift in philosophical ground nurtured the growth of chaos theory.

Fundamental to the Postmodern stance is a rejection of the Modern search for unity – for one Truth, for one external source of authority, for a unique cause for any effect, even for a single unifying concept of the universe. The Law of the Excluded Middle is demoted and individual experience revalued.

Instead of a single, external Truth investigated by an objective rationality, Postmodernists see subjective, fallible, culture-bound human researchers relating to the external world as best they can, while they construct their models of reality. The scientific effort looks more like the six blind men with the elephant. One man's version of what's out there depends both on what part he grabs hold of and how his past experience shapes his understanding of what he is touching. Can we be sure that the act of touching the elephant has not somehow deformed it? Not always. Frequently the very presence of an observer changes the object being observed. Furthermore, our interpretation of what we "see" is based on subjective factors that have nothing to do with the elephant: what we thought we might find in the first place, what our culture has taught us to see, what we hear others saying they see, what kind of an impression we want to make with our report, and so on. Perhaps there is some superhuman intelligence that could stand outside this whole scene and define the elephant, but we'll never know. All we can do is feel around in the dark and make up a story that explains our experience, filtered through our own perceptions, psychology and culture. We cannot claim to be telling the Truth, but from our experience we *construct* truth. We can even be said to construct *reality* through our interpretation of our interaction with the outside world. What we think about our experience becomes our reality.

Umberto Eco (1983) writes about the struggle between Modern and Postmodern ways of seeing the world in his novel *The Name of the Rose*. Set in a 14th century monastery, the story revolves around a series of murders that the monk, William, is trying to solve with the assistance of his novice, Adso. After solving the mystery, William addresses these words to Adso:

> "...The Antichrist can be born from piety itself, from excessive love of God or of the truth, as the heretic is born from the saint and the possessed from the seer. Fear prophets, Adso, and those prepared to die for the truth, for as a rule they make many others die with them, often before them, at times instead of them. Jorge did a diabolical thing because he loved his truth so lewdly that he dared anything in order to destroy falsehood. Jorge feared the second book of Aristotle because it perhaps really did teach how to distort the face of every truth, so that we would not become slaves of our ghosts. Perhaps the mission of those who love mankind is to make people laugh at the truth, *to make truth laugh*, because the only truth lies in learning to free ourselves from insane passion for truth" (p. 491, italics in the original).

The only truth lies in learning to free ourselves from insane passion for truth. That could be the rallying cry of Postmodernism. The myth of Unity that had guided the Modern era was being replaced by a Postmodern myth of pluralism: many peoples, many truths. The myth of objectivity was yielding to the myth of relationship. The search for simplicity was enriched by respect for complexity. The belief in Order began to make space for confidence in Disorder.

It was in such an intellectual matrix that chaos theory and fractal geometry developed. Although its name had a certain amount of shock value, chaos theory did not propose radical new physical laws or contradict scientific assumptions. In one way, the chaologist's approach is no different from the most dedicated Newtonian's: Both are looking for patterns. But the chaologist now looks for patterns in disordered data where the old patterns of stability, static and cyclical patterns, do not appear. The fractal geometer looks for self-similar patterns instead of circles and squares. We are still making models, but in the Postmodern era we feel freer to attend to the turbulence of the real world with the new models of chaos theory and fractal geometry.

Determinism

As a specific example of the mutual influence of chaos theory and the cultural climate of the Postmodern era, let us look more closely at the concept of *determinism*, one of the guiding myths of classical science. Determinism holds that the present state of the universe was completely determined at the outset, and everything since that moment has been a gradual unfolding of the inevitable. This includes even the fact that I am writing this book and you are reading it, that my sinuses are bothering me today and that you just had a thought that had nothing to do with chaos theory. *Everything.* A determinist believes that there are mathematical laws governing every single atom in its connection to and movement among all other atoms in the universe, and that knowledge of those laws, along with perfect information about the present state of the universe, would allow us to predict all future states of the universe and to retrodict all past states. In effect, life is like a film unrolling one frame at a time. We can see only the present frame, but the future frames are already waiting to unroll; they are already determined. The past frames have already rolled onto the take-up reel, and we could run the projector backward if we wanted to see them. There is only one possible film for this universe, the one that contains the unique frame we're seeing at this moment. Even if we don't know what's on the rest of the film, the filmmaker does; and if we were smart enough, we could figure it out too.

Determinism is comforting to those who cherish their own experience of the universe as orderly and intelligible, and it is reassuring to any who are disturbed by a vision of many possible futures. On the other hand, a vision of a completely determined universe is disturbing to those who cherish their own experience of autonomy and free will in a constantly changing universe. To them, determinism promises order at the expense of spontaneity, and safety at the expense of surprise.

But determinism received strong support from the remarkable success of classical science in explaining planetary motion, and has remained a central cultural belief throughout the Modern era. Even when limitations of Newton's Laws were exposed by Einstein's theory of general relativity and by quantum mechanics, determinism remained the dominant hypothesis. Chaos theory, however, has raised significant questions. To understand the challenge chaos theory poses to determinism, we need to look more closely at four layers of determinism identified by Stephen Kellert in his book *In the Wake of Chaos*.

I call Kellert's first layer of determinism *mathematical dependence*: the future depends on the present in a mathematically specifiable way that includes no statistical or probabilistic reference. There are no if-then decisions, no branches. At any point in time, the future state of the universe is determined by applying mathematical formulas to the real numbers that capture the essence of the present state.

A second level of determinism, *unique evolution*, is based on the film-in-the-can notion: A complete instantaneous description of the present fixes the past and future with no alternatives. Only one universe could have arrived at this particular state from the singularity marking its birth. In other words, if two universes agree on everything at one moment in time, then they agree on everything at all moments in time. If two universes look the same for one nanosecond, then they are identical. There is only one universe that looks just like this one at this moment.

A third level of determinism specifies that physical quantities have *exact values*. We may be limited in our ability to measure these values, but the values themselves are precise. A physical quantity is not spread out over a range of possible values. It is not an average of a huge number of unspecifiable values. Values are not themselves indistinct or fuzzy. They are exact to an infinite number of decimal places.

The final and most comprehensive level of determinism is called *total predictability*: The universe is predictable, in principle, by an all-powerful intelligence or computational scheme, given complete information of instantaneous conditions and the complete set of physical laws. As fallible human beings with inadequate measuring devices, we may not be able to come up with complete information about any instant, we may not have the right set of physical laws, and we may not apply them with 100% accuracy. But our failure to predict accurately is due to our own shortcomings not to some confused quality of the universe. If we were only smart enough, we could do it, for the universe simply hums along according to the rules, and it remains, in principle, predictable.

Now we will show how science itself peels back these layers of determinism, working backwards from the fourth to the first. Chaos theory begins by eliminating total predictability. According to Kellert, "Chaotic systems scrupulously obey the strictures of [mathematical dependence], unique evolution, and [exact values], yet they are utterly unpredictable. Because of the existence of these systems, we are forced to admit that the world is not totally predictable (p. 62)." Furthermore, the sensitivity of chaotic systems renders the notion of total predictability at least useless. No measurement can be made with infinite accuracy, so the instantaneous state of a system – let alone the whole universe! – could never be completely specified. Perhaps one would wish to believe in a god who has such infinite capacity; if so, then total predictability could be retained as a spiritual belief although empty of any methodological import.

Second, quantum mechanics eliminates exact values. To specify the state of a system one needs to pinpoint its position and fully describe its motion. Equipped with this information, one can then apply the laws of motion to predict its next state. However, we know from quantum mechanics that position and momentum cannot be fully specified simultaneously. When we know the position of a particle (with whatever degree of accuracy), we have a range of possible values for its momentum as well as a probability distribution to tell us where in that range the momentum is likely to be. The more certain we are about position, the less certain we can be about momentum, and vice versa. The best we can do is plot position and momentum on a two dimensional graph as a point surrounded by a fuzzy rectangle of probability. These are not exact values, and if you require the universe to provide exact values in your definition of determinism, then you have to conclude that the universe is not deterministic.

Third, chaos theory and quantum mechanics together eliminate unique evolution. If by *identical* you mean that two universes must have the same position and momentum to an infinite number of decimal places, then quantum mechanics guarantees that the condition can never be met. If you mean that two universes must have the same position and momentum *only so far as physics can specify*, then two systems that start within the same small area of quantum indeterminateness *are identical* in all physically relevant aspects. But if they are *chaotic* systems, they can and will evolve in such a way that the patch of vagueness will soon include the entirety of the systems, rendering judgment about their identity impossible. Kellert concludes,

> In other words, chaos theory together with quantum mechanics invites us to participate in the following imaginative exercise: picture another universe, created at just this very moment, which is physically identical to this one. Let the physical descriptions of the two universes be identical (never mind that such descriptions could never be written down, the point is that the two worlds agree on "all physically relevant properties"). Now imagine them unfold in time (again, never mind where you are supposed to be watching them from). After a while they will be noticeably different – an atom will decay in one and not in the other, a hurricane will strike Florida in one and not in the other, two asteroids will collide in one and not in the other. Determinism fails (pp. 74-75).

Finally, we are left with mathematical dependence. The future depends on the present in a mathematically specifiable way. But not necessarily very far into the future. Knowledge of the state of the system at time n is sufficient to determine and predict the state at time $n + 1$. This is true for any n. In fact we could determine and predict any state for some finite number of time periods in the future, the number depending on the stability of the system and on the accuracy and completeness of information we are able to gather about the system at any moment. For stable systems such as missiles and planets, we will have an accuracy horizon that extends quite far into the future. For chaotic systems, however, the accuracy horizon tends to be relatively short – about two weeks for the weather, even less for the stock market. For all practical purposes, we have a limit on determinism. We could call this *local determinism*, a Postmodern kind of determinism.

Summary

Chaos theory developed in the context of Postmodernism, and Postmodernism developed in the context of chaos theory. Each influenced and shaped the other. As a result, the major tenets of classical science, such as determinism, have been called into question. As human beings, we are developing a new view of the universe and our relationship to it. By focusing on patterns within disorder, chaos opens our eyes to the richness of the natural world in a new way. In the overused term of Thomas Kuhn, it provides a paradigm shift, a new model for understanding our universe and our place in it. New doors stand open and invite us to enter into a new relationship with the world.

§3. Exercises

1. What aspect or aspects of the Modern era do you find most appealing? most threatening?

2. What aspects of the Postmodern era do you find most appealing? most threatening?

3. What made the Postmodern era a nourishing context for chaos theory?

4. In what ways does chaos theory challenge classical science? In what ways is it part of classical science? compatible with?

5. The word *myth* is frequently used in a negative way to mean a belief that is silly or untrue. Explain the use of *myth* in this section. Does it carry a pejorative meaning? If you believe it does, what word would you use that is neutral?

6. The text describes some myths of the Modern and Postmodern eras. Can you identify other myths that have served as guides in the past or the present?

7. Name or describe a myth that is powerful in
    a) your own life.
    b) your family.
    c) this school.
    d) the United States of America.

8. What aspects of determinism seem right to you?

9. How could you modify the film-in-the-can image to include sensitivity?

10. It has been said that chaos theory reveals the order hidden in disorder. Do you agree with this statement? Justify.

11. In a dualistic system of thought, *order* and *disorder* would be separate categories to classify one's experience of the world. In a non-dualistic system, order and disorder would reside at opposite poles of a continuum. (Think of a straight line with perfect order off at one infinite end and perfect disorder at the other.)
    a) Where do you find yourself on this line, more toward the order end or the disorder end? How do you experience yourself as ordered and how as disordered? When are you more comfortable with order, when with disorder?
    b) In some models, the infinite ends of a straight line meet. In what ways do perfect order and perfect disorder resemble each other?
    c) Describe how order and disorder have both positive and negative qualities.

BIBLIOGRAPHY

Books and Articles

Abraham, Ralph H. *Chaos, Gaia, Eros: A Chaos Pioneer Uncovers the Three Great Streams of History*. New York: HarperCollins Publishers, 1994.

Anderson, Walter Truett, Ed. *The Truth about The Truth: De-confusing and Re-constructing the Postmodern World*. New York: Jeremy P. Tarcher/Putnam, 1995.

Avnir, David, Ricardo Gutfraind and Dina Farin. "Fractal analysis in heterogeneous chemistry," in *Fractals in Science*, Armin Bunde and Shlomo Havlin, Editors. Berlin: Springer-Verlag, 1994.

Baker, Gregory L. and Jerry P. Gollub. *Chaotic Dynamics: An Introduction* (2nd Edition). New York: Cambridge University Press, 1996.

Barnsley, Michael F. *Fractals Everywhere*. San Diego: Academic Press, 1988.

Borges, Jorge Luis. "The garden of the forking paths," in *Ficciones*. Anthony Kerrigan, Editor. New York: Grove Press, 1962 (pp. 89-101).

Briggs, John. *Fractals: The Patterns of Chaos*. New York: Touchstone, 1992.

Briggs, John, and F. David Peat. *Turbulent Mirror: An Illustrated Guide to Chaos Theory and the Science of Wholeness*. New York: Harper & Row, Publishers, 1990.

Buldyrev, Sergey V., Ary L. Goldberger, Shlomo Havlin, C.-K. Peng, and H. Eugene Stanley. "Fractals in biology and medecine: from DNA to the heartbeat," in *Fractals in Science*, Armin Bunde and Shlomo Havlin, Editors. Berlin: Springer-Verlag, 1994.

Capra, Fritjof. *The Tao of Physics: An Exploration of the Parallels Between Modern Physics and Eastern Mysticism*. Boston: Shambala Publications, 1991.

Crichton, Michael. *Jurassic Park*. New York: Ballantine Books, 1991.

Devaney, Robert L. *Chaos, Fractals, and Dynamics: Computer Experiments in Mathematics*. Menlo Park: Addison-Wesley Publishing Co., 1990.

—. *A First Course in Chaotic Dynamical Systems: Theory and Experiment*. Reading, MA: Addison-Wesley Publishing Co., 1992.

Dimotakis, Paul E. "Turbulence, fractals, and CCDs," in *Engineering & Science*, Volume LIX, Number 3, pp. 23-34, 1996.

Eco, Umberto. *The Name of the Rose* (English translation). New York: Harcourt Brace Jovanovich, 1983. (Original work published 1980.)

Falconer, Kenneth. *Fractal Geometry: Mathematical Foundations and Applications*. Chichester, England: John Wiley & Sons Ltd., 1995.

Gardner, Martin. "Mathematical Games: White and brown music, fractal curves and one-over-f fluctuations" in *Scientific American*, Volume 238, pp. 16-31, April, 1978.

Gleick, James. *Chaos: Making a New Science*. New York: Penguin Books, 1988.

Goldberger, Ary L., D. R. Rigney and B. J. West. "Chaos and fractals in human physiology" in *Scientific American*, Volume 262, pp. 42-49, February, 1990.

Gulick, Denny. *Encounters With Chaos*. New York: McGraw-Hill, Inc., 1992.

Hayles, N. Katherine, Ed. *Chaos and Order: Complex Dynamics in Literature and Science*. Chicago: The University of Chicago Press, 1991.

Kauffman, Stuart. *At Home in the Universe: The Search for Laws of Self-Organization and Complexity*. New York: Oxford University Press, 1995.

Kellert, Stephen H. *In the Wake of Chaos: Unpredictable Order in Dynamical Systems*. Chicago: The University of Chicago Press, 1993.

Littell, Robert. *The Visiting Professor*. New York, Random House, 1994.

Mandelbrot, Benoit B. *The Fractal Geometry of Nature*. New York: W. H. Freeman and Co., 1977.

Marshall, William. *Roadshow*. New York: Henry Holt & Co., 1985.

McGuire, Michael, *An Eye for Fractals: A Graphic and Photographic Essay*. Redwood City, CA: Addison Wesley Publishing Co., 1991.

Mucherino, Nicholas. *Recursion: A Paradigm For Future Music?* http://www-ks.rus.uni-stuttgart.de/people/schulz/fmusic/recursion.html.

Paulson, William. "Literature, complexity, Interdisciplinarity" in *Chaos and Order: Complex Dynamics in Literature and Science*, N. Katherine Hayles, Editor. Chicago: The University of Chicago Press, 1991.

Peitgen, Heinz-Otto, and P. H. Richter. *The Beauty of Fractals: Images of Complex Dynamical Systems*. New York: Springer-Verlag, 1986.

Peitgen, Heinz-Otto, Hartmut Jürgens and Dietmar Saupe. *Chaos and Fractals: New Frontiers of Science*. New York: Springer-Verlag, 1992.

Peitgen, Heinz-Otto, Hartmut Jürgens, Dietmar Saupe, Evan Maletsky, Terry Perciante, and Lee Yunker. *Fractals for the Classroom: Strategic Activities*, volumes 1 and 2. New York: Springer-Verlag (in cooperation with the National Council of Teachers of Mathematics), 1992.

Peitgen, Heinz-Otto, and Dietmar Saupe. *The Science of Fractal Images*. New York: Springer-Verlag, 1988.

Porush, David. "Fictions as Dissipative Structures: Prigogine's Theory and Postmodernism's Roadshow" in *Chaos and Order: Complex Dynamics in Literature and Science*, N. Katherine Hayles, Editor. Chicago: The University of Chicago Press, 1991.

Prigogine, Ilya and Isabelle Stengers. *Order out of Chaos: Man's New Dialogue with Nature*. New York: Bantam Books, 1984.

Sandefur, James T. *Discrete Dynamical Systems: Theory and Applications*. Oxford: Clarendon Press; New York: Oxford University Press, 1990.

Schroeder, Manfred R. *Fractals, Chaos, Power Laws: Minutes from an Infinite Paradise*. New York: W. H. Freeman and Company, 1991.

Stoppard, Tom. *Arcadia*. London: Faber and Faber, Limited, 1993.

Voss, Richard F. and J. Clarke. "1/f noise in music: Music from 1/f noise" in *The Journal of the Acoustical Society of America*. Volume 63, No. 1, pp. 258-263, January, 1978.

Wegner, Timothy and Mark Peterson. *Fractal Creations*. Mill Valley, CA: Waite Group Press, 1991.

Zukav, Gary. *The Dancing Wu Li Masters: An Overview of the New Physics.* New York: Morrow, 1979.

Videos and CDs

Davids, Zach. *Heartsongs: Musical Mappings of the Heartbeat.* Wellesley, MA: Ivory Moon Music, (BMI), 1995.

Devaney, Robert L. *Chaos, Fractals, and Dynamics: Computer Experiments in Mathematics.* New York: The Science Television Company, 1989.

———. *Professor Devaney Explains The Fractal Geometry of the Mandelbrot Set.* Berkeley, CA: Key Curriculum Press, 1996.

Software

James Gleick's Chaos: The Software. Sausalito, CA: Autodesk, Inc., 1990.

FRACTINT. Available as shareware on the Internet. An early version with complete documentation in Wegner (1991), 1995.

Georges, J., D. Johnson, and R. L. Devaney. *A First Course in Chaotic Dynamical Systems Software.* For Macintosh. Reading, MA: Addison Wesley, 1992.

Interactive Physics. San Mateo, CA: Knowledge Revolution, 1994.

Parris, Richard L. *WINFEED.* Available on the Internet as part of Parris's *Peanuts Software.* http://academy.exeter.edu/~rparris/, 1997.

ANSWERS
To Selected Exercises

Chapter 1

§1.1 Exercises

1. 4, 2, 1, 0.5, 0.25, 0.125

3. 0. 4, -0.2, -0.6, 0.2, -0.6, 0.2

5. 256, 16, 4, 2, 1.414, 1.189

7. a) $a_n = 0.5^n a_0$

c) $a_n = \left| \cos(n\pi / 2) \right|$

9. all approach 0.7390851...

11. 0.2 and 0.8 approach 0.5; $1 \to 0 \to 0 \to ...$; 2 approaches $-\infty$.

13. all approach 0.567143...

15. 50; $a_0 = 2, a_n = a_{n-1} + 2n + 1$

17. $\dfrac{1}{5}$; $a_0 = \dfrac{1}{5}, a_n = 2\left|a_{n-1}\right| - 1$

19. 20; $a_n = 2 + 3n$, $n = 0, 1, 2, ...$

21. 127; $a_n = 2^n - 1$, $n = 1, 2, 3, ...$

§1.2 Exercises

1. 5, 8, 11, 14, 17, 20

3. 6, 5, 4, 3, 2, 1

5. 1, 3, 9, 27, 81, 243

7. 5, 50, 500, 5000, 50000, 500000

9. neither

11. geometric: $r = 5$

13. geometric: $r = 0.5$

15. arithmetic: $d = -10$

17. 612

19. 1/27

21. nMin=1, u(n)=−2+3(n−1), TblStart=1
a) −2, 1, 4, 7, 10, 13, 16
b) u(25)=70
c)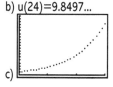

23. nMin=1, u(n)=2^(n/(n+1)), TblStart=1
a) 1.4142, 1.5874, 1.6818, 1.7411, 1.7818, 1.8114, 1.834
b) u(25)=1.9473...
c)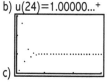

25. nMin=0, u(n)=1.1u(n−1), TblStart=0
a) 1, 1.1, 1.21, 1.331, 1.4641, 1.61051, 1.771561
b) u(24)=9.8497...
c)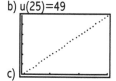

27. nMin=0, u(n)=1/√(u(n−1)), TblStart=0
a) 48, 0.14434, 2.6321, 0.61637, 1.2737, 0.88606, 1.0624
b) u(24)=1.00000...+
c)

29. a) nMin=1, u(n)=2n−1
b) u(25)=49
c)

31. nMin=1, u(n)=3^(1/n)
b) u(25)=1.044924...

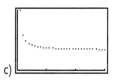
c)

§1.3 Exercises

1. 240

3. 280

5. 605

7. 295

9. a)210; b)5050; c)131328; d)1113778

11. $7\dfrac{63}{64} = 7.984375$

13. $12\dfrac{205}{256} = 12.80078125$

15. 12.49984

17. a)8/33 b)70/33 c)1

§1.4 Exercises

1. ClrHome
Disp "SUM OF INTEGERS"
Disp "FROM 1 TO N"
Prompt N
N(1+N)/2→S
Disp S

3. ClrHome
Input "FIRST NUMBER? ", A
Input "LAST NUMBER? ", B
Disp (A+B)/2

5. ClrHome
Disp "COEFFICIENTS..."
Prompt A
If A=0
Then
Disp "NOT QUADRATIC"
Goto 1
End

Prompt B
Prompt C
B²–4AC→D
If D<0
Then
Disp "NO SOLUTIONS"
Goto 1
End
(–B+√(D))/(2A)→P
(–B-√(D))/(2A)→Q
Disp "SOLUTIONS ARE", P, Q
Lbl 1

7. For(J,1,3,1)
Disp "HAVE A NICE DAY"
End

9. ClrHome
Input "NUMBER OF TESTS?",N
0→S
For(J,1,N,1)
Input "SCORE? ",T
T+S→S
End
Disp "AVERAGE=",S/N

§1.5 Exercises

1. $a_n = \dfrac{n+1}{n}$; $\lim_{n\to\infty} a_n = 1$

because $\dfrac{n+1}{n} = 1 + \dfrac{1}{n}$ and

$\dfrac{1}{n} \to 0$.

3. $a_n = 16 + 4n$, $n = 0, 1, 2, \dots$
Unbounded

5. $a_n = \dfrac{n^2+1}{n^2}$; $\lim_{n\to\infty} a_n = 1$

because $\dfrac{n^2+1}{n^2} = 1 + \dfrac{1}{n^2}$ and

$\dfrac{1}{n} \to 0$.

7. $a_n = \left(\dfrac{3n-1}{3n}\right)(-1)^{n+1}$; no

limit; alternate terms approach 1
and –1.

9. $a_n = \dfrac{n(n+1)}{2}$, $n = 0, 1, 2,$

...; unbounded.

11. 1

13. 0

15. 1

17. Unbounded because

$a_n = \dfrac{n^2}{2n-1} \to \dfrac{n}{2} \to \infty$.

19. Unbounded because

$a_n = \log\left(\dfrac{1}{n}\right)$. As $n \to \infty$,

$\dfrac{1}{n} \to 0$ so $\log\left(\dfrac{1}{n}\right) \to -\infty$.

21. Approaches limit 0 because

$a_n = \dfrac{5\sqrt{n}}{n-3.5} \to \dfrac{5\sqrt{n}}{n} \to \dfrac{5}{\sqrt{n}} \to 0$

23. 2, 8/3, 26/9, 80/27, 242/81.
Series converges to 3.

25. ½, 5/8, 21/32, 85/128,
341/512. Series converges to 2/3.

27. 6.9282, 11.8272, 15.2913,
17.7408, 19.4728. Converges to

$\dfrac{\sqrt{48}}{1-\left(1/\sqrt{2}\right)} \approx 23.6544$.

29. 1, –0.2, 1.24, –0.488,
1.5856. Series diverges.

31. 2/3

Chapter 2

§2.1 Exercises

1. a)

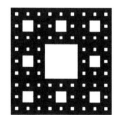

b) 64; 512; 8^n
c) 64/81, 512/729, $(8/9)^n$
d) area $\to 0$
e) Strictly self-similar

3. a)

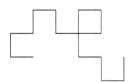

b) RRLRRLLRRRLLRLL
c) RRLRRLLRRRLLRLLRRRLRRLLL
RRLLRLL at next stage. Notice the
R in the middle and work away from
the middle toward the ends.
e) Join every other vertex at stage
n and you get stage n–1.

7. A centimeter magnified by 100
is an exact reproduction of the
meter stick (with infinitely fine
gradations marked).

9.

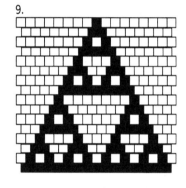

§2.2 Exercises

1. Change of base theorem: For

any base x, $\log_r n = \dfrac{\log_x n}{\log_x r}$.

(Proof: $r^{\log_r n} = n$
$\log_x r^{\log_r n} = \log_x n$
$\log_r n \cdot \log_x r = \log_x n$)

Therefore both $\dfrac{\log_a n}{\log_a r}$ and $\dfrac{\log_b n}{\log_b r}$

are equal to $\log_r n$.

3.

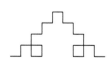

(continued)

5.

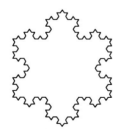

7. $f(x) = 81x - 8$

9. a)

	0.4	0.6	
.16	.24	.76	.84
.064	.304	.664	.904
.096	.336	.696	.936

b) 0.861353...

11.

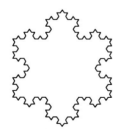

b) Self-similar, not strict.

---

c) 4, 16/3, 64/9, 256/27,

$4^n / 3^{n-1}$

d) Perimeter $\to \infty$

e) 0.5773..., 0.6415..., 0.6700...,
0.6826...; geometric series starts
at Stage 1 with $a_1 = \sqrt{3} / 12$,
$r = 4 / 9$. Area at stage n is

$$\sqrt{3} / 4 + \frac{\sqrt{3} / 12 \left(1 - (4/9)^n \right)}{(1 - 4/9)}$$

f) Area approaches a limit:

$$\sqrt{3} / 4 + \frac{\sqrt{3} / 12}{1 - 4/9} \approx 0.6928...$$

12. {0, 1/27, 2/27, 1/9, 2/9,
7/27, 8/27, 1/3, 2/3. 19/27,
20/27, 7/9, 8/9, 25/27, 26/27, 1}

13. 81

14. 2^{n+1}

15. a) RRRRR...; b) LRLRRR...;
c) LRLRLLL...

16. Address ends in infinite string
of L's or R's.

17. LRLRLRLR..., for example.

18. a) $\frac{2}{3} + \frac{2}{3^2} = \frac{8}{9}$

b) $\frac{2}{3^2} + \frac{2}{3^4} + \frac{2}{3^5} + \frac{2}{3^6} + \cdots =$

$$\frac{2}{3^2} + \frac{2/3^4}{1 - 1/3} = \frac{7}{27}$$

c) $\frac{2}{3^2} + \frac{2}{3^4} = \frac{20}{81}$

d) $\frac{2}{3^2} + \frac{2}{3^4} + \frac{2}{3^6} + \ldots =$

$$\frac{2/9}{1 - 1/9} = \frac{1}{4}$$

§2.3 Exercises

1. D ≈ 1.013

r	4	8	16	32
n	11	22	45	90

3. D ≈ 1.548

r	4	8	16	32
n	16	45	152	271

---

5. D ≈ 1.548

r	4	8	16	32
n	16	59	195	581

7. D ≈ 1.244

r	4	8	16	32
n	14	39	84	192

8. D ≈ 1.606

r	4	8	16	32
n	12	42	98	370

9. Answers may vary depending on
placement of boxes.
a) D≈1.6026...
b) D≈1.6298...
c) Answers will differ from the
results of (a) and (b) but remain in
the same range.

11. Answers may vary depending
on placement of boxes.
a) D≈1.2385... which differs slightly
from the results in the text. b)
D≈1.4245... Use of 8 data points
differs slightly from (a).
c) Randomizing corners also
changes the data slightly.

Chapter 3

§3.1 Exercises

1.

0	0.5	2	−1
1	2	5	−1
3	5	11	−1
7	11	23	−1
15	23	47	−1

3.

1/3	½	2/5	1
−1/3	0	−1/5	1
−1/3	−1	−3/5	1
−1/3	1	1/5	1
−1/3	1	−3/5	1

5. a) Slowly approaches 0
b) Approaches 0.6
c) Approaches a 4-cycle
d) Approaches an 8-cycle
e) Approaches a 3-cycle

7. $\sqrt[64]{32} = 1.0556...$

9. $\cos(\cos(\cos(2\pi))) = 0.8575...$

11. a) 2/3; b) 2/3; c) 0; d) 0; e)−128; f) 0.8

13. 0 stays at 0; 1 stays at 1; −1 goes to 1 and stays there; seeds between −1 and 1 are attracted towards 0; seeds less than −1 or greater than 1 orbit to infinity.

15. All seeds orbit to infinity.

17. $\frac{1+\sqrt{5}}{2}$ stays at $\frac{1+\sqrt{5}}{2}$; $-\frac{1+\sqrt{5}}{2}$ goes to $\frac{1+\sqrt{5}}{2}$ and stays there; $\frac{1-\sqrt{5}}{2}$ stays at $\frac{1-\sqrt{5}}{2}$. All other sees between $-\frac{1+\sqrt{5}}{2}$ and $\frac{1+\sqrt{5}}{2}$ approach a 2-cycle {0, −1}. All seeds less than $-\frac{1+\sqrt{5}}{2}$ or greater than $\frac{1+\sqrt{5}}{2}$ approach infinity.

19. The two seeds $\frac{1\pm\sqrt{13}}{2}$ are fixed; all other seeds approach infinity.

§3.2. Exercises

1. a) 1; b) 0,1; c) −0.5, 1.5; d) 0, −2, 3; e) All non-negative x; f) ±1

3. 0, 1−1/r

5. a) $9x - 36x^2 + 54x^3 - 27x^4$; 0, 2/3
b) $x^4 - 2x^2$; 0, −1, $(1\pm\sqrt{5})/2$
c) $x^9 - 3x^7 + 3x^5 - 2x^3 + x$; 0, ±√2

7. a) 0 is neutral: weakly attracting on the right, weakly repelling on the left; b) 0.5; c) 0; d) ±1.895...; e) 0; f) 0 is neutral but weakly attracting.

9. a) All points are fixed, so no orbits approach any point but stay on the seed.

b) Fixed points are ±1, but all other seeds in the domain fall into a 2-cycle, none getting closer to or further from either fixed point.

c) All non-negative points are fixed, negatives are fixed after one iteration. No orbits approach any point (as in part (a)).
d) Fixed point 0.5 is weakly attracting on the left, weakly repelling on the right.

11. −2/3 is attracting, 1 is repelling

13. 0, 1; both repelling

§3.3 Exercises

1. repelling

3. attracting

5. {0.1494..., 0.4880..., 0.9594...} is attracting; {0.1694..., 0.5403..., 0.9537...} is repelling.

7. In the domain [0, π], f has 2 fixed points, ^2f has 4, ^3f has 8, and ^nf has 2^n.

§3.4 Exercises

1. a) −1; b) 13.5

3. a) −1; b) 0.2

5. a) 0.5 neutral: weakly attracting on left, weakly repelling on right
b) 0 attracting, 1 repelling
c) $\frac{1+\sqrt{2}}{2}$ repelling, $\frac{1-\sqrt{2}}{2}$ attracting
d) $\frac{1\pm\sqrt{6}}{2}$ both repelling

7. a) 0, repelling; 1, attracting; 2, repelling;
b) 0 neutral but weakly attracting on right and weakly repelling on left; ±√2 both repelling

c)−1 repelling, 1 attracting, 2 repelling
d) 0 repelling, 2/3 neutral but weakly attracting.

§3.5 Exercises

1. a) $x^2 + 3x - 10$; b) −5, 2

3. Other factor: $x^2 + 2x - 2$; solutions: −2, −2/3, $-1\pm\sqrt{3}$

5. {0.5580..., 0.7645...} attracting

7. { ±√2 } repelling

9. {−0.6, 0.2} repelling

11. a) {0.3454..., 0.9045...} repelling
b) {0.1882..., 0.6112..., 0.9504...}, {0.1169..., 0.4131..., 0.9698...}, both repelling

Chapter 4

§4.1 Exercises

1. a) 0; b) 0, 0.375; c) 0, 0.5833...; d) 0, 0.6774...; e) 0, 0.7142...

3. a) attracting; b) attracting; c) neutral; d) repelling; e) repelling

5. a) 0 attracting; b) 0 attracting; c) 0 repelling, 0.4285... attracting; d) 0 repelling, 0.5454... attracting; e) 0 repelling, 0.6428... attracting

7.

	Fixed Pt.	Slope	
0.5	0	0.5	att
1.0	0	1	neut
1.5	0	1.5	rep
	1/3	0.5	att
2.0	0	2.0	rep
	½	0	att
2.5	0	2.5	rep
	0.6	-0.5	att
2.9	0	2.9	rep
	0.6551...	-0.9	att
3.1	0	3.1	rep
	0.6774...	-1.1	rep

3.4	0	3.4	rep
	0.7058...	-1.4	rep
3.5	0	3.5	rep
	0.7142...	-1.5	rep

9. {0.4794..., 0.8236...}
a) attracts 0.5; b) slope is −0.29

11. Choose $r = 3.5$, for example
a) The orbit of 0.5 is attracted to a
4-cycle. Conjecture: 2-cycles end
at $1 + \sqrt{6}$ and 4-cycles begin.
b) {0.4285..., 0.8571...} is
repelling and slope is −1.25,
greater than 1 in absolute value

§4.2 Exercises

1. The orbit: 0.5, 1, 0, 0, 0...
Virtually any other seed's orbit
wanders unpredictably throughout
the whole unit interval. (While
there are many other seeds that
are fixed, periodic, eventually fixed
or eventually periodic, your
probability of picking them at
random is essentially 0. Some are
explored in Exercise 18 of §4.4.)

5.

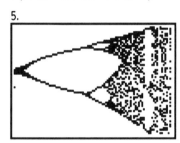

a) $r \approx 3.5639...$ A 16-cycle
begins
b) If $r = 3.566$, the orbit of 0 is
attracted to a 16-cycle.

7.

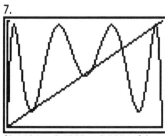

{0.1494..., 0.4880..., 0.9594...} is
attracting (slope = -0.8755...);
{0.1694..., 0.5403..., 0.9537...} is
repelling (slope = 2.7436...).

§4.3 Exercises

1. a) 0.1127..., 0.8872...
b) −0.3660..., 1.3660......
c) −0.6180..., 1.6180...;
d) −0.8228..., 1.8228...
e) −1, 2

3. Attractor	Endpoints
0.2	±0.7236...
−0.4	±1.3062
−0.7	±1.4746

5. FnOff
"X²+C"→Y₁
"X"→Y₂
-2→Xmin
2→Xmax
1→Xscl
-2→Ymin
2→Ymax
1→Yscl
For(C,-2,.25,.25)
Tangent(Y₁,(1-√(1-4C))/2)
nDeriv(Y₁,X,(1-√(1-4C))/2)→M
Text(1,10,"C=",C)
Text(1,70,"M=",M)
Pause
End

Attracting when $−0.75 < c < 0.25$

7. a) no non-trivial 2-cycle
b) no non-trivial 2-cycle
c) attracting 2-cycle {−0.8872...,
−0.1127...}; tangent slope = 0.4
d) attracting 2-cycle {−1.1708...,
0.1708...}; tangent slope = −0.8
e) repelling 2-cycle {−1.3660...,
0.3660...; tangent slope = −2

9. FnOff
"(X²+C)²+C"→Y₁
"X"→Y₁
-2→Xmin
2→Xmax
1→Xscl
-2→Ymin
2→Ymax
1→Yscl
For(C,-2,-.75,.25)
(-1-√(-3-4C))/2→P
Tangent(Y₁,P)
nDeriv(Y₁,X,P)→M
Text(1,10,"C=",C)
Text(1,70,"M=",M)
Pause

End

Attracting for $-1.25 < c < -0.75$

11. With $c = -1.76$, an attracting 3-
cycle is {0.0238..., -1.7594...,
1.3356...}; a repelling 3-cycle is
{-0.1332..., -1.7422..., 1.2754...}

13. a) ClrDraw
ClrHome
FnOff
Disp "WINDOW"
Prompt Xmin
Prompt Xmax
Prompt Ymin
Prompt Ymax
1→Xscl
1→Yscl
(Xmax-Xmin)/94→S
For(C,Xmin,Xmax,S)
0→X
For(J,1,200,1)
X²+C→X
If J>50
Pt-On(C,X)
End
End

Compare graph with Figure 4.41.

b) ClrDraw
ClrHome
FnOff
Disp "WINDOW"
Prompt Xmin
Prompt Xmax
Prompt Ymin
Prompt Ymax
1→Xscl
1→Yscl
(Xmax-Xmin)/94→S
For(K,Xmin,Xmax,S)
.5→X
For(J,1,200,1)
Ksin(πX)→X
If J>50
Pt-On(K,X)
End
End

Compare graph with Figure 4.43.

§4.4 Exercises

1. a) 13: u(14)=0.0463...,
v(14)=0.1486...

b) $u(15) < 0.5$, $v(15) > 0.5$
c) $u(17)$-$v(17)$=0.9720...

3. Orbits differ by 10^{-10} at $n = 7$, and by 0.5 at $n = 40$.

5. a)

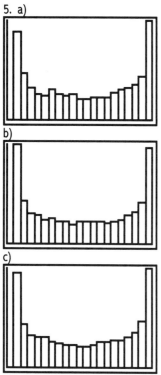

b)

c)

All roughly the same as each other and as Figure 4.51.

7. $\dfrac{5 \pm \sqrt{5}}{8} \approx 0.9045084972...$

and 0.3454915028...
b) The calculated orbit point after 13 iterations differs from the point of the cycle by 10^{-10}. Gradually the calculated orbit wanders away from the 2-cycle. Because the decimal approximations are not exact, and because this cycle is repelling, the sensitivity of the function eventually takes over and moves the orbit off the approximations.

9. a) $f(1) = 4 \cdot 0 = 0$

b) $f(0.5) = 1$ and $f(1) = 0$

c) a_3 is the smallest positive solution to $4x(1-x) = 0.5$.

$\therefore a_3 = \dfrac{2 - \sqrt{2}}{4} \approx 0.1464...$, an

eventually fixed point with orbit
$a_3 \to a_2 \to a_1 \to 0 \to 0 \to \cdots$

d) The smallest positive solution to $4x(1-x) = a_3$ is

$a_4 = \dfrac{1 - \sqrt{1 - a_3}}{2} \approx 0.0380...$,

eventually fixed because a_3 is.
e) An infinite, decreasing sequence approaching 0.
f) If you take the *larger* solution to $f(x) = 0.5$, and then continue as with the a's except always taking the larger solution, you generate an infinite increasing sequence of b's approaching 1. Then each member of both the a and the b sequence spawns an infinity of sequences, all of which are eventually fixed points. A similar process with cycles would produce infinitely many eventually periodic points. The unit interval is packed with fixed, eventually fixed, periodic and eventually periodic points, virtually all invisible to the finite approximations of a calculator.

11.

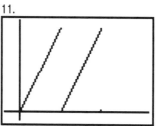

Stretches both halves of the domain, but layers instead of folding.

13. ClrHome
ClrAllLists
FnOff
PlotsOff
4 * rand−2→X
Disp "SEED"
Disp X
For(J,1,20,1)
J→L1(J)
0→L2(J)
End
For(K,1,3000,1)
X²−2→X
int(5X)+11→A
L2(A)+1→L2(A)
End
Plot1(Histogram, L1, L2)
PlotsOn 1

0→Xmin
21→Xmax
1→Xscl
0→Ymin

max(L2)→Ymax
0→Yscl
DispGraph

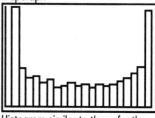

Histogram similar to those for the logistic function.

Chapter 5

§5.1 Exercises

1. $2+8i$

3. $-8+6i$

5. -8

7. $6/13 + 4/13i$

9. $-1/5+2/5i$

11. $-6i$

13. $2-12i$

15. $1-10i$

17. $2/29-5/29i$

19. $12/13+5/13i$

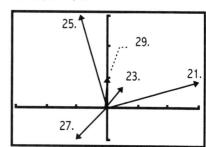

Absolute values: 21. $\sqrt{10}$; 23. 1; 25. $\sqrt{10}$; 27. $\sqrt{2}$ 29. 1

31.

$\left(-1+i\sqrt{2}\right)^2 + 2\left(-1+i\sqrt{2}\right)+3 =$

$\left(-1-2i\sqrt{2}\right)+\left(-2+2i\sqrt{2}\right)+3 = 0$

and

$$\left(-1-i\sqrt{2}\right)^2 + 2\left(-1-i\sqrt{2}\right) + 3 =$$
$$\left(-1+2i\sqrt{2}\right) + \left(-2-2i\sqrt{2}\right) + 3 = 0$$

33. ½-4i

35. $1/2 \pm i\sqrt{3}/2$

37. $-2+i$

39.

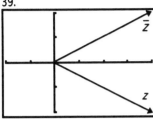

$|\bar{z}| = 2\sqrt{5} \approx 4.4721$

41. $(a+bi)(a-bi) = a^2 - (bi)^2$
$$= a^2 + b^2$$

43. If $z = a + bi$ and $w = c + di$,
then $zw = (ac - bd) + (ad + bc)i$
and $\overline{zw} = (ac - bd) - (ad + bc)i$.
Also $\bar{z} = a - bi$ and $\bar{w} = c - di$,
so
$$\bar{z} \cdot \bar{w} = (ac - bd) + (-ad - bc)i .$$
Therefore $\overline{zw} = \bar{z} \cdot \bar{w}$.

§5.2 Exercises

1. a) 5; b) 13;
c) $4\sqrt{2} \approx 5.6568...$

3. $18 + 8\sqrt{2} \approx 29.3137...$

5. a) All points outside the circle of radius 2 centered at the origin.
b) All points inside and on the circle of radius 5 centered at the origin.
c) All points inside the circle of radius 4 centered at $z = 3$.

7. a) All points on the non-negative real axis.
b) All points on the vertical line at $x = 2$.
c) All points on two horizontal lines at $y = \pm 1$.

9. a)

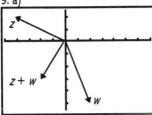

b)

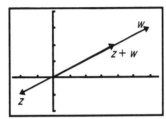

c)

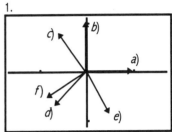

11. Let $z = a + bi$ and
$w = c + di$.
Then $zw = (ac - bd) + (ad + bc)i$
$$|zw| = \sqrt{(ac-bd)^2 + (ad+bc)^2}$$
$$= \sqrt{(ac)^2 - 2abcd + (bd)^2 + (ad)^2 + 2abcd + (bc)^2}$$
$$= \sqrt{(ac)^2 + (bd)^2 + (ad)^2 + (bc)^2} .$$
But $|z| = \sqrt{a^2 + b^2}$, and
$|w| = \sqrt{c^2 + d^2}$, so
$$|z| \cdot |w| = \sqrt{(a^2 + b^2)(c^2 + d^2)}$$
$$= \sqrt{a^2c^2 + b^2d^2 + a^2d^2 + b^2c^2} = |zw|$$

13.

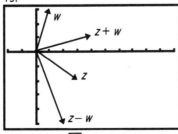

a) $|z + w| = \sqrt{17} \approx 4.1231...$

$|z| + |w| = \sqrt{13} + \sqrt{10} \approx 6.7678...$
Therefore $|z + w| < |z| + |w|$.

b) $|z - w| = \sqrt{29} \approx 5.3851...$

$|z| - |w| = \sqrt{13} - \sqrt{10} \approx 0.4432...$
Therefore $|z - w| > |z| - |w|$.

§5.3 Exercises

1.

a) $1 + 0i$; b) $0 + i$;

c) $-\frac{1}{2} + \frac{\sqrt{3}}{2}i$; d) $-\frac{\sqrt{2}}{2} - \frac{\sqrt{2}}{2}i$;

e) $\frac{1}{2} - \frac{\sqrt{3}}{2}i$; f) $-\frac{\sqrt{3}}{2} - \frac{1}{2}i$

3. a) $e^{(-\pi/4)i}$; b) $5e^{\pi/i}$;
c) $8e^{(\pi/3)i}$; d) $10e^{0i}$;
e) $e^{(-\pi/2)i}$; f) $2e^{(-\pi/2)i}$

5. -4

7. $\pm 2i$

9. $e^{-30°i}, e^{90°i}, e^{-150°i}$

11. a) $e^{\theta i} = \cos\theta + i\sin\theta$

b) $|e^{\theta i}| = |\cos\theta + i\sin\theta|$
$$= \sqrt{\cos^2\theta + \sin^2\theta} = 1$$
c) The unit circle.

13. $\dfrac{1}{e^{\alpha i}} = \dfrac{1}{\cos\alpha + i\sin\alpha}$
$$= \frac{\cos\alpha - i\sin\alpha}{\cos^2\alpha + \sin^2\alpha}$$
$$= \frac{\cos\alpha + i\sin\alpha}{1} = \cos\alpha - i\sin\alpha$$
$$= \cos(-\alpha) + i\sin(-\alpha) = e^{-\alpha i} .$$

But $\cos\alpha - i\sin\alpha = \overline{\cos\alpha + i\sin\alpha}$,

so also $\dfrac{1}{e^{\alpha i}} = \overline{e^{\alpha i}}$

15. a)
$f(0) = e^{0i} = \cos 0 + i\sin 0 = 1$ b)
sin and cos are both periodic with a period of 2π; therefore so is f since
$f(x) = \cos x + i\sin x$.
c) The unit circle.
d) $f(a)\cdot f(b) =$
$(\cos a + i\sin a)\cdot(\cos b + i\sin b) =$
$[\cos a\cos b - \sin a\sin b] + ...$
$\qquad [\sin a\cos b + \cos a\sin b]i =$
$\cos(a+b) + i\sin(a+b) = e^{(a+b)i}$
$= f(a+b)$

§5.4 Exercises

1. Translates the plane 5 right and 1 down

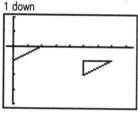

3. Reflects the plane over the real axis.

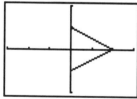

5. Rotates the plane clockwise around the origin by 90° and stretches the plane out from the origin by a factor of 2.

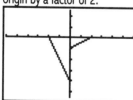

7. Reflects the plane over a line through the origin inclined at 30° from the positive real axis.

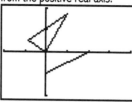

9. Reflects the plane over a line through the origin inclined at –60° from the positive real axis.

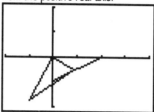

11. Reflects the plane over a line through the origin, inclined at –45° to the positive real axis, and stretches the plane out from the origin by a factor of 2.

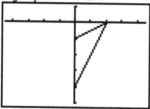

13. The midpoint of the segment joining (a,b) to (c,d) is
$\left(\dfrac{a+c}{2}, \dfrac{b+d}{2}\right)$. Therefore
$m = \dfrac{a+c}{2} + \dfrac{b+d}{2}i$. The endpoints of the new segment are
$f(z) = a + 2 - bi$ and
$f(w) = c + 2 - di$. The midpoint of this segment is
$\left(\dfrac{(a+2)+(c+2)}{2}, \dfrac{-b-d}{2}\right)$, or
$\left(\dfrac{a+c+4}{2}, -\dfrac{b+d}{2}\right)$. But this is the graph of $f(m)$ because
$f(m) = \dfrac{a+c}{2} + 2 - \dfrac{b+d}{2}i$.

15. $k = i$

17. $\left|f(z) - f(w)\right| =$
$\left|(z+k) - (w+k)\right| = |z-w|$

19. $\left|f(z) - f(w)\right| =$
$\left|\overline{z}e^{\alpha i} - \overline{w}e^{\alpha i}\right| = |\overline{z} - \overline{w}|\cdot\left|e^{\alpha i}\right| =$
$|\overline{z} - \overline{w}| = |z-w|$

21. If $z = e^{\theta i}$, then
$f(z) = e^{\theta i}\cdot e^{\alpha i} = e^{(\theta+\alpha)i}$.
Therefore, f adds α to the angle of every z, which rotates the points through the angle α.

Chapter 6

§6.1 Exercises

3. a) tends to 0; b) tends to ∞; c) tends to 0; d) tends to 0; e) eventually periodic in a 6-cycle; f) does not tend to an attractor and is not eventually fixed or periodic, but moves unpredictably around the unit circle; g) tends to ∞; h) tends to 0.

5. a) tends to ∞; b) eventually periodic in a 2-cycle $\{0, -1\}$; c) tends to attracting 2-cycle $\{0, -1\}$; d) tends to ∞.

7. $\{1, -1\}$

9. a) If z is on the unit circle then $|z| = 1$, so $\left|z^2\right| = 1$, and therefore iteration through f keeps the orbit on the unit circle.
b) (i) All have absolute value 1. (ii) But the calculator gives accurate results only for z_2 (eventually fixed at 1) and z_3 (periodic in a 2-cycle with $e^{(4\pi/3)i}$). The calculator shows incorrectly that z_1 and z_4 tend to ∞. (iii) Because of the sensitivity of the system, a small error gets amplified under iteration. With z_2 and z_3, the orbital time to being fixed was short enough that the calculator gave accurate results. Under longer iteration for

z_1 and z_4, the calculator's inaccuracies in approximating the seed eventually were magnified to give inaccurate results.

c) Let $z = e^{(2\pi/k)i}$, where k is chosen as follows:

cycle	3	4	5	n
k	7	15	31	$2^n - 1$

§6.2 Exercises

3.

5.

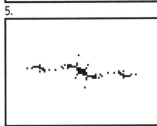

7.

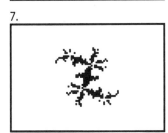

9. a) By definition, Prisoner Points tend to a finite attractor. If there were a finite attractor, the orbit of 0 would find it. Since the orbit of 0 escapes, there is no finite attractor and hence no Prisoner Points.
b) No points are plotted. Every point tried by the calculator escapes, implying that the entire plane is the Escaping Set.

c) The fixed points are $\dfrac{1 \pm i\sqrt{5}}{2}$.

Because their orbits stay on the plane and to not tend to an attractor, they are Julia Points.
d) All the Julia Points for this parameter are repelling. The calculator could only find and plot them if it picked them with complete accuracy. The fixed points in (c)

are irrational and are not specified with sufficient accuracy by the looping procedure of $\mathtt{JULIA1}$.

11. The fixed points are $\dfrac{1 \pm i\sqrt{11}}{2}$, the 2-cycle is
$$\left\{\frac{-1 + i\sqrt{15}}{2}, \frac{-1 - i\sqrt{15}}{2}\right\}.$$

Neither fixed points nor 2-cycle is attracting. However, all are Julia Points because they stay on the plane without tending to an attractor.

13. a) The midpoint is:
$$\left(\frac{p + (1-p)}{2}, \frac{q + (-q)}{2}\right) = \left(\frac{1}{2}, 0\right)$$

b) $f(1 - p - qi) =$
$$[-a(1-p)^2 + a(-q)^2 + a(1-p) - b(-q) + 2b(1-p)(-q)]$$
$$+ i[-b(1-p)^2 + b(-q)^2 + b(1-p) + a(-q) - 2a(1-p)(-q)]$$
$$= [-ap^2 + aq^2 + ap - bq + 2bpq]$$
$$+ i[-bp^2 + bq^2 + bp + aq - 2apq]$$
$$= f(p + qi).$$

14. If $|z| > \dfrac{1}{|r|} + 1$, then

$|z| - 1 > \dfrac{1}{|r|}$. Therefore,

$|f(z)| = |rz(1-z)| = |r||z||1 - z|$

$= |r||z||z - 1| > |r||z|(|z| - 1)$

$> |r||z|\dfrac{1}{|r|} = |z|$. Then

$|f(z)| \geq |z|(1 + \varepsilon)$ for some small number ε. Iteration shows
$|{}^n f(z)| \geq |z|(1 + \varepsilon)^n$, and so
$|{}^n f(z)| \to \infty$.

15. ClrHome
ClrDraw
FnOff
AxesOff
a+bi
−2→Xmin
2→Xmax
0→Xscl

−2→Ymin
2→Ymax
0→Yscl
Input "PARAMETER? ",R
1/abs(R)+1→B
ClrHome
4/94→S
4/62→T
For(U,-2,2,S)
For(V,0,2,T)
U+Vi→Z
0→J
Lbl 1
RZ(1-Z)→Z
If abs(Z)>B:Goto 2
J+1→J
If J<50:Goto 1
Pt-On(U,V)
Pt-On(1−U,-V)
Lbl 2
End
End

a)

b)

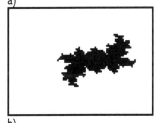

c)

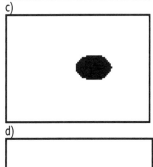

d)

§6.3 Exercises

1. No point of the Julia Set is an attractor because attractors are Prisoner Points. Nearby non-Julia Points tend toward an attractor or toward infinity, in either case away from the Julia Set.

3. a) $\pm\sqrt[4]{18}e^{(\pi/8)i}$;

b) $\pm e^{(3\pi/4)i}$; c) $\pm\sqrt{2}e^{(\pi/6)i}$

5.
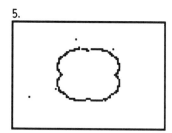

7.
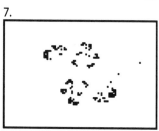

9.
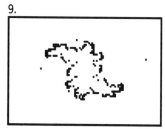

11.
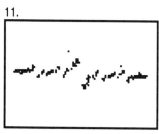

13.
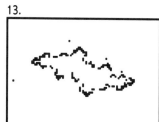

15.
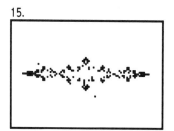

17. Input "PARAMETER? ",C
$(1+\sqrt{(1-4C)})/2\rightarrow A$
$(1-\sqrt{(1-4C)})/2\rightarrow B$
Disp A,B

a) 1.3002...−0.6248...*i*, repelling;
−0.3002...+0.6248...*i*, repelling
b) 1.3406...−0.2379...*i*, repelling;
−0.3406...+0.2379...*i*, attracting
c) 1.1525...+0.6130...*i*, repelling;
−0.1525...−0.6130...*i*, repelling
d) 1.2745...+0.3872...*i*, repelling;
−0.2745...−0.3872...*i*, attracting

19. A point z is on the unit circle if and only if $|z| = 1$. If $|z| = 1$, then $|z^2| = 1$. Hence if z is on the unit circle, then so is $f(z)$. The circle is invariant under f.

§6.4 Exercises

1. a) 0 is attracted to 0.2763..., Julia Set is connected; b) 0 is eventually periodic so does not escape, and Julia Set is connected. (To see connectedness, raise the number of iterations to 5000 or use WINFEED.) c) 0 is attracted to a 3-cycle, Julia Set is connected; d) 0 escapes, Julia set is totally disconnected.

3. a) connected; b) totally disconnected; c) connected; d) totally disconnected

5. Changing sign of imaginary part flips image horizontally across the imaginary axis. Changing sign of real part changes Julia Set from connected to totally disconnected (in this case, but not in general).

7. a) Hard to tell because there appear to be some black spaces

implying the existence of Prisoner Points, implying connectedness. b) 0 escapes, so there is NO attractor. c) There can be no Prisoner Points since there is no attractor, contradicting the apparent black regions. d) The black regions disappear. e) Backwards iteration seems to show a connected boundary around a large interior; this is a misleading image; the default graph is a better image when the number of iterations is sufficiently high.

9. Not strict. Compare the Julia Set for $c = i$ with the fractal tree in Figure 2.4. Well chosen portions of the image will reproduce the original under sufficient magnification, but not any arbitrary portion

11. Results are not reliable. The Julia Sets in (b) and (d) are totally disconnected, but the power regression analysis gives a boxcount dimension greater than 1. Since a totally disconnected set is fractal dust, its dimension must be less than 1.

§6.5 Exercises

1. The orbit of 0 approaches the following fixed point attractors:
a) -0.2227...+0.4151...*i*;
b) -0.3944...−0.2236...*i*;
c) -0.4357...−0.1602...*i*;
d) 0.0527...+0.2236...*i*

3. The orbit of 0 approaches the following 2-cycle attractors:
a) {−1.0339...+0.1872...*i*, 0.0339...−0.1872 *i*}
b) {−0.9255...−0.1762...*i*, −0.0744...+0.1762...*i*}
c) {−1.1718...−0.0372...*i*, 0.1718...+0.0372...*i*}
d) {−1.1136...+0.1629...*i*, 0.1136...−0.1629...*i*}

5. Tends to a 3-cycle.

7. a)

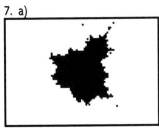

c) 5-cycle for $c = -1.256 + 0.381i$

9. There is evidence of fine structure, complex irregularity and (non-strict) self-similarity. The Mandelbrot Set is defined by a recursive process: the behavior of the orbit of 0. Fractal dimension is evident from the complexity of the boundary and antennae but is hard to substantiate numerically.

§6.6 Exercises

5. Attractor is a 3-cycle; Julia Set has a rabbit shape as in Figure 6.33 with three regions together at each juncture point.

7. A clockwise analysis of the next largest bulb starting from the 3-bulb generates the sequence 4, 5, 6, 7, 8, ...

9. a) Period is 7; b) Period is 14; c) Period is 28; d) Period is 21; e) 7 antennae at juncture points.

11. In order, counterclockwise from the period-21 "arm" of the period-7 bulb, the next largest bulbs have periods of 28, 35, and 42.

13. The red dot inside the main body is the attracting fixed point for the orbit of 0. Toward the center of the main body, convergence is rapid, and the white dots stream into the red dot. Toward the edge, convergence is slower and a spiral pattern develops. Closer to the edge, convergence is very slow and a whole region is covered by white dots.

15. The single large Julia Set seen in the main body is pinched off at each side into three main sections. One fixed point is at the extreme right of the Julia Set, the other at the juncture of the middle and left regions. The orbit of 0 is attracted to a 2-cycle, seen most clearly toward the edge of the Mandelbrot head where a spiral pattern identifies the points in the attractor.

19. Outside the main body, the orbit of 0 is not attracted to a fixed point (represented by the red dots).

Chapter 7

§7.1 Exercises

1. a) $3 - 9x^2$; b) $10x - 3$; c) $4x^3$; d) $4x^3 - 6x^2 + 8x$; e) $12x + 5$; f) $6x - 9x^2$

3. a) $y = x - 1$;

b) $4y + 8x = 9$;

c) $y = 4x - 16$;

d) $16y + 40x + 3 = 0$

5. a) 0 is the only fixed point; $f'(0) = 0.5$ so 0 is attracting.

b) 0 is the only fixed point; $f'(0) = 1$ so 0 is neutral.

c) 0 and 0.6 are fixed points; $f'(0) = 2.5$ so 0 is repelling; $f'(0.6) = -0.5$ so 0.6 is attracting.

d) 0 and 0.6875 are fixed points; $f'(0) = 3.2$ and $f'(0.6875) = -1.2$ so both are repelling.

7. a) $\{0.7994..., 0.5130...\}$ Derivative of ^2f is 0.16 at these points: cycle is attracting.

b) $\{0.8571..., 0.4285...\}$ Derivative of ^2f is -1.25 at these points: cycle is repelling.

c) $\{0.1708..., -1.1708...\}$ Derivative of ^2f is -0.8 at these points: cycle is attracting.

d) $\{0.3660..., -1.3660...\}$ Derivative of ^2f is -2 at these points: cycle is repelling.

e) $\{1, -1\}$ Derivative of ^2f is 9 at these points: cycle is repelling.

f) $\{\sqrt{2}, -\sqrt{2}\}$ Derivative of ^2f is 25 at these points: cycle is repelling.

§7.2 Exercises

1. $^2f(x) = f(f(x))$, so $^2f(x) = f(rx(1-x)) = r(rx(1-x))(1 - rx(1-x)) = r^2x(1-x)(1 - rx + rx^2) =$

$r^2x\left(1 - rx + rx^2 - x + rx^2 - rx^3\right) = r^2x\left(1 - (r+1)x + 2rx^2 - rx^3\right) = r^2x - r^2(r+1)x^2 + 2r^3x^3 - r^3x^4$

3. Let $S = \sqrt{r^2 - 2r - 3}$; show $f\left(\dfrac{(r+1)+S}{2r}\right) = \dfrac{(r+1)-S}{2r}$.

$f\left(\dfrac{(r+1)+S}{2r}\right) = r\left(\dfrac{(r+1)+S}{2r}\right)\left(1 - \dfrac{(r+1)+S}{2r}\right) = r\left(\dfrac{(r+1)+S}{2r}\right)\left(\dfrac{2r - (r+1) - S}{2r}\right) =$

$r\left(\dfrac{(r+1)+S}{2r}\right)\left(\dfrac{(2r - r - 1) - S}{2r}\right) = r\left(\dfrac{(r+1)+S}{2r}\right)\left(\dfrac{(r-1) - S}{2r}\right) =$

$$r\left(\frac{r^2-1+(r-1)S-(r+1)S-S^2)}{4r^2}\right)=\frac{r^2-1+rS-S-rS-S-r^2+2r+3}{4r}=\frac{2r+2-2S}{4r}=\frac{(r+1)-S}{2r}$$

5. Let $S=\sqrt{r^2-2r-3}$. Show that $^2f'\left(\frac{(r+1)+S}{2}\right)=-r^2+2r+4$.　　　$^2f'\left(\frac{(r+1)+S}{2}\right)=$

$$r^2-2r^2(r+1)\left(\frac{(r+1)+S}{2r}\right)+6r^3\left(\frac{(r+1)^2+2(r+1)S+S^2}{4r^2}\right)-4r^3\left(\frac{(r+1)^3+3(r+1)^2S+3(r+1)S^2+S^3}{8r^3}\right)=$$

$$\frac{2r^2-2r(r+1)[(r+1)+S]+3r[(r+1)^2+2(r+1)S+S^2]-[(r+1)^3+3(r+1)^2S+3(r+1)S^2+S^3]}{2}=$$

$$\frac{2r^2-2r(r+1)^2-2r(r+1)S+3r(r+1)^2+6r(r+1)S+3rS^2-(r+1)^3-3(r+1)^2S-3(r+1)S^2-S^3}{2}=$$

$$\frac{2r^2+r(r+1)^2-(r+1)^3-3S^2+4r(r+1)S-3(r+1)^2S-(S^2)S}{2}=$$

$$\frac{2r^2+r^3+2r^2+r-r^3-3r^2-3r-1-3(r^2-2r-3)+[4r^2+4r-3r^2-6r-3-(r^2-2r-3)]S}{2}=$$

$$\frac{-2r^2+4r+8+[0]S}{2}=-r^2+2r+4.\text{ A similar proof shows that }^2f'\left(\frac{(r+1)-S}{2}\right)=-r^2+2r+4.$$

7.

$$x^2-x+c\overline{\smash{\big)}\,\begin{array}{l}x^2+x+(c+1)\\ x^4+2cx^2-x+c^2+c\end{array}}$$

$$\begin{array}{l}\underline{x^4-x^3+cx^2}\\ x^3+cx^2-x\\ \underline{x^3-x^2+cx}\\ (c+1)x^2-(c+1)x+c^2+c\\ \underline{(c+1)x^2-(c+1)x+c^2+c}\\ 0\end{array}$$

Using the quadratic formula to solve
$x^2+x+(c+1)=0$:

$$x=\frac{-1\pm\sqrt{1-4(c+1)}}{2}=\frac{-1\pm\sqrt{-3-4c}}{2}.$$

9. $^2f'(x)=4x(x^2+c)$. If $x=\dfrac{-1+\sqrt{-3-4c}}{2}$, then

$$x^2+c=\frac{-1-\sqrt{-3-4c}}{2}.\text{ Therefore}$$

$$^2f'\left(\frac{-1+\sqrt{-3-4c}}{2}\right)=$$

$$4\left(\frac{-1+\sqrt{-3-4c}}{2}\right)\left(\frac{-1-\sqrt{-3-4c}}{2}\right)=$$

$$4\left(\frac{1-(-3-4c)}{4}\right)=1+3+4c=4(1+c).$$

§7.3 Exercises

1. a, b, c)

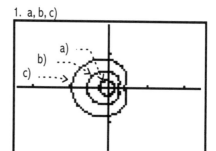

d, e)

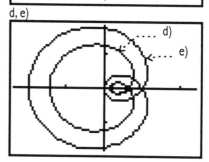

3. For initial values of θ, choose $0<\theta<\dfrac{\pi}{2}$.
Then $0<\sin\theta<1$ and $0<\cos\theta<1$. Also $k>0$.
If $k\sin\theta-k^2\sin2\theta<0$, then $k\sin\theta<k^2\sin2\theta$, or
$k\sin\theta<2k^2\sin\theta\cos\theta$ using a formula for $\sin2\theta$.
Therefore, $1<2k\cos\theta$ since $k\sin\theta>0$, and so
$k>\dfrac{1}{2\cos\theta}$. But $0<\cos\theta<1$, so $\dfrac{1}{\cos\theta}>1$ and

$\dfrac{1}{2\cos\theta} > \dfrac{1}{2}$. Therefore, the condition implies $k > \frac{1}{2}$.

5. Period 7, then 11, 15, 19. The period of the largest intermediate bulb is the sum of the periods of the end bulbs.

7. $\dfrac{f(z+h)-f(z)}{h} = \dfrac{(z+h)^2 + c - [z^2 + c]}{h}$

$= \dfrac{z^2 + 2zh + h^2 + c - z^2 - c}{h} = \dfrac{2zh + h^2}{h} = 2z + h$.

Therefore $\lim\limits_{h\to 0} \dfrac{f(z+h)-f(z)}{h} = \lim\limits_{h\to 0} 2z + h = 2z$.

§7.4 Exercises

1. $1/7 \to 2/7 \to 4/7 \to 1/7 \to ...$ The calculator's approximation to 1/7 is sufficiently inaccurate for sensitivity to move the orbit away from the cycle which is repelling.

3. a)
$1/3 \to 2/3 \to 1/3 \to ...$
$1/5 \to 2/5 \to 4/5 \to 3/5 \to 1/5 \to ...$
$1/9 \to 2/9 \to 4/9 \to 8/9 \to 7/9 \to 5/9 \to 1/9 \to ...$
$1/17 \to 2/17 \to 4/17 \to 8/17 \to 16/17 \to 15/17 \to$
$\qquad\qquad 13/17 \to 9/17 \to 1/17 \to ...$

Number	1/3	1/5	1/9	1/17
Period	2	4	6	8

b) 1/33 should have a period of 10:
$1/33 \to 2/33 \to 4/33 \to 8/33 \to 16/33 \to 32/33 \to$
$\qquad\qquad 31/33 \to 29/33 \to 25/33 \to 17/33 \to 1/33 \to ...$

c) Seeds of the form $1/(2^n + 1)$ are periodic with a prime period of length $2n$.

5. Not fixed, periodic, eventually fixed, or eventually periodic, but remains in the unit interval.

7. a) 4/7; b) 6/7; c) 1/12

9. a) 0.100100100...; b) 0.1110111111...;
c) 0.01001100110011...; d) 0.010111111...;
e) 0.01011001100110011...; f) 0.010111011110111...

11. Suppose we require x_0 to be within $1/2^N$ of $x = 0.a_1 a_2 a_3 ...$, and we require its orbit to pass within $1/2^M$ of $w = 0.b_1 b_2 b_3 ...$. Choose $x_0 = 0.a_1 a_2 a_3 ... a_N b_1 b_2 b_3 ... b_M c_1 c_2 c_3 ...$ where the c's are any pattern of 0's and 1's. Then x_0 is within the required distance of x, and its Nth iterate is within the required distance of w.

Chapter 8

§8.1 Exercises

1. If $n = kr^D$, then $\log n = \log(kr^D)$. Using the properties of logarithms:
$\log n = \log k + \log r^D = \log k + D \log r$.

3. a)

Stage	1	2	3
r	1	3	7
n	3	15	63

b) $r = 2^S - 1$, $n = 2^{2S} - 1$

c) At stage 4, $r = 15$ and $n = 255$.

d) At any finite stage S, $D = \dfrac{\log n}{\log r} = \dfrac{\log(2^{2S} - 1)}{\log(2^S - 1)}$. As

$S \to \infty, D \to \dfrac{\log 2^{2S}}{\log 2^S} = \dfrac{2S \log 2}{S \log 2} = 2$.

e) Boxcount dimension is 1.6040...

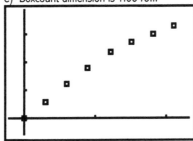

f)

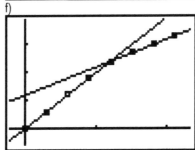

Lower values of r give a log-log graph with slope 2 while higher values have a slope of 1. There is no middle range where the graph straightens out with an intermediate slope.

g) Stage 4 is too early to approximate well the infinite Hilbert curve.

h) Boxcount dimension is 1.9915...

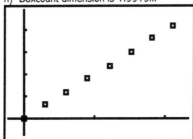

INDEX